MAN AND WILDFOWL

For

Peter, Andrew, Joe, Mike

and Myrfyn

'Man and Wildfowl' – Sir Peter Scott painting. Photograph by J. F. Leach.

Man and Wildfowl

by JANET KEAR

T & A D POYSER

London

© Janet Kear 1990

ISBN 0 85661 055 0

First published in 1990 T & A D Poyser Ltd
24–28 Oval Road, London NW1

Text set in Monophoto Bembo
Printed and bound in Great Britain by
Mackays of Chatham PLC, Chatham, Kent

British Library Cataloguing in Publication Data
Kear, Janet
  Man and wildfowl.
  1. Birds. Relationships with man   2. Man. Relationships
with birds
  I. Title
  598.26

  ISBN 0–85661–055–0

Contents

List of illustrations

A number of uncaptioned headpieces, tailpieces and other engravings by Thomas Bewick, his apprentices and school appear throughout the book.

Acknowledgements

This book is dedicated to all my colleagues at The Wildfowl and Wetlands Trust, and especially to Andrew Dawnay, Joe Blossom, Mike Ounsted and Myrfyn Owen, in gratitude for friendship and the pleasure of a shared enthusiasm. Sir Peter Scott was a colleague of a rather special sort; as founder and Honorary Director of The Wildfowl Trust he was also our boss. I hope that he was occasionally as pleased with us as we were with him.

Dozens of people, apart from those five (of whom Joe painted the cover and many of the illustrations), have helped in the book's preparation. Sue Hazeldine has done other drawings and been immensely helpful and painstaking in her research; Joanna Cecil-Wright made some of the earlier collations. Professor Geoffrey Matthews had confidence that the book might be worth writing, has read the resulting text and made many helpful comments. The Trust gave me five weeks off at Caerlaverock in order that I might get on with its preparation – there is no nicer place to be, and no nicer people to work among. I have been assisted by the staff at Ormskirk public library who, while cheerfully observing that I was straying far from my usual interests, have traced obscure books. Dr Colin Ogilvie has also read everything, and been most encouraging. Jonathan Leach and Rob Edwards have done wonderful things with the photographs.

Chapter 2 depended on help from Dr Pat Morris who lent me some of his books and kindly photographed a number of old prints for me, Dee Wallis (of 'Mastermind'), Dr M. J. Scott of Seattle who suggested that geese be used to keep snakes away, Sir Harry Llewellyn Bt, CBE who told me of his brother's searches for Brecon Buffs, John William-Davies of the Welsh Folk Museum, Frances Neale who gave me information about the pre-enclosure goose-feather industry in the Somerset Levels, Eileen Preston who photographed geese being shod on ancient misericords, Dr Geoff Parker of Liverpool University and H. Nott, Agricultural Director of Cherry Valley Farms Ltd, for advice on domestication, and Mrs Myrtle Ashmole who sent me the correspondence between her great-grandfather and Charles Darwin. Richard Green Gallery kindly allowed me to use A. M. Koester's beautiful painting of domestic ducks resting, and Greenpoint Films Ltd lent me a video of 'Laughterhouse'. Dr B. Glofcheskie told me about his research on the fly-catching habits of domestic Muscovies.

Assistance with Chapter 3 was obtained from Professor W. G. Hale who first found the site of the Martin Mere decoy, Tony and Anne Cook and Don and Pam Revett who shared their books and experiences; Anne Cook took many excellent photographs for me. Jack Dodds, a descendent of decoymen who knows everything about early decoys, answered my queries and is (I hope) writing a book himself, Dr Bob McCabe told about the Delta decoy and of the one at Salem, and James Fox of County Kildare, who has traced and written about Irish decoys, sent me details. Linda Birch of the EGI and Jennifer Owen copied manuscripts, and Barbara and Jack Owen brought carvings of preaching foxes to my attention. Richard T. Mills of Cork allowed me to use his photograph of fox and Whooper Swan, and David Morgan of the NCC answered my questions about exports of dead ducks. The Local Studies Librarian, Newcastle upon Tyne City Libraries kindly supplied the heading illustration for this chapter.

Martin Brown lent me his library of books by Payne-Gallwey for Chapter 4, and Dr Pamela Harrison photographs of her husband Jeff. Chapter 6 is enhanced by a portrait of my hero, Lord Derby, which was taken by Mrs Iris Young, the present Lord Derby's librarian who has been most kind, as has his Lordship. Dr Stephen Davies was good enough to supply the Aboriginal drawing of a family of Magpie Geese, and recommended other Australian sources. Sam MacKenzie drew some lovely White-winged Wood Ducks in their natural settings, David L. Tranger of the US Fish and Wildlife Service sent information on the Aleutian Canada Goose, and Neil Hayes on the New Zealand Brown Teal. Clem Fisher and Tony Morgan of the Liverpool Museum searched their records, as did Peter Olney of the Zoological Society of London.

'Aliens' was much improved by enthusiastic help from Kit Savage, who is revising his book on the Mandarin but, nevertheless, generously shared his ideas and recalled conversations with the late Jean Delacour. Sir Christopher Lever and Lawton Shurtleff gave me additional information.

Mrs B. Potter, Headmistress of St Werburgh's Primary School, Mr. R. Bridgett, author of St Werburgh's life, many vicars of churches dedicated to her (the Rev. Geoffrey Marshall, Rev. Peter Barnett, Rev. Donald Felix, Rev. E. G. Seddon and Father David Mellor) helped with parts of Chapter 8. Sir Peter Scott gave me permission to photograph paintings from his books, and Lady Scott provided me with photographs of a Bewick's Swan caught in fishing line, and of three swans preening.

Jeffery Boswall and Dr M. Desfayes advised on the language section of Chapter 9, as did other linguists including Dorothy Evans, Roger Spencer and the Rev. A. Mayes. Dr D. Owen supplied information on inn signs, Linda Tilbury on St Hugh of Lincoln, Rosalind Hall on ancient Egyptian wildfowl, J. E. Vaughan on children's literature, Professor Vincent Megaw of Flinders University on Celtic ducks, Lionel Lambourne of the Victoria and Albert Museum on prints and Robert Gillmor on wildfowl art.

Robin Prytherch and John Harrison of the BBC, Simon Anstey, R. H. Blakeman of MAFF, Professor N. T. Boaden, Professor R. Bray, Mandy Callard, Harriet Drummond, Christie's drawings department, Captain R.de L. Cazenove, Wendy Dickson, Pat Earnshaw, Dr Tony Fox, Brian Gadsby, Irene Halliday, Doug Hulyer, Patrick Humphries, Dr A. G. Irwin of the Norfolk Museums Service, Dr J. Kirkwood, Hugh Macandrew, F. W. Manders, Tony Marshall, Judy and Michael Molesworth, Donald Ogilvie, Su Page of *Country Life*, Dr C. M. Pond, Dr Erika Price, Dr Eileen Rees, David Salmon, Lynda Seddon, Dr James Serpell, Pat Wisniewski, Sandra and Derek Williams and Mary Wilkinson of the Imperial War Museum have been helpful in various ways, and I thank them all. Trevor and Anna Poyser, my publishers and dear friends, have been kinder than most writers can expect, and John Turner has done much more than go half-shares on a word-processor, draw the diagrams and correct my spelling.

1: Introduction

Human involvement with ducks, geese and swans is probably closer than that with any other group of birds. Geese and ducks were brought into the farmyard thousands of years ago and, in many parts of the northern world, became an important part of the economy. Our imagination has found symbols of gentleness and purity in swans, of domesticity in the family life of geese, and of charm and whimsy in the duck.

We have a particular love of birds, and see wildfowl as both familiar and magical. The English-speaking world has exploited them for sport and food, and conserved them with almost equal enthusiasm. By custom every child has a 'Donald' as a toy, an eiderdown as a bedcover and is taken to the park to feed the ducks. The UK Department of Transport even has a special sign to indicate and warn of a road that ducks may be crossing. Hundreds of birdwatchers count wildfowl on Sundays during the worst of the winter weather in the expectation that their combined efforts will be for the good of the birds.

This close relationship will be examined in the following pages, in particular our involvement with domestic ducks and geese, decoys, wildfowling, agricultural conflict, refuge management, the keeping of wildfowl in captivity and re-introduction to the wild. There will be mention of legend and art, of Leda and Jemima Puddle-duck, and of the many other ways in which these birds give us pleasure.

The writing was started during the 40th anniversary of the founding of The Severn Wildfowl Trust by Sir Peter Scott in 1946 and was intended to honour his 80th birthday on 14 September 1989. Sadly, 'the patron saint of conservation' to quote Sir David Attenborough, died on 29 August. By then his unique Gloucestershire-based enterprise had been enjoyed by more than eleven million visitors and become an important part of the conservation, research, education and leisure scene. Only in Britain, it seems, could an organisation devoted to one group of wetland birds have flourished with such conspicuous success.

The book is first and foremost about wildfowl, but is not all about them – only some aspects of their lives that impinge on ours are considered. Secondly it is about Sir Peter Scott – but by no means all about him either – I have merely selected events and achievements from his eight decades – principally, the creation and development of what has now become The Wildfowl and Wetlands Trust. And very much last, it is about myself. I celebrated 30 years of employment by The Trust in the autumn of 1989; during the course of my work I have become fascinated by wildfowl and the effect that they have on people, and am committed to Sir Peter's premise that the two can be brought close together – always for our benefit, and sometimes for theirs.

THE WILDFOWL GROUP

'Wildfowl' is the word that in Britain is applied to the 142 or so species of medium to large-sized ducks, geese and swans in the family Anatidae of the order Anseriformes (3,6). This close-knit group is found throughout the world in freshwater, coastal and marine habitats, reaching right into the far northern latitudes where it is represented in large numbers. The birds all hatch with open eyes and a covering of dense down that protects them from the water into which they are able to plunge at one day old; their bills are typically broad and somewhat flattened but differ in order to deal efficiently with diets as varied as grass, fish and tiny seeds. Many are common birds which everyone knows; the Mallard Duck *Anas platyrhynchos* teems in millions; others, like the Hawaiian Goose or Nene *Branta sandvicensis* which today can be seen in almost every zoo, have recently numbered in the low hundreds.

Swans are the largest flying birds and, like their relatives the grazing geese, have strong pair-bonds and a prolonged family life. Both mature slowly and are almost always territorial when breeding, defending their mates, nests and young ones vigorously. Their acute powers of sight and hearing enable them to guard against threats to their territorial integrity and, in the winter or non-breeding season, families assemble in large flocks and any individual will warn the others of danger; man has used geese as 'watchdogs' for many centuries (Chapter 2). Ducks are smaller than swans and geese, and are much less uniform in appearance and social behaviour. In a few species, the male helps rear the young and has an association with his mate that lasts longer than a few months but, in many more, the pair comes together only until the eggs are laid so that parental duties are solely the task of the female and she stays with the ducklings until they are fledged.

Ducks are more thoroughly adapted to water-living than swans or geese, and their feathers need to provide better waterproofing, which is why they replace their feathers by moulting twice every 12 months. Thus, they are able to show two different plumages in the course of each year (3,6). The two sexes of tropical ducks, despite their double moults, tend to resemble one another, but in almost all high-latitude, migratory species, the courting male is brighter than his female who remains like a juvenile in appearance for the whole of her life.

As we shall see later, the waterproof and insulating plumage of wildfowl was one of the most useful products of their domestication. The beautiful feathering of many wild male ducks meant that in Victorian times, especially, they were favoured subjects of the taxidermist who stuffed

This fine example of the taxidermist's art stuffed and mounted by Thomas Gunn of Norfolk in 1922, shows a family of Shelducks emerging from a rabbit burrow (see Chapter 7). Photograph by J. F. Leach.

their skins and sold the mounted specimens, cased in glass, for decorating drawing rooms. Duck feathers have also been used on fishing hooks – to catch another animal for man's pleasure; a series of 'winged wet flies' that to the trout's eye resemble insects near the water surface have 'wings' constructed of speckled feathers from the shoulder of the Mallard. The most famous of the series (traditionally the most 'deadly') is called 'Mallard and claret' and has its body of seal's fur dyed dark red.

THE MALLARD

The Mallard may be regarded as the typical duck. Towards the end of May in Britain, the drake shows the first signs of a change in colour on the breast and back; in a few days, the curly feathers at the centre of the tail drop out and the glossy green around the eye becomes grey; by the third week of June scarcely any green remains and, soon after the beginning of July, the bird resembles the female – only the bill remains greeny-yellow and unspotted so that it is always possible upon close inspection to tell the difference between the two. In the early part of August, his sombre plumage will be moulted out until, by the second week in October, he is again in his finery with a new set of bright feathers, and courtship and the search for a new wife begin once more. Like many waterbirds, wildfowl moult all their wing-quills simultaneously and cannot fly for some weeks while the next set of flight feathers grows. Male ducks go through this flightless stage while their conspicuous colours are 'eclipsed' and cryptic and, in the company of other drakes, pass the time in safety from land-based predators, such as foxes and man, by gathering on lakes and ponds.

The annual cycle of the female Mallard is rather different; she also changes her body feathers twice, but her plumages are identical and brown. Her hormones, like those of the drake, will respond to the lengthening daylight hours of spring and bring her into breeding condition; in the main, however, it is the male's courtship that will determine exactly when she lays. In England, she will produce the first of about ten eggs in March, at the rate of one a day, and then incubate them for 28 days. Nests are constructed, usually on the ground, in a variety of wetland habitats, from the smallest fish pond to large lakes and reservoirs. Her feathers and down will provide a soft bed, and she will weave the surrounding vegetation into an overhanging screen so that the nest is almost invisible. After

Thomas Bewick's wood-engraving of a wild Mallard drake from *History of British Birds* published in 1797.

incubation, but about four weeks later than her mate, she also becomes flightless while still caring for the ducklings. They fly when they are six or seven weeks old, and family ties will then be broken.

The Mallard occurs throughout subarctic and temperate Europe, Asia and North America, and its habits have been studied intensively. It is Britain and Ireland's most widely distributed and commonest duck; about 150,000 pairs breed and a further 700,000 individuals join them from other parts of Europe for the winter. Although 700,000 are shot annually (see Chapter 4), wildfowlers themselves hatch, rear and release an estimated 400,000 every autumn in order to add to the stock that may be harvested.

COMMUNICATION WITH WILDFOWL

Village-pond Mallard may see us as a friendly meal-ticket but, to most wild ducks, geese and swans, the human being is a foe. Until the coming of guns, man was not an important enemy of adult wildfowl but he made use of the fact that they cannot fly when young or during their annual wing-moult to round them up with boats and to take them as food. Because he has long been regarded as potentially harmful, many ducks with helpless ducklings (indeed, all except the few that have evolved on remote islands) respond to him by 'pretending' to be flightless and invite attack upon themselves by giving a 'broken-wing display'. The virtuoso performance of a mother duck, surprised at the pond's edge by the sight of man and/or his dog, suggests thousands of years of interaction during which females who behaved this way left more offspring than those who did not. She will fly in a laboured manner towards the land, collapsing repeatedly just ahead of any pursuer as if her back and wings were broken.

Confrontation – the white gander is threatening the lad, apparently unmoved by his reciprocal threatening gesture involving a raised hat. Engraved by Thomas Bewick.

In a series of apparently narrow escapes and painstaking recoveries, she succeeds in luring the chase well away from her precious offspring and finally, the hood-wink complete, will return to the water on well-trimmed, easy wings.

Communication of a different kind between bird and man occurs during 'imprinting' when, to a duckling or gosling just a few hours old, the sight and sound of a human being may represent a parent duck or goose who will 'care', and whose closeness is something to be desired and strived for (see Chapter 5). And we communicate directly when we call wild birds for food; Call Ducks in decoys are whistled at feeding time (Chapter 3), and the wintering swans at Wildfowl and Wetlands Trust reserves have learnt to fly or walk in for grain (Chapter 5) on hearing and seeing sounds and people that may vary a bit from place to place but convey the same message. At most Centres, the visiting public take the greatest pleasure from the accessibility of tame ducks and geese that feed from the hand and demonstrate a trust that is both astonishing and delightful.

PUBLIC ATTITUDES

Our feelings about animals have probably changed in detail many times, as have other contemporary values. In some instances, a personal relationship between man and bird results in the animal receiving a name, and there are not a few books describing the course of what becomes a love affair. Perhaps women are especially associated with such experiences (1,8) – but I remember meeting a racy Irish fashion designer who had the improbable title of the Marquis MacSwiney of Mashanaglas and whose moated schloss in Germany was the summer home of a pair of Mute Swans *Cygnus olor* called Hans and Leda. He wrote an excellent account of his observations, with acknowledgements to the birds that had 'brought great joy into my life' (5). And a journalist who lived on Sydney harbour has told with relish of his 'adoption' by a white Muscovy *Cairina moschata* who he christened Dora, and for whom he went to considerable trouble to provide food, fresh water and security for her ducklings (2).

In a survey of American public opinion carried out in the 1970s (4), 57% of those questioned said, surprisingly, that they disapproved of the filling in of wetlands for housing developments if the marshes were used by wild ducks. Sixty percent were opposed to hunting of waterfowl if it were solely for the purpose of recreation or sport; however, 64% approved of that hunting if it were done for the meat – in other words, the killing of wild animals for sport was generally acceptable when the dead body was to be consumed.

On a scale of America's favourite animals (4), the swan ranked third (after the dog and horse, and ahead of the American Robin *Turdus migratorius* and butterfly). It was the 'most liked' wild creature, but may have been perceived to be as domestic as the dog and horse since it was probably the tame, non-American Mute Swan, that will approach for food, that was being identified. A later German survey, using the same questionnaire, put the swan sixth after *Erithacus rubecula*, another species of Robin altogether, dog, butterfly, horse and 'ladybug' (7). The goose was not included in the selection but, in earlier times, it might also have scored high as a natural part of the household. 'Mother Goose' has a special place in juvenile hearts (Chapter 9) although, once past childhood, we try not to become too fond of those we kill and eat. Man usually shows more affection for a tame wild animal than for a domestic one. Our equivocation can be acute, especially about gourmet delicacies such as *pâtés de fois gras* (Chapter 2).

I have written this book mainly about what interests me in the historical and recent relationships of man and wildfowl. The paradox in our attitudes – of admiration for the beauty that is apparently best preserved by stuffing the dead duck, or for the wildness that is such a challenge to the wildfowler or the decoyman – is especially fascinating. The first subject dealt with in detail is domestication, the process through which we have tamed and altered wild animals and plants so that we may exploit them more readily – often as food – and one in which wildfowl have been much involved.

REFERENCES

1. Irvine, L. 1960. *Field with Geese*. London: Hamish Hamilton.
2. Fraser, B. 1971. *Sitting Duck*. London: MacGibbon.
3. Kear, J. 1986. *Eric Hosking's Wildfowl*. London: Croom Helm.
4. Kellert, S. R. 1980. American attitudes and knowledge of animals: an update. *Int.J.Stud.Anim.Prob.* 1(2): 87–119.
5. MacSwiney, Marquis. 1971. *Six Came Flying*. London: Michael Joseph.
6. Matthews, G. V. T. 1974. Anseriformes, article in *Encyclopaedia Britannica*.
7. Schulz, W. 1987. Attitudes towards birds and other wildlife in West Germany and America, in *The Value of Birds*, ICBP Technical Publication No.6.
8. Wiggin, K. D. 1902. *The Diary of a Goose Girl*. London: Gay & Bird.

2: Domestication

Domestication has been called the largest biological experiment ever undertaken; indeed Charles Darwin's study of *The Variation of Animals and Plants under Domestication* (11), published in 1868, was as important to his understanding of the processes of evolution as his observations of wild creatures made during the voyage of The Beagle. From man's point of view, wildfowl have been conspicuously successful. The Greylag Goose *Anser anser*, along with the Rock Dove *Columba livia*, has the distinction of being the first bird to be domesticated, some 5000 years ago (44,49). As it was the eastern sub-species of the Greylag *A.a.rubirostris* that was involved, we may guess that the process occurred first in western Asia (9). Some centuries later, the Red Jungle Fowl *Gallus gallus* of the Indus River and the Mallard were brought into human settlements.

It is possible that the Mallard was tamed in many parts of the Old World, as it has a wide distribution at latitudes occupied by early man. The Swan Goose *A.cygnoides* of eastern Asia and the Muscovy Duck of Central and South America were also farmed, but we do not know when the process started (8,9,18). At the time that the conquistadors reached the New World, the Muscovy was already a household animal; it was brought back to Spain from Mexico along with the Turkey *Meleagris gallopavo* and the guinea pig – all three bearing most misleading common names. Two centuries later, when the Europeans settled in North America, Turkeys and Muscovies were to return with them (49).

In Egypt during the Old Kingdom, which ended around 2300 BC, the Egyptian Goose *Alopochen egyptiacus* was the principal domestic bird. The goose played a role in the creation myth and was identified with Geb the earth god. It was commonly eaten, although its eggs were not, as they were shaped somewhat like the sun and had religious significance. The Egyptian Goose was not domesticated outside Egypt and, when the

Persians conquered the country in 525 BC, the bird ceased to be a farm animal (49).

Domestication is a relatively recent human activity and was very gradual in its development (49,50). Man has been making tools for a million years and roasting meat for half that time, but evidence of domesticated plants and animals is available from only about 8–10,000 BC. Indeed, some 99.9% of our total time as a species has been spent as non-agriculturalists, and our relationship with other animals has been typically one of hunter and prey. When it happened, domestication of animals occurred in Asia rather than Europe, most of our farm stock originating in the Near East. Cultivated plants, on the other hand, have come mainly from tropical America and China as well as southwest Asia (47). Domestic animal breeding started with dogs, sheep and goats, accelerated and broadened in Greek and Roman times but, after that, most domestic breeds did not change much until quite recently. This will be obvious when we look in more detail at the goose. Geese were practical animals to farm because (like cattle, sheep, camels and reindeer) they were adapted to survive on plants that man could not consume himself; they were not in competition with him and could convert grass into protein, fat and such valuable commodities as feathers. Significantly, the numbers of domestic geese in Britain during the last war (just over 600,000) did not drop, unlike all other classes of poultry, including ducks.

It is suggested that geese (and perhaps ducks) were tamed as pets before their other, more utilitarian, advantages became obvious (18,47,50). It was the young birds that would have been chosen as companions – a gosling or duckling is an engaging plaything and one can imagine a child delighting in its obvious sociability. Eventually they were supplying flesh and eggs, fat for ointments, oil for lamps and for preserving meat, feathers for arrows and ornamentation, and down for bedding and padded clothing. White individuals, which appear from time to time in most birds, would be seen as extraordinary symbols of purity and thus suitable as sacrificial offerings to the gods (44).

What do we mean by domestication, and why did the Greylag, the Swan Goose, the Mallard and the Muscovy accept the process so easily? Domestication implies that, by controlling the mating choice of an animal or plant, man can alter its genetic potential. He can select features of value to him from the natural variation available and breed only from individuals showing these traits, preventing the reproduction of those that deviate from his ideal. Thus the stock is changed gradually to suit a man-selected, rather than the naturally selected, situation. Geese and ducks are grazers and seed-eaters that would have come into association with early man through raids on his crops (32,44,49). After adoption into the family, perhaps as pets, domestication would be helped by an ability to eat a range of plant foods, by adaptable breeding behaviour and by easy accommodation to the proximity of human beings.

A long life, efficient parental care, maximum production of down and feathers, good food conversion and rapid growth rates were features from which the farmer could select his wildfowl stock – even if, as seems likely, the selection was at first unconscious. Of particular importance was the tendency of ducks and geese to live in social groups and to 'imprint' early in life and to accept as companions the first things that they see after hatching (32,44). Obviously this is usually the parent, but it could be man himself (the subject is further examined in Chapter 5). Earlier maturity, longer laying seasons, and larger clutches were features that gradually distinguished domestic geese and ducks from their wild relatives. Flightlessness and a heavier body were also achieved. Protection was given from predators and the ability to escape them became less and less important; thus the breeder could control the parents of the next generation.

Why are white forms so common in domestication? Feathers without pigment occur every so often in many dark-coloured birds but, in the wild, white individuals seldom survive. The white feathers are not so robust (which is why many pale birds, such as the migratory Snow Goose *Anser caerulescens*, have black primary wing feathers, for strength) and the birds are often picked off by predators because they are conspicuous. The religious significance of white ducks and geese as sacrificial objects has already been referred to, but there is another important feature that whiteness imparts. A white bird puts on weight more quickly and, although it needs more food, converts that food faster than a dark form. For instance, the white phase of the Lesser Snow Goose *A.c.caerulescens* hatches half a day earlier and fledges faster than the blue phase. Why, then, are not all domestic birds white? Because the dark ones, once mature, start to lay earlier in the year and, as they lay for longer, can produce more eggs. So early man had the choice of eggs and potential chicks from slow-growing dark birds, or meat from faster-growing ones. Eventually he had other choices, because the speed of growth affects the flavour of the meat. Mrs Beeton (3) noted the difference in taste between white and brown-plumaged ducks, pointing out that the light ones were more delicate and milder in flavour. She does not relate this to their rapid growth, but that was the principal reason. Charles Darwin (11) recorded that Roman gourmets preferred the livers of white geese; perhaps there is a difference there too.

TYPES OF DOMESTIC GEESE; GREYLAG GOOSE DESCENDANTS

We can conjecture that it was the Eastern Greylag rather than the Western race *A.a.anser* (with which the British are more familiar in the wild) that was first domesticated, by just looking at our common modern breeds. The grey cast to the feathers and the pinkish bill and eye-ring are all characters of the Eastern Greylag and of many farmyard geese. (Curiously, the legs and feet of most domestic geese are orange, although in both races of wild Greylag they are pink). Our guess is confirmed by

An Eastern Greylag painted nearly 3,400 years ago during the reign of Akhenaten in Egypt. Its swollen white belly suggests that it is on the point of laying and was therefore domestic (sadly, the painting no longer exists).

the fact that early depictions of the domesticated bird come from areas that the Western race does not reach. There was an excellent rendering of a goose in laying condition in the North Palace of Akhenaten at El-Amarna, Egypt, painted about 3360 years ago. It is shown here in black-and-white, but the original had all the features of the Eastern Greylag. This race would have been in greater contact with early man because it bred further south than the Western race. It is also heavier, lays earlier in the spring and over a longer period, so it already had a number of desirable farmyard qualities. However, it is likely that, once domestic geese reached Britain, they did at times mate with the local Western bird. It is said that it was this 'outbreeding' that kept the old English Grey Goose 'unimproved' for so long.

The domestic goose was bred selectively with increasing success by the Greeks and, particularly, by the Romans. Penelope, in Homer's *Odyssey*, owned 20. Aesop, the Greek story-teller of the 6th Century BC, wrote of the fabulous goose that laid golden eggs (see Chapter 9) which may have symbolised the great wealth enjoyed by early farmers with large goose flocks. The birds were kept mainly for meat, as watchdogs and to provide feathers for arrows. Pliny, the Roman naturalist of the 1st Century AD, recorded that 'our people esteem the goose chiefly on account of the excellence of the liver which attains a very large size when the bird is crammed'. So there is nothing new in what the French, Hungarians and Israelis do to geese today. There is even an Egyptian frieze from a tomb

This wood-engraving by Thomas Bewick shows an old women who has come to fill her jug and is furious to find a gaggle of geese at the well. The most aggressive bird, who is threatening her, is probably the flock gander and is whiter than the others.

of the 6th Dynasty at Saqqara (about 2300 BC) showing geese and cranes being forcibly fed (47). I shall return later to the subject of *foie gras*.

There was a tame goose in Britain when the Romans arrived, for which the Celts were said to have had a special reverence. They did not eat it, only sacrificing it as part of a seasonal religious ceremony. Wild geese that migrated were seen as harbingers of death and the bearers of departed souls; the tame bird must have been, to some extent, a surrogate for those magical messengers. By Saxon times, the English Grey Goose was

Bewick's 1797 wood-engraving of the 'tame goose', an example of the old Grey Goose that was the common English domestic bird before improvement by strains imported from the Continent.

important as food, and this breed remained immensely popular until about 150 years ago. Thomas Bewick's many woodcuts showing domestic geese suggests that the ganders were often of a lighter colour than the females, so the breed probably tended to be auto-sexing (see below, under Pilgrims). However, almost all modern farm geese in Britain are of foreign breeds imported from the Continent relatively recently (2,9,28,34,36,43). A few are described here; most have been bred for their meat, some for eggs and one for its plumage. Rapid growth is a feature of the white breeds, while epicurean flesh and, on the continent, fat livers come from the brown ones (2,3,34).

The **Embden** was imported into England in the early 19th Century from the region around the Prussian seaport (43). In 1815 both male and female were referred to as being white and of a very uncommon size; by 1872, weights of over 14 kg (30 lb) had been obtained and, in 1929, the British standard was 14–16 kg (30–34 lb) for the gander and 9–10 kg (20–22 lb) for the goose, or three to four times the weight of the wild Greylag. The American-bred Embden gosling is described as the fastest growing domestic bird, weighing about 113 g (4 oz) when hatched and 2.6 kg (5.8 lb) at four weeks. This represents a 24-fold increase in weight (and it is 46 times at ten weeks) which is vastly better than the domestic chicken can achieve.

The **Toulouse** Goose is as large as the Embden when adult but is grey and brown and does not, as a consequence, grow so fast. It is a dual purpose bird being bred for both meat and eggs (34,43). Toulouse females lay more eggs than their Embden counterparts but, primarily, this was the goose that in the Dordogne region of France provided the livers for the famous *pâté de foie gras*. That uncertain honour now goes to the smaller grey-brown Landes Goose from Alsace (20). The Toulouse was introduced into Britain in about 1840 by the 13th Earl of Derby, when it was also referred to as the Mediterranean or Marseilles Goose. This was the same nobleman that first bred the Hawaiian Goose in captivity at Knowsley Hall near Liverpool in 1834 (see Chapter 6). Today, the Toulouse's vast bulk may prevent it from copulating successfully and some of the best show specimens are reproduced by artificial insemination, as are most large varieties of Turkey.

The **Pilgrim** or West of England Goose is small to medium-sized, weighing about 6 kg (13–14 lb) (34,43). It has been suggested that these were the birds taken to Massachusetts in the Mayflower in 1620, although other histories say that the Pilgrim fathers obtained them in the Netherlands. The gander is white while the goose is a soft grey. It is the only domestic goose breed that is always auto-sexing: that is, even at hatching, the sex of the gosling can be determined by its colour, because the genes for grey and for female gender are carried on the same pair of chromosomes. This feature undoubtedly made it popular, and it is surprising that it has become almost extinct in Britain. The US Declaration of Independence was signed with a goose-quill pen presumably taken

Drawings by Joe Blossom of the common domestic ducks and geese.

from this particular breed.

In the 1920s, Sir Rhys Llewellyn decided to establish a smaller variety suitable for cooking in the modern oven rather than roasting before an open fire. He collected buff-coloured geese from various Breconshire hill farms, bred them and called them **Brecon Buffs**. They were recognised by the British Poultry Club in 1934, the males weigh 8.7 kg (19 lb), and the females at 7.3 kg (16 lb) regularly lay more than one clutch of eggs as well as being good eating. Alone among British domestics they have pink legs, so some recent outbreeding with wild Greylags, or even Pinkfeet *A.brachyrhynchus* (although this is much less likely as Pinkfeet do not breed readily at Welsh latitudes) may have occurred.

The **Roman Goose** is often said to be a descendent of the white geese that saved Rome during the seige by the Gauls; however, the first reports of its existence in Britain did not appear until the early part of this century, and it more probably originates in Romania. It is another medium-sized bird, economical in terms of food conversion and useful for fitting into the modern oven; where geese are reared intensively for meat, the Roman is now the usual stock chosen.

The **Sebastopol** is a large white goose with long curling feathers growing either all over the body or on the back and wings only. It is fairly common in the Black Sea area and is also found in parts of Hungary, the Balkans and the Lower Danube. It was imported into Britain as an ornamental bird after the Crimean war in 1856, but in its native home was developed and kept because the curling feathers were useful for filling pillows and quilts. Constant inbreeding produces the frizzled plumage that is similar to that of the 'silky' fowl.

SWAN GOOSE DESCENDENTS

Two domestic breeds are descended from the wild Swan Goose of Asia, the Chinese and the African. Because this species originates even further south than the Eastern Greylag, and tends to swim less, it naturally lays down less fat. Chinese and Africans are thus more tolerant of warm climates and are usually the farm geese kept in tropical countries. In Hong Kong and Thailand, for instance, these are the common geese, often kept overnight in sheds built over ponds, so that their droppings fall through the slatted floors and fertilise the fish. The domesticated birds often have two egg-laying seasons, a major one in the early part of the year, like the wild birds, and a shorter one in autumn when the number of hours of daylight is similar to that of spring.

The **Chinese** is an elegant small-bodied goose with a long swan-like neck (29). Two colour forms occur: fawn, like the Swan Goose, and the rarer white. The fawn variety is an excellent layer and nests regularly in spring and again in November, producing up to 140 eggs a year, many more than any Greylag type. The gander is distinguished by a large bill-

Bewick's 1797 wood-engraving of 'swan geese'. The difference in appearance between the Grey Goose and this Chinese newcomer to the farmyard is obvious. Compare it also with a painting (below) made in India of a domestic goose that is nearer to the wild type, and with Buffon's Chinese Goose (opposite) which has many features that today we would call 'African'.

Domestic Chinese Geese, an 18th Century painting in miniature from the National Museum of Ethnology in Leiden; attributed to the great Ustad Mansur.

knob, and 'good' specimens (that is, not crossed with those of Greylag ancestry) can be sexed at six to eight weeks by this feature. The Chinese is recommended by enthusiasts as a useful breed for keeping the grass down and for providing meat and eggs; it is ornamental and a good watchdog, having acquired a loud voice and a greater inclination to use it during the course of domestication.

Although it is now rather unusual in Europe, the **African** breed apparently reached this continent ahead of the Chinese variety, at least 200 years ago. Count de Buffon published the first description in his *Natural History*

The Chinese Goose according to Count de Buffon in 1793. This is obviously an African Goose imported into Europe at a fairly early date. Redrawn by Sue Hazeldine.

of 1793 and called it the Cape Goose; he mentions that the skin of the dewlap beneath the throat was used by Cape Colony soldiers as a pouch for tobacco (29). Thomas Bewick (1753–1828) also referred to this curious appendage, so one must assume that he too was more familiar with the African breed than the Chinese. The bird resembles the Chinese in colour and general shape, but is less swan-like, with a shorter neck and a larger, deeper body. Its most striking character is the pronounced dewlap or gullet, similar to that of the Toulouse. It has remained a popular breed in Africa and the USA.

MICHAELMAS GEESE

The widespread custom of eating a goose at Michaelmas (the feast of St Michael and All Angels on 29 September) probably has its roots in the ancient Celtic ritual at which a bird was sacrificed to increase crop fertility during the next season. The idea that it was lucky to do so certainly caught on: 'Whoso eats goose on Michaelmas Day shall never lack money his debts to pay'. There is an often repeated tale that Queen Elizabeth was dining on goose when the news of the defeat of the Armada was brought to her, and that she decreed that roast goose should be served on the anniversary of the day (29 September 1588) in celebration and remembrance. The story is mentioned in Alfred Suzanne's *La Cuisine Anglaise* (1904) and therefore appears in *Larousse* (1938); Monsieur Suzanne may have read it in Mrs Beeton's *Book of Household Management* (1861), where we are given the detail (3) that Her Majesty was at the table of an English baronet (said by other authorities to be Sir Neville Umfreyville). The trouble with the detail is that the baronetage was not created until 1611, and with the theory itself is that the Armada was defeated in July. We know that the glad tidings were not kept from the Queen for two months: indeed the thanksgiving sermon for the victory was preached in St Paul's Cathedral on 20 August.

Michaelmas is also the quarter day when many rents are due and tenancies end and begin; others have suggested, therefore, that a fat goose was the gift that softened the landlord's heart. Geese were associated with Michaelmas before the reign of the Tudors (the poet George Gascoigne, who was born in 1535 and died before the Armada sailed, wrote 'At Christmas a capon, at Michaelmas a goose') probably for the prosaic reason that they were ready and partly because of a link to that pre-Christian sacrifice to the success of next year's crops. Geese were plucked in large numbers and the word 'gossamer', meaning fine cobwebs beaded with dew, derives from the Middle English 'goose-summer' – warm autumn days when masses of goose-down hung in the air.

Michaelmas was, as well, the time when men and women were looking for new employment; this they did at Michaelmas Fairs, most contracts running from one fair to the next. So important were domestic geese in the rural economy, and so critical were these autumn gatherings for the sale of that season's birds, that many were called Goose Fairs (4, 37).

GOOSE FAIRS

A European agricultural community required the existence of markets and fairs (37). Markets were held in quick succession for the sale of perishable produce, while fairs were less frequent and involved the seasonal sale of animals. In Britain, many fairs were associated with ancient sanctuaries where a deity hallowed the ground and superstition maintained an

Gossamer on an autumn morning. Tennyson wrote the lovely line: 'all the silvery Gossamers that twinkle into green and gold'. Drawn by Sue Hazeldine.

uneasy peace between the traders. This sacred truce which lasted for the days of the fair was, in Christian times, symbolised by the market cross. The point has been made that the old and prestigious universities of Oxford and Cambridge were established on the sites of autumn fairs (St Frideswide's and Sturbridge) rather than as, on the Continent, near religious houses; for hundreds of years, trading has had a major influence on the culture of the British!

Fairs were subject to their own rules administered at 'Pie Powder' Courts, a title corrupted from *pieds poudrés* or 'dusty footed' – a reference to the state of the walking trader and his beasts. The justice dispensed included heavy fines for those who 'forestalled'; it was an offence to buy goods on the way to market and to sell them at a profit. There is an account of 22 geese that were forfeited by the Sheriffs of London because, on 13 October 1375 'after dinner', they had got only so far as Holborn on their way to the City market when they were forestalled. Geese had to walk all the way with their original master and, often, it must have been a long trek as fairs attracted people from a wide area.

A goose fair, for which a charter was granted in 1105, is still held at Tavistock in Devon every October, and follows a smaller but more famous Widecombe Fair which dealt mostly with the sale of horses. The ditty 'Widecombe Fair' is a version of the 'Tavistock Goosey Fair Song':

> *'Tis just a month come Friday next*
> *Bill Champernown and me*
> *Us drove across old Dartymoor*
> *The Goosey Fair to see.*

Colyford Goose Fair, also in Devon, takes place on 28 September, the charter having been granted by King John in 1208; and Ovingham, where Thomas Bewick is buried, near the Roman wall in Northumbria, has a recently revived one held in June. This suggests a change of date, or perhaps the event was originally a Green-goose Fair. These smaller events were for the sale of goslings up to four months of age, which presumably could not walk far. In 1724, for instance, Daniel Defoe (14) recorded that Stamford on the Great North Road – called Ermine Street in Roman times – had three fairs: St Simon and St Jude (28 October), St James (25 July) and a Green-goose Fair.

An ancient track known as Sewstern Lane linked Stamford with England's greatest Goose Fair which is held annually at Nottingham 62 km (40 miles) away. King Edward I granted the charter in 1284 and by the mid-16th Century it was known as the Goose Fair. It lasts three days and starts on the first Thursday in October, although it was originally a September event during which, in medieval times, 20,000 geese changed hands annually. They walked in via the Fosse Way, another Roman road, and Sewstern Lane, through the Goose Gate on the eastern side of the town, to the Old Market Square. D. H. Lawrence, who was educated at Nottingham High School, wrote a short story *Goose Fair* (31) which begins: 'Through the gloom of evening, and the flare of torches of the night before the fair, through the still fogs of the succeeding dawn came paddling the weary geese, lifting their poor feet that had been dipped in tar for shoes, and trailing them along the cobble-stones into the town.

A GPO stamp was issued to commemorate a variety of old English fairs and markets; this poem refers to Nottingham's Goose Fair:

'Twas Goose Fair cracked the merriest wheeze
Where Babel's babble filled the breeze;
Glad Goose Fair's gambols oft would cheer
The country side throughout the year'.

Last of all, in the afternoon, a country girl drove in her dozen birds, disconsolate because she was so late'.

Geese descended from the Greylag have only one spring breeding season. Traditionally, first eggs are laid on 2 February, and by Michaelmas the resulting youngsters were required to walk long distances in order to be sold. There was nothing new in this. Pliny recorded that they walked from Morini to Rome: 'the weary geese are placed in front, and those following by a natural pressure urge them on'. Geese bred by the peoples of Gaul and Germania were even driven across the Alps for sale in Italy. The longest journeys expected of them in Britain were from Norfolk to London, a distance of about 128 km (80 miles), from the East Anglian coast ports where birds were landed from Holland, and from Wales to London, about 160 km (100 miles) (4,27).

GEESE TO LONDON

The Poultry is a City of London street that runs eastward from Cheapside to the Royal Exchange. It bears the name of the commodity once sold there, as do Milk Street, Bread Street, Silver Street, Honey Lane, Wood Street and Ironmonger Lane nearby. Cheapside, when first called Cheape, was the main market for the capital and its centre was filled with stalls. It derives its name from the Old English word 'cieping' (19), meaning a market (as in Chipping Camden and Chipstead and even, apparently, in Copenhagen). John Stow, in his 1598 *Survey of London* (45), says that 'Men of trades and sellers of wares in this city have often since changed their places as they found their best advantage ... poulters of late (have) removed out of the Poultrie, betwixt the Stockes and the great Conduit in Cheape, into Grasse Street and St Nicholas shambles'. He goes on to describe the adjacent Scalding Alley where the poulters had scalded their birds although they were 'but lately departed'. So Poultry had lost its principle tradesmen by Elizabethan times. We do not know when they arrived and gave the street its name, but the word comes from the Old French *pouleterie*, so it was probably post-1066. An ordinance of 1345, in the reign of King Edward III, directs poulters who were not freemen of the City to sell their birds at the new Leadenhall (where the market still specialises in poultry today) and, by 1375, freemen also were being ordered to set their stands before the Church of St Nicholas Shambles. Stow lists the monuments to poulters that had been buried by Scalding Alley at the church of St Mildred; none died later than 1487. St Mildred's was destroyed in the Great Fire of September 1666, one of nearly 90 churches to be burnt. Although rebuilt by Wren, it was again demolished to make way for a bank and, today, the only trace of the poulters' parish church and their nearby scalding ground is an alley called St Mildred's Court.

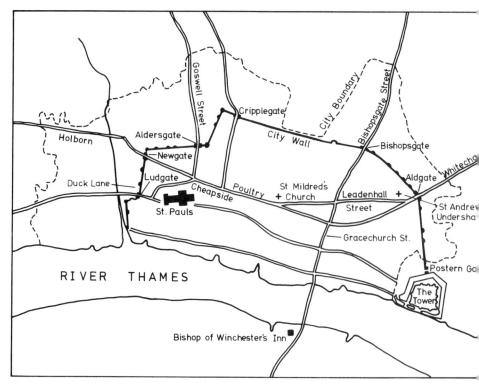

A map of medieval London showing some of the streets and places referred to in the text. Redrawn by John Turner.

Treatment with hot water is still an essential part of the preparation of duck and goose carcasses. The modern recommendation is that the temperature should be 63–66°C, and immersion for $1\frac{1}{2}$–3 minutes guarantees that feathers can be picked off easily. It is not hard to imagine why the mess (or shambles) of slaughter and scalding in the open centre of medieval London needed regulation and containment. In 1416, the Wardens of the Worshipful Company of Poulters were instructing members to sell geese with feet, head and intestines 'entire' (30) in an attempt to make the streets a little cleaner. And, later, anyone keeping swans, geese, herons and other poultry was told to move to the outskirts of the City. Duke Street (now Little Britain), near Smithfield Market, started as Duck Lane, and was just outside the old Roman Wall; this was where ducks were fattened.

How did the domestic geese, ducks and fowl reach Poultry, Duck Lane, Grasse (later Gracechurch) Street and Leadenhall? The 'drove road' for cattle was wide Whitechapel which came through Aldgate. Almost certainly most of the geese were driven in via the western and northern gates in the City wall; the small birds may have been carried but the geese walked. Aldersgate, the narrowest of the five Roman entrances, opens into Goswell Road and goes on to Islington to join the Great North Road (to the east) or Watling Street (to the west). Goswell Road was originally a rather shorter Goswell Street (where Charles Dickens lodged Mr Pickwick with Mrs Bardell) and ran from Aldersgate Street to just beyond Old Street; its name 'Goose Well Road' is a reminder of the thousands of weary geese that passed this way and of their need for a watering place. Streets known as 'Gospelgate' at Louth and Lincoln are similar legacies of ancient goose pools near the towns' minor access points, while Gosford Street in Coventry, which went through the city wall and across the River Sherbourne on the western side, held a market until 1822. (The right 'to guse gate' or 'goosegate' in the Lake District, incidentally, used to be conferred as part of a parson's fee, and meant that he might pasture birds on the open common.)

Traditionally geese for the London market were hatched and reared in eastern England. Here wild Greylag bred until 1500 or so, and goslings were probably caught and added to the stock indiscriminately; as already said, it was this practice that kept the old English Grey Goose so variable into modern times. Mrs Beeton, in 1860, gave her opinion that the best geese came from Suffolk, Norfolk and Berkshire, but the largest flocks

'Lincolnshire Geese at Home' fattening for Christmas in December 1877. From Rowley's *Ornithological Miscellany* of 1878.

'Lag 'em, Lag 'em.' Lincolnshire gossards with their driving sticks on the road from Kirton to Boston, November 1877. From Rowley's *Ornithological Miscellany* of 1878. Goose and duck farmers in many parts of Asia use similar sticks tipped with flags to drive their flocks.

were reared in the fens of Lincolnshire and Cambridgeshire where they had easy access to water (3). Defoe (14), in his *Tour through the Whole Island of Great Britain* published in 1727, tells us that goose-driving started in August 'by which time the harvest is almost over, and the geese may feed on the stubbles as they go. Thus they hold on to the end of October, when the roads begin to be too stiff and deep for their broad feet and short legs to march in'. He went on to describe the latest contraption, a four-storied carriage in which the geese could be put 'one above another, by which invention one cart will carry a very great number and for the smoother going, they drive with two horses a-breast, like a coach ... Changing horses they travel night and day; so that they bring the fowls 70, 80 or 100 miles [112, 130 or 160 km] in two days and one night ... and infinite numbers are thus carried to London every year.' Presumably the geese arrived in better condition for the table than if they walked. However, they probably were not killed immediately: 'large herds of them are sent every year to London to be fattened by the Metropolitan poulters' (Mrs Beeton again).

Geese, guided by a 'gozzerd' and in droves of 1,000 or 2,000, could cover about $1\frac{1}{2}$ kmph (1 mph) and, at most, 16 km (10 miles) a day (4,42);

on 2 September 1783, a drove of about 9,000 geese passed through Chelmsford on their way from Suffolk to London (42). An Act of Charles II laid down that all droves (of cattle, sheep, pigs and ponies, as well as geese) stopped on Sundays. To make the long walk a little easier, they were sometimes, as D. H. Lawrence (31) wrote, given 'shoes' of tar and sand. A letter in *Country Life* of November 1977 tells of the writer's grandfather, of Holmwood, Surrey, shoeing geese in 1896 before driving them to market at Dorking about three miles distant. 'He constructed a trough about 18 in [45 cm] high and 15 ft to 16 ft long [4.5–4.8 m], in which he put about 6 in [15 cm] of dry sand. The feet of each goose was coated with Stockholm tar and then driven through the sand'. This footwear was so effective that a wager for 500 guineas (£525) is said to have been laid in 1740 between Lords Orford and Rockingham (42) that a flock of geese with tarred feet would beat a flock of Turkeys in leather boots in a race from Norwich to London. The geese won by a clear two days because the Turkeys insisted on spending the nights in trees and the drovers wasted valuable time getting them down before they could be on their way every morning!

In Whalley Church, Lancashire, not far from Martin Mere, there is a misericord that depicts a man shoeing a goose (4). It was carved about

'Shoeing the Goose' – a misericord made in the 15th Century for Whalley Abbey, Lancashire, now in Whalley Parish Church. Photograph by Eileen Preston.

1430 and the inscription in Old English reads 'Whoso melles him of that al men dos, let hym cum hier and shoe the ghos'. The goose is held in a vice-like contraption, with a rope harness around its bill. An obvious blacksmith, backed by anvil and bellows, is raising a hammer to the bird's foot. It is hardly likely that the scene is meant to show real life; the witty message probably means 'if you are going to come here and meddle in our affairs, we'll put you to the absurd task of making iron shoes for waterfowl'. A similar scene is depicted on a misericord at Beverley Minster, Humberside, which was carved about 90 years after the Whalley one.

The subject of goose-shoeing is ambiguous (4). The birds were certainly given boots of tar and sand, or tar and sawdust. The tar was applied in layers by walking the flock through a bath of it a number of times, and was eventually peeled off leaving a clean skin. Sometimes little pads of felt seem to have been added (4). But more than that – apparently there was a smith near Dolwyddelen, Gwynedd, who had his own method of shoeing geese which involved a device that fastened on their feet and had a spike an inch or so in length underneath. It is difficult to see how this would have allowed the birds to walk, but a smithy near Aylesbury is said to have re-shod Welsh geese on their long walk to London (27). At Ilchester, Somerset, 'a saddler and harness-maker made boots of soft leather for the travelling geese. These boots were carried by the drovers and placed on the feet of the geese that became lame or suffered damage to their feet in the long walks'.

The confusion comes because 'to shoe a goose' is also a saying that means to engage in a foolish or fruitless undertaking – to fritter away one's time on unnecessary work. The Beverley misericord actually shows horse-shoes being used on the birds, and probably records a medieval joke; the same witticism was known in Old French: *ferroit les oyes* means to play about or trifle.

Because much poultry, especially geese and ducks, breeds in spring, the young birds were ready to eat only between August and February. By the end of the 18th Century, when London had a million inhabitants, an early statistician calculated that in a week they consumed: 1,000 geese for six months (or 26,000 annually), 1,000 'turkies' for six months, 2,000 capons, 500 dozen chickens, 4,300 ducks and 2,000 dozen pigeons for eight months. Turkeys were introduced into England in the late 15th Century; the navigator and Yorkshireman William Strickland seems to have brought the bird to Bristol in 1497 and been allowed to have a 'turkey in its pride' on the crest of his coat of arms. James I began the Christmas tradition of serving Turkey instead of swan or peacock (see also Chapter 6), and the taste gradually spread until by 1790, as we have seen, equal numbers of Turkeys and geese were being bought by London's residents. With one exception in the 1980s, the last troops of geese walked to London in 1838 (42) – the growth of the railways, improvement of road surfaces, and the decline of free vergeside grazing had put an end to over 300 years of the drover's trade (4). The recent exception was a journey from Norfolk

A misericord in Beverley Minster, Humberside, carved about 1520, with a fox preaching to a congregation of geese (see Chapter 3), and a supporter showing a man shoeing a goose. Photograph by Eileen Preston.

to Smithfield market undertaken for a film called '(S)laughterhouse' (see Chapter 5).

GEESE AS FOOD

In past centuries, the importance of the peasant family's goose was emphasised by the Middle German name of *Federnaschwein* or 'feathered pig'! All parts had immediate value and the fat preserved joints for winter consumption (25). In Germany, goose stuffed with chestnuts was as important in the cuisine as beef was in Old England (42), and the foremost use of goose that comes to the English mind is as a roast dinner. St Wulfstan (1009–1095), Bishop of Worcester, is said to have been so distracted by the smell of roast goose drifting from the monastery kitchens while he served High Mass that he vowed to abstain from meat thereafter. The *Form of Cury* ('A Method of Cookery'), our first collection of recipes written down about 1390, contains one for stuffed goose. From Piers Ploughman to Bob Cratchit, geese have been esteemed for their delicious taste and reserved for special occasions. The nobility may have eaten swan or peacock on 25 December, roasted before a huge fire, but ordinary folk had goose. Only during the Commonwealth, when extreme puritanism abolished all festivals and holy days (a minister in Scotland in 1659 actually searched houses to rid them of the Christmas goose (1)), did the custom lapse under protest. The bird was stuffed with sage and onions, and, from the 18th Century, cooked at the local baker's, since most people would

The graves of Ann and George Basey, goose and Turkey farmers of Norfolk in the 19th Century. These gravestones are at Ashby St Mary. Photograph by Eileen Preston.

have lacked a large grate and lots of fuel. It was, in the Cratchit's festive meal (17), served with mashed potatoes and apple sauce – 'there never was such a goose, its tenderness, size and cheapness were the theme of universal admiration'. Afterwards, the family ate Christmas pudding boiled in the wash-house copper and blazed with brandy, apples, oranges and roasted chestnuts, and drank a punch of gin and lemons. Scrooge sent, too late to go to the baker's oven, a monster Turkey, 'foreign' but fashionable: one wonders which the Cratchits preferred.

So good was roast goose in popular esteem that various substitutes were devised for the real thing. For instance, 'Colonial Goose' was boned leg of mutton whose cavity had been filled with onions, breadcrumbs and herbs; it was intended to vary the monotony of the Australian sheep farmer's diet. Roast Black Swan served with a port-wine sauce was another more fashionable item in the 19th Century Australian cuisine. At Michaelmas, the really poor cottager of East Anglia made do with 'goose in disguise' – a couple of baked sheep's hearts, stuffed and wrapped in pastry carefully moulded to form a 'breast bone'. 'Bombay Duck', by the way, is a further colonial curiosity – a small fish that is dried and eaten as a relish.

Consumer preference in England changed from the Grey Goose to the larger Continental strains throughout the 19th Century; and the curtailment of free grazing made the homegrown ones scarcer anyway. G. D. Rowley (42) obtained the following information as to the number of geese consumed by Londoners at Christmas 1877:

'In Leadenhall market arrived about 38,000. These were thus divided, viz.:-

French	20,000
Dutch, fed in England	5,000
Irish, fed in England	5,000
Irish, killed in Ireland	5,000
English natives	1,000
Hamburg and Belgium (very large)	2,000

'A great many Geese, both English and foreign, were sold direct to cooperative stores and clubs, which never came to market.

'It is calculated by the above authority that about 100,000 Geese passed through the London trade; each Goose averaged from 10 to 11 lb [4.5–5.0 kg], and sold at from 8d. to 9d. per lb [7p–8p per kilo]. These figures show how much the breeding of English native Geese has declined.'

In the accounts kept at Berkeley Castle in the 13th Century, a goose was valued at 3d, pigeons were $\frac{1}{4}$d each and a fat pig was 2s. In 1274, in the reign of Edward I, the price of geese varied three times a year: between Easter and Pentecost they were 5d, Pentecost to 1 August 4d, and, for the rest of the year when they were plentiful, 3d (a wild goose cost 4d). From

A flock of 800 geese moving along the Horncastle road by Bargate drain, Boston, Lincolnshire in December 1877. From Rowley's *Ornithological Miscellany* of 1878.

1363–1512, the price remained at 6d, but then started to rise (30). By 1627, Turkey cocks were 4s 6d, hens 3s, cock pheasant 6s, hen pheasant 5s, a goose 2s and a dozen pigeons 6s★. Game was still pricey in 1786 when *The London Adviser and Guide* (46) listed pork chops at 7–8d a lb, a goose weighing 10 lb (4.5 kg) at 5s, a duck 3s, a couple of wild ducks 2s 6d and a pheasant at 5s. Turkey cost about 2s 6d more than goose until the middle of the 20th Century when intensive farming of the former began to tip the scales; by 1985 a goose ready for the oven was £15.20, a Turkey £8.10 and a pig some £80.00.

A recipe from *The Complete Housewife* of 1773 tells us how to pot a goose and a Turkey and it sounds delicious. 'Potting' as a method of preserving cooked meat in a deep crock of butter had been known since Elizabethan times – although this dish was obviously for immediate consumption: 'Take a fat goose, a fat turkey; cut them down the rump, and take out all the bones. Lay them flat open, and season them very well with white pepper, nutmeg and salt, allowing three nutmegs, with the like proportion of pepper, and as much salt as both the spices. When you have seasoned them all over, let your turkey be within the goose, and keep them in season two nights and a day. Then roll them up as collared beef, very tight, and as short as you can, and bind very fast with strong tape. Bake it in a long pot, with a good store of butter, till it is very tender, as you may feel by the end. Let it lie in the hot liquor an hour, then take it out and let it stand till next day. Then unbind it for use, and slice it out thin.'

Sage, onion, salt and pepper, with sometimes nutmeg or mace, were the traditional English seasoning for geese – with 'apple sauce in a bason' (1773). Onions cooked in milk, then chopped and the whole thickened with flour and butter, made a sauce for both duck and boiled goose.

The use of goose fat in cooking and preserving has influenced greatly the cuisine of the Dordogne and Languedoc regions of France where other oils such as olive oil and butter are relatively scarce (13). The rich grease of the goose, which melts at a lower temperature than other animal fats, goes into the pan for frying eggs, sausages or steak, for cooking a daube of beef, or a thick cabbage and bean soup. Goose pieces are preserved for late winter use in jars of *confit* – cooked until they are meltingly tender and covered in a layer of goose fat. From Languedoc comes the famous *cassoulet*, an amalgam of haricot beans, sausages, pork, mutton and preserved goose, cooked for hours in an earthenware pot with garlic and herbs. Elizabeth David (13) calls the dish 'sumptuous' and reminds us that the Greeks thought goose fat an aphrodisiac.

Goose eggs are also good at 170–280 g (6–10 oz) in weight, but have never been widely available since most were needed to hatch and grow into the next generation. Goose egg yolk was found to be a durable vehicle

★6d = £0.025 (2.5p), 2s = £0.10 (10p) – these are coinage equivalents, not value equivalents with present day decimal coinage. There were twelve pennies (12d) to a shilling (1s) and twenty shillings to a pound (£1).

for pigment, and its use allowed the development of painting *in tempera* (see Chapter 9).

PÂTÉ DE FOIE GRAS

To many Frenchmen, fattened goose liver or *foie gras* is the perfect food; in fact, the French currently import some 1,500 tonnes a year, much of it from Israel, because home-grown supplies are inadequate. However, they tend to regard *foie gras* as an expensive and seasonal dish, eaten particularly at Christmas, so one must suppose that a lot is re-exported after preparation, perhaps to England where gourmets are not far behind in their appreciation for its 'silky smoothness'. Fresh raw *foie gras* was selling in London in 1988 at £27.50 per kilo (£12.45 per pound). Sydney Smith (1771–1845), the journalist and cleric, characterised heaven as 'eating *pâté de foie gras* to the sound of trumpets' (hell, on the other hand, was a thousand years of tough mutton).

Why are ducks and geese the only domestic birds that are overfed to the point where their liver cells grossly enlarge with deposited fat? Wild-fowl seem to be particularly prone to the disease of fatty degeneration. As water-birds they naturally carry more fat beneath the abdominal skin than other poultry and, being migratory, have a tendency to eat more and lay down stores of lipids in the autumn and spring. Migratory cranes, as well as geese, were force-fed by the Egyptians (47).

The English have almost never indulged in the practice of force-feeding domestic birds but, as well as the Egyptians, Greeks, Romans, many other Europeans and the Israelis did and still do. In the 2nd Century AD, Plutarch the Greek was recording the sewing up of the eyes of swans and

The forcible feeding of geese and cranes, a relief carving from the tomb of Mereruka at Saqqara, in Eygpt, about 4,000 years old.

cranes to 'shut them up in darkness' so that they could be fattened. Mrs Beeton (3) wrote that 'we would rather abstain from the acquaintance of a man who ate *pâté de foie gras*, knowing its component parts', and she gives a disturbing account of the 19th Century treatment of Rouen ducks in Brittany and Normandy. 'The poor birds are *nailed* by the feet to a board close to a fire and, in that position, plentifully supplied with food and water. In a few days, the carcase is reduced to a mere shadow, while the liver has grown monstrously'. Geese and ducks still have mash pumped down their gullets, but selective breeding and careful husbandry ensure that those birds that are forced to overeat 'accept their gross meals of ground corn willingly'. Cruelty is no longer so apparent.

The liver, as well as storing fat, is the body's sieve and a scrapyard for substances that reach it via the bloodstream. Fatty degeneration is not unusual in any bird that is overfed on carbohydrates and kept relatively short of fibre – the Romans and medieval French used ripe figs, the modern French employ the more effective maize. If the animal is also under-exercised in warm weather, further symptoms of disease are likely. The liver enlarges as lipids are deposited, and it starts to press on the other organs; in the last stages of degeneration, liver tissue is replaced in a condition known as cirrhosis, and the heart, kidneys and other parts of the gut are affected. The *foie gras* farmer must kill his stricken bird before

The 'cramming' of a goose for the production of *foie gras*. Photo supplied by Compassion in World Farming.

fibrous cirrhosis nodules appear and vital body functions cease of their own accord. A 6.5 kg (14$\frac{1}{4}$ lb) Landes Goose will be fed over 700 g (1$\frac{1}{2}$ lb) daily in three meals for a three week period and produce a liver weighing 1.14 kg (2$\frac{1}{2}$ lb) (20). In a duck, cramming, or *le gavage*, occurs during the same last 21 days of life, when the liver enlarges sixfold.

Presumably it would be difficult to cram an animal that had some natural ability to regurgitate. Wildfowl never bring their food back; they do not feed their young on pre-digested items, nor cast pellets of indigestible matter, neither are they sick merely as a method of rejecting something unpleasant from their crops. Thus they seem to have been first class candidates for producing 'the supreme fruit of gastronomy'.

The French changed to the large-scale stuffing of ducks, especially hybrid ducks, rather than geese because a demand for *foie gras* for export was made outside the traditional pre-Christmas period when geese and truffles were naturally mature. Muscovies (known as Barbary Ducks) and hybrid Muscovy/Mallards (called Mulards) could be made available over a longer season than geese (see later).

The best *foie gras* is reputed to come from Alsace, around Strasbourg (13); it matures with age, like a good wine, and is the most esteemed dish in the Alsatian cuisine, being served and given as gifts on many special occasions. It can be bought in heart-shaped presentation jars with the inscription *et puis voici mon coeur* – here is my liver, 'now take my heart'! Nevertheless, the Dordogne, where the Périgord truffle flourishes, is *foie gras*'s natural home. There trained dogs and pigs search oak woods for the prized fungus which may be found up to a foot deep in the calcareous soil. Tiny pieces of truffle are inserted into the liver before it is steamed and after it has been separated from the bile sac and soaked for a while in milk. Lesser quality livers are made into spreads for sandwiches; the most choice are served cold at the start of a meal, often with a sweetish white wine, or sautéd with salt and pepper.

How did the idea of force-feeding or cramming originate? As so often in human evolution, a religious requirement seems to have provided the inspiration, and the practice is a very ancient one. Animals were either fattened for sacrifice, or they were considered to be an incarnation of a god and maintained in temples as cult objects (47). They were selected from the wild because they had particular markings or other attributes thought to be divine but, whatever the reason, it was not because they would settle and live contentedly in captivity. Routinely, they had to be force-fed if they were to be kept alive. Perhaps cranes and geese were chosen because their migratory habits appeared magical to the Egyptians, and their arrival every year coincided with a significant stage in the flooding of the Nile. Other sacred animals were kept for fattening and were hand-fed, such as oryx, hyena and certain cattle (47). These practices arose among pre-agricultural men, at an early stage of religious development, when the animal spirit was something to be appeased and propitiated. So the cult purpose was older than the utilitarian one, but the measures necessary to maintain an animal for the gods were eventually to prove useful in domestication.

FEATHERS

Goose quills – the primary feathers of the wing – provided the flights for arrows, for shuttlecocks and for the pens of many generations of our ancestors (the word 'pen' comes from the Latin *penna* meaning a feather). The hollow quill allowed sufficient ink to be retained to complete a few words of script (48). The Brent Goose has the local name of Quink, and it is suggested that the brand of ink of the same name was called after its quills (24). At the beginning of the last century, it was said that half the pens in Europe came from Meckleberg in Germany where geese were particularly numerous (42). The Declaration of Independence, as already pointed out, was signed with a goose feather, and thousands of important literary and musical works have been composed and recorded by this means. Indeed, between the 6th Century and the early 19th, until steel nibs were introduced (and Birmingham, England, became the centre of the pen trade), quills were the major writing implement of the civilised world. Although they were chiefly obtained from geese plucked live in the spring, feathers from swans and crows were occasionally employed. Only the five outer primaries were serviceable and, of these, the second and third were considered the best; left wings were preferred by right-handed persons as they curved out and away from the writer. 'A goose-quill is more dangerous than a lion's claw' is a proverb that suggests that

The musician Thomas Tallis (1505–1585); the greatest of early Tudor composers used, as did all calligraphers until the 19th Century, a goose quill pen. Drawn by Sue Hazeldine.

The flights of shuttlecocks were made from goose quills. This wood-engraving, from a series illustrating children's games, is entitled 'battledore and shuttlecock' and is by Luke Clennell (1781–1840), one of Thomas Bewick's apprentices.

the written word can do lasting injury. John Stow has been referred to as the chronicler of 16th Century London (45); his effigy in the Church of St Andrew Undershaft, Leadenhall Street, writes for ever in a large ledger and, around 5 April every year, the Lord Mayor and Sheriffs offer a prayer of thanksgiving for Stow's industry and leave a new white goose quill in his stony hand.

The use of stiff pinion feathers to provide vanes to an arrow's shaft (fletching) is so old and universal that we have no evidence of where or how the system was invented (26). The vanes control the yaw of the arrow as it passes through the air, and this discovery must have revolutionised hunting with a bow. Paper and, more recently, plastic have been used for fletching; Roger Ascham, in his *Toxophilus* of 1571, emphatically preferred goose feathers. 'The goose is man's comfort in war and in peace, sleeping and waking . . . how fit as her feathers be only for shooting, so be her quills fit only for writing . . . the old goose feather is still and strong, good for a wind . . . the young goose feather is weak and fine, best for a swift shaft'. In the days of archery, England is said to have been saved by 'the crooked stick and the grey goose wing', a reference to the supremacy of the bow and arrow in combat.

The game of battledore and shuttlecock, which employs a 'ball' made of cork and 14 to 16 goose feathers about 60 mm ($2\frac{1}{2}$ in) long, also originated in antiquity. There are Greek drawings representing the game, and it has been popular in the Far East for at least 2,000 years. In Europe it was a children's game until the last century when badminton, played over a net, was developed and the trimmed feathers of the shuttlecock were replaced eventually by plastic.

Beds stuffed with goose down seem not to have been found much in England before Elizabethan times. Straw and wool were the normal stuffing in a bedstead's mattress, but 'beds' (loose upper mattresses), bolsters and pillows were increasingly filled with down obtained after the birds were killed at Michaelmas, or by plucking the geese live four or five times a year. There were important feather industries in Lincolnshire and

Luke Clennell's wood-engraving of a flock of domestic geese on their way to feed. Until arable fields became normal, grazing stock roamed free on common land; so enclosure was not popular with country folk, provoking the anonymous lines published in 1821:

> *The fault is great in man and woman*
> *Who steals a goose from off a common;*
> *But what can plead that man's excuse*
> *Who steals a common from a goose?*

Somerset during the 18th Century (41). Large flocks of up to 900 birds grazed the commons and produced, for every four birds, 1lb (450 g) of feathers a year; the barbarous business of live-plucking only stopped in England when enclosures limited access to free grazing. Horsehair, much of it imported from South America, thereafter became the usual filling for mattresses (42), and in 1797 goose-owners on the Somerset levels burnt an effigy of a drainage agent whose activities preceded their loss of commoner's rights (41).

Live-plucking began with the Romans and today occurs mainly in Hungary where birds are stripped of their breast feathers several times before the Christmas slaughter (43); without feathers, they eat more to maintain body heat and end up at higher weights for killing. In Somerset around Wedmore during the 1740s, goose feathers were sold at 9d a lb, and a flock of 100 birds produced annually 25 lb (11.3 kg) in weight. By 1871, the value of feathers in London varied from 1s 2d to 1s 4d per lb for the best grey, and 1s 8d to 1s 10d for white. During dressing, the feathers lost about a quarter of their weight and retailed at 2s 6d or 3s 6d per lb (42). The proportion of foreign feathers was then about two thirds, with 775 tonnes coming from the Continent, mainly Russia, and 300 tonnes being home-produced from living birds. The modern British feather industry uses dead geese and expects to collect 1lb (453 g) of dry feathers from three birds, so a total of 4 oz (113 g) produced from four live pluckings a year would not have denuded an 18th Century goose completely – just under one fifth of its plumage was being removed at any time. It was obviously a very unpleasant procedure (36), and the end was no better; according to Francis Grose's *Dictionary of the Vulgar Tongue* published in 1811, 'cagg maggs' were old Lincolnshire geese which, having been plucked for ten or twelve years, were 'sent up to London to feast the cockneys'.

It is because the goose is a water bird and needs insulation from the cold while swimming that its plumage has the qualities of warmth, lightness, elasticity and softness that are so beneficial for quilts and cushions. The feathers of the domestic fowl (or 'chicken') are much harsher and less fluffy. Obviously, white geese are preferred by the bedding trade and, nowadays, 'pure white goose down' pillows and duvets seem part of the movement back to things natural. In the Poitiers region of France, white goose skins are cured with the soft down still attached, and manufactured into 'swansdown' trimmings and powder puffs. Swansdown used to come from the real thing – and the trade from North America in wild Trumpeter Swans' *Cygnus buccinator* skins once brought that bird to near extinction. extinction.

GEESE AS FIGHTERS, GUARDS AND WEEDERS

For many centuries, Russian geese were bred selectively for male aggression (28). In 1842, a book by Bonington Moubray (36) described the goosepits of St Petersburg where ganders, who pecked and beat their opponents hard with their wings, were put together until they drew blood and sometimes killed one another. Unlike cock-fighting, the sport was restricted to the start of the breeding season, and the birds' mates were present to shout encouragement. The breast muscles were enhanced by developing the wings as weapons and, although it was said to be impossible to fatten fighters to the same extent as Toulouse Geese, their table properties were excellent. Goose-fighting was banned a century ago so that the pure breeds, the Tula and Arsamas (43), have largely disappeared.

As sentinels and guards, geese have legendary qualities. It is the same territorial behaviour (mostly threat rather than fight), plus a tendency to call and warn the mate and the rest of the flock of danger, that is invoked. Their eyesight is acute and their awareness of sounds at night has been especially praised. F. O. Morris in 1897 (35) pointed out that 'you may drive over a cat, dog, hen, pig, or even pigeon, but few, if any, can record an instance of driving over a tame goose'. They seem to lack the agitation that we associate with most birds, and to be 'as intelligent, responsive and biddable' as any flocking mammal. Undoubtedly these virtues are the bases of much of the respect shown to the goose since its early domestication. To have called a children's nurse Mother Goose ('*Ma Mère l'Oye*' in French and '*Fru Gosen*' in German) seems to have been a natural expression of the affection felt for a trusted member of the family.

When the Gauls attacked Rome in 390 BC, some advanced up the Capitoline Hill so quietly that the leader reached the top unchallenged. As he climbed over the rampart, however, the sacred geese cackled and awoke the garrison. The Gaul was hurled back over the precipice and the

Jacob the goose in the contemporary painting, reproduced by kind permission of Col. Sir Brian Barttelot Bt, OBE, DL, Regimental Lieutenant-Colonel of the Coldstream Guards.

city saved (43). To commemorate the event, a golden goose was carried in procession to the Capitol every year and the dogs whipped as a punishment for their silence.

The Coldstream Guards had a pet goose called Jacob (21) who was acquired in 1838 by a post near Quebec that was pestered both by rebels and foxes. One day the sentry saw a goose fleeing in his direction chased by a fox. His first inclination was to shoot the pursuer, but he knew that the sound of a shot would signal an alarm, so he watched in despair until the goose ran between his legs to safety in the sentry box. Thereafter, the goose stayed by the side of every successive sentry and, remarkably, was to save in turn the life of his preserver – a silent enemy approached at night to knife the guard, but Jacob flew at him and shouted a warning. In the fullness of time, he came to London with the battalion and was admired by the great Duke of Wellington; when he died, he was buried with military honours – except for his head which is mounted in the regimental museum (21).

We still read of domestic geese being used as watchdogs. Typically they are of Swan Goose descent, with the same excellent sight and hearing, and with vocal qualities that rouse and carry. At Lamberhurst in Kent, a grower of Christmas trees had 60 birds running loose in his woodland, and a whisky warehouse on Clydeside has had Chinese Geese since 1959 to alert the human guards to intruders. They have an 'obvious advantage over micro-electronic devices: since the flock includes a gander, the system reproduces itself'.

In Malaysia, flocks are employed for a related but different purpose: they are kept to drive snakes away from cocoa and rubber plantations. The deadly black cobras are small enough to be difficult to see among the layers of fallen leaves. Geese detect them, however, and create 'such a racket and a nuisance that the snakes readily depart from the area'. Many fatal bites among the workers are thus prevented. Presumably, the geese are of Swan Goose type to whom snakes might be a natural hazard. I have never seen a confrontation between a wild goose and a snake – normally their ranges would not overlap. Does a Greylag-descended domestic goose react to a reptile in the same manner as a Swan Goose?

Today's Egyptian scarab-makers have been known to render their modern works ancient by having a goose swallow them (6) – a little grinding against the grit in the gizzard knocks off any sharp edges! And in Yorkshire, a flock of domestic geese is found to be useful for training sheep dogs. The birds stay together and can 'put sides' on a dog by allowing it to practise gentle turns to the left and right.

Robert Gillmor's cartoon of 'Weeder Geese'.

A further use of geese (both Greylag and Swan Goose types) harnesses another aspect of their normal behaviour. In the United States, goslings weed cotton, onions, asparagus, hops, mint and strawberry fields by eating the quick-growing grass, clover, chickweed, groundsel and buttercups without harming the established crop which they find relatively unpalatable. In the early 1960s, there were 250,000 'working geese' in California, and six to eight fast-growing hungry goslings could control the weeds on 0.4–0.8 ha (1–2 acres). In money terms, the farmer paid £124 per acre for labourers to hoe, £119 for chemicals and only £98 an acre to hire geese. White goslings were preferred – they grow faster, must eat more in order to do so and therefore carry out the job more thoroughly. Sadly, selective weed-killers are now improved, and fewer birds are needed.

Two British plants have declined to near-extinction since large herds of geese stopped grazing common land. Pennyroyal and small fleabane were once frequent on wet commons in the south of England where geese traditionally foraged watched over by a goose-girl. Both plants are hairy, with glandular leaves and stems, and geese avoid the strongly aromatic and downy leaves while removing much of the surrounding vegetation. With the grazing pressure on competing plants now lifted, pennyroyal and small fleabane are dominated and very rare.

TYPES OF DOMESTIC DUCK; MALLARD DESCENDANTS

The duck has been farmed for only half as long as the goose; it was not domesticated in Egypt, Assyria, Babylon, nor by the ancient Greeks and the Jews (7,44,50). It seems to have been the Romans who initiated domestication in Europe and the Malays in Asia. Ducks, other than wild ones, were not included in lists of poultry sold in London (30) until 1363 (when they were called 'tame Mallard' – the term 'duck' is not seen until 1528, although Teal were named and priced by 1274, Shoveler in 1507, and Wigeon from 1541). They then became quite common. Unlike geese, ducks tend to be food competitors with man although, thriving as they do in marshy places, this was not a crucial drawback. The Mallard has produced more domestic breeds than all other ducks and geese together and some 20 are found in the British Poultry Standards Manual. However, this list ignores the numerous varieties developed in south and east Asia where 75% of all domestic ducks are kept (5,7), and is a long way short of the 100 different kinds of domestic fowl – a bird that was, elsewhere, more amenable to increasing urbanisation. Only five breeds of domestic Mallard have attained any degree of commercial popularity in the West: the Aylesbury, Pekin, and Rouen were developed for meat production, the first two being white, and the Khaki Campbell and fawn Indian Runner as excellent egg-layers.

The **Aylesbury** was named sometime in the early 1800s when duck production was a principal springtime industry in Buckinghamshire's Vale

'The White Drake' – an Aylesbury Duck painted about 1890 in gouache on holland by the Glaswegian artist Joseph Crawhall (1861–1913). From a private collection, on loan to the National Gallery of Scotland. Photograph courtesy of Hugh Macandrew.

of Aylesbury (3,7,34). This white duck was reared in scanty numbers by numerous cottagers and labourers (rather than in large flocks by wealthy farmers), and it was the business of the wife and children to tend the ducklings. Small ponds with thatched shelters were provided for the daytime and the birds would crowd into the living room or even the bedroom with the family at night. Mrs Beeton (3) described the rows of boxes lined with hay that were fixed around the walls for the ducks' use. Sometimes the stock birds were the cottager's own but, more often, they were left in his care by a wholesaler who would pay for the ducklings reared when the time came for market – usually at nine or ten weeks and at weights of 5–6 lbs (2.25–2.72 kg). The Aylesbury's bill is pink or flesh coloured and its feet orange. In Britain it was considered the *deluxe* table bird, with its deep body, pale skin and broad breast. It is a spring breeder, ready to eat about 25 July on the feast of St James so that, on the Sunday nearest to that date, duck and green peas were traditionally served for dinner. The pure stock has now become quite uncommon, being mixed with the more recently imported flocking breed known as the Pekin.

The **Pekin** is smaller, also white with a more upright carriage, and originated in China where ducks are, as already said, regarded as better than chickens for both meat and eggs (7,34). The Chinese method of keeping ducks, and some geese as well, recycles food that is unavailable

Pekin

Aylesbury

Rouen

Domestick ducks, drawn by Joe Blossom.

directly to humans; enormous numbers are kept on carp and mullet ponds so that their droppings fertilise the water, adding nitrogen and phosphates. These nutrients stimulate the growth of small plants which in turn become the food of invertebrates and small fish on which the ducks thrive. A group of nine Pekins was imported into the USA in 1873 by a clipper ship captain, and the breed gained wide popularity as a table bird in the east, where it is also called the Long Island Duck. The skin is yellow and the bill and legs orange. It is a much better egg-layer (in other words, it lays during a longer season and fewer females become 'broody') and more fertile than the Aylesbury. It is the basis of much of the intensive production for British supermarket freezers by firms such as Cherry Valley of Norfolk, who sell millions of ducks and, interestingly, export large numbers of their tongues and feet as food to China. Statistics of duck consumption are not easy to obtain but, in the middle 1970s for example, Canada was importing 1.8 million lbs (815 tonnes) of duck meat a year, in the early 1980s Cherry Valley was producing 8 million birds annually, and in Japan the consumption of duck meat was expected to rise from 6,000 tonnes in 1987 to over 10,000 tonnes by 1988.

The famous 'Peking duck' was a court dish of the Northern Sung Dynasty (AD 960–1127) and the recipe can be followed easily in western kitchens. A fresh plucked duck has a kettleful of boiling water poured over it and is hung up to dry in an airy place overnight. Next day, the skin is brushed with honey before roasting in a hot oven for $1\frac{3}{4}$ hours. The bird is carved into small pieces, keeping the skin and flesh separate; slivers of crisp skin and succulent meat are placed with strips of cucumber, spring onions and a thick soy sauce at the centre of a thin pancake. The pancake is then rolled up and eaten with the fingers. Traditionally, a soup made of cabbage and the duck carcass is drunk at the end of the meal.

The **Rouen** was developed, as its name suggests, in the city of that name in France. It is a huge duck, weighing about 5 kg (11 lb) whose colouring closely resembles that of the wild Mallard. It lays in the spring and, because it is not white, takes a long time to mature for market – up to five or six months – and has a delicious flavour. For those reasons, it is highly prized and relatively expensive. In French cuisine, the Rouen, the Nantes Duck, Muscovy and the various kinds of wild duck, are the only ones much used for cooking.

Until the last century, the Hook-billed Duck (which is seldom seen today) was the variety kept in Britain as a springtime egg-layer (3). The reddish-fawn **Indian Runner** was introduced into the Solway region of Scotland from Indonesia soon after 1835, probably from the island of Lombok east of Java and, until displaced by the Campbell, was the egg-laying duck *par excellence*. One of the earliest farmers to keep it was Mr Brisbane of Bankend Mill, Caerlaverock, not far from The Wildfowl and Wetlands Trust's Eastpark reserve, and it was first exhibited at the Dumfries Poultry Show of 1876 (10). Its outstanding feature is its perpendicular

Anas rostro adunco
The Hook-bill'd
Duck

The Hook-billed or Bow-billed Duck was the egg-laying domestic variety kept in Britain before the import of the Runner; it had the disadvantage of breeding only in the spring. Drawing from Francis Willughby's *Ornithologia* of 1676–78.

carriage; much of the table flesh around the breast has gone, while its reproductive regions are thoroughly accentuated. It is shaped much like a bottle and runs rather than waddles. It is good at foraging for its own food and can range some distance on strong legs and feet. All domestic ducks are adept at removing slugs and snails and, left with sheep on marshy ground, can reduce the incidence of liver fluke because they eat the molluscs that are the parasite's secondary host. The Runner-type was bred, perhaps 2,000 years ago, for a droving life in the rice paddies where it fed on seeds, snails and insects, and laid non-seasonally and prodigiously even while moulting. They are walked, goose-like, to the rice fields at mid morning behind a rag tied to the end of a pole, and returned at night to roost and lay. Eventually, they will follow the same rag to market and slaughter. Few females construct nests and even fewer become broody, so artificial incubation (sometimes under hens or Muscovies) is the norm for those eggs not salted immediately for human consumption. Charles Darwin (11) regarded the Indian Runner as the most remarkable of all domestic ducks, and his research into its ancestry is discussed in Chapter 5.

The Campbell Duck was developed in 1902 by Mrs A. Campbell, the

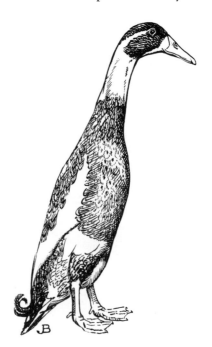

The Indian Runner Ducks that were landed on the north Solway in the 1830s were fawn in colour; some that went to the Cumberland region developed a pied brown-and-white plumage like this drake drawn by Joe Blossom.

The Khaki Campbell Duck was developed, partly from the Indian Runner, by the wife of a village doctor, not far from Slimbridge in Gloucestershire. Like all domestic ducks descended from the Mallard, the drake has a curly tail that is lost in the 'eclipse' plumage shown on the right. Drawn by Joe Blossom.

wife of the village doctor in Uley not far from Slimbridge in Gloucestershire. It was the result of crossing an Indian Runner female, a wild Mallard and a Rouen (although its true ancestry is somewhat mysterious), and was intended from the start as an egg-layer whose production was not tied to the increasing daylength of spring (7). The **Khaki Campbell** is a variety of that original Campbell and was named for its warm brown feathers. Khaki is a Hindustani word for the colour of dust and, to quote from one manual on *Profitable Duck Keeping*: 'the serviceable colour of the plumage is an asset where laying birds are concerned, as Khaki does not easily show discolouration from mud'! One is reminded that Khaki uniforms were first worn by the army during the Indian Mutiny by a famous squadron whose nickname was 'the mudlarks'. The drake Khaki Campbell has a head, neck, stern and wing bar of green bronze while the remainder of his plumage is the same brown as the female. The breed became increasingly popular during the 1920s and 1930s, when it seems often to have been fed on waste potatoes. Individual productions of almost one egg per day for 12 months were not uncommon; one bird laid 291 eggs without a pause, and 333 eggs in 336 days. A White Campbell was also developed which laid fewer eggs – about 200 a year being the maximum – but which, being white-fleshed, found a readier market as meat and commanded higher prices. Coincidentally, while she was developing the breed, Mrs Campbell lived in the house since occupied by the late Colonel Ralph Hodgson, until his death the volunteer museum curator at The Wildfowl Trust's headquarters at Slimbridge. In those days the house was known as Rose Villa and is, in fact, the site of a Roman settlement.

Duck eggs, and the egg-laying breeds, went out of fashion in Britain after the last war. This was partly because domestic hen's eggs become mass-produced and cheap, and partly because of a number of cases of human *Salmonella* poisoning during the 1920s in which duck eggs were implicated. The UK poultry industry is again finding infection by *Salmonella* troublesome, but this time domestic hens are the carriers. Elsewhere, duck eggs are a most important item of diet; in the Philippines (5) where domestic ducks are fed largely on snails, and in other parts of southeast Asia and the Pacific islands, eggs are often eaten hard-boiled. They may be incubated for 13 days and found to be infertile after testing or, as a particular delicacy, fertile and at the 18th or 19th day of development.

In addition to meat and egg-producing breeds, **Call Ducks** and some purely ornamental types, like the Crested Duck, have been developed (2). Call Ducks are usually white, but also come in buff and natural, like the Mallard. All are smaller and noisier than the wild bird and their function was to lure their cousins into traps or decoys (see the next Chapter). They were bred small so that they ate less and, unlike most of the domestic ducks so far mentioned, can fly readily. Today, they are not raised for decoying but for their pretty looks, as are varieties like Silver Appleyard Bantams (2).

Bewick's 1797 wood-engraving of a 'Muskcovy' duck — white domestic strains were already common in the New World when European man arrived at the end of the 15th Century, although the dark forms probably laid more eggs.

Muscovy Ducks, drawn by Joe Blossom; the ancestral wild bird is at the top.

THE MUSCOVY DUCK

After the Greylag, Swan Goose and Mallard, the last of the four domestic waterfowl species is the **Muscovy** of South America. It is a perching duck related to the Mandarin *Aix galericulata* and Carolina *A. sponsa* (or North American Wood Duck) and is common in Amazonian rain forests. The first European reports did not appear before the 16th Century – it is said to have been imported into England in 1550 and spread rapidly in France – and it is not certain why it was called the Muscovy (8,18,49). It may have been after the Muscovite Company that traded to South America. Other authorities suggest that it was procured from the Mosquito Coast of Nicaragua, the country of the Muysca Indians, and that the name was originally the Musco Duck.

The Muscovy was probably domesticated by the South American Indians as a pet: it had sentimental value in the main, but was also useful for its feathers, and in ridding houses of ants, crickets and other insect pests (18). It was sometimes eaten, and so were its eggs: indeed, it is a dual purpose animal – the male puts on weight faster than the female and is a better food converter, ending up at about 5 kg (12 lb) in weight or twice her size. The social system is polygamous and there is little mating display, the male tending to overcome the female by sheer weight. Being polygamous even in the wild, one drake can be kept with a number of females and his brothers taken for the pot. Clutches are laid in the wild at any time of the year and, even in England, from early spring through mid-summer to the autumn. Surprisingly, Muscovies are said to be hardier than Mallard types in the English climate and 'more intelligent', but few are produced for the market. British food firms have imported them from the continent as Barbary Ducks for roasting – and very good they are. In tropical countries, they are seen and eaten more (18); like the Chinese Goose, they are tolerant of warm weather and, because they rarely swim, lay down relatively little fat. On a few modern farms, Muscovies are kept with cattle and pigs to reduce unpleasant insect populations much as they were when originally domesticated in South America. They are more efficient and environmentally acceptable than flypapers and chemicals, and taste better on the farmer's table. They will cross with other domestic ducks, producing sterile offspring which mature fast and also taste excellent. These 'mules' or Mulards are not bred commercially in Britain, but have been in France since the middle of the 19th Century (18) and in Israel, Taiwan (18), Australia and South Africa (39) more recently. They are lean-breasted birds that, in France and Israel as already pointed out, are force-fed for *foie gras*; they are also kept for their breast fillets – called

Muscovy Duck jug from Peru, *c.* 600 AD. The British Museum copyright.

magrets – which each weigh about 400 g (13 oz) and are often smoked or dried like Parma ham.

The Amerindians of the southern shores of the Caribbean and/or those of Paraguay and eastern Peru probably farmed the Muscovy first (18). They changed it hardly at all; that is, they did not greatly interfere with its choice of mate in order to select for particular traits. The domesticated form is larger than the wild bird and occurs in a variety of colours (sooty brown feathering with green and purple iridescence is normal, and in captivity birds may be white and grey) but there are no recognised breeds, unlike the other ducks and geese just discussed. It flies relatively little (the females occasionally take to the wing and cause problems of identification for British birdwatchers), seldom swims and is less inclined to roost in trees – all of which suggest some adaptation for living in proximity to man (8).

Far more plants have been domesticated than animals, and it is clear that New World man has been responsible for a disproportionate number of agricultural plants, while peoples of Asia have contributed most of our relatively few farm animals. From South America the world obtained beans (the basis of *cassoulet* (13)), tomatoes, potatoes, maize (with which geese and ducks are now crammed), peanuts, squash, avocados, manioc, tobacco, chilli or sweet peppers, pineapples and cocoa; all were domesticated by the native Indians and, in many cases, were altered greatly from the wild form (47). Man in Central and South America seems to have farmed few animals and changed none of them to any extent; only the Turkey, Muscovy, llamas and alpacas, guinea pigs and capybara were domesticated. The North American Indian tamed none of these, neither the Mallard nor the Canada Goose *Branta canadensis*. He had the dog, whose domestication 12,000 years ago had pre-dated all other animals and plants (47,50), and which had presumably accompanied him across the Bering Straits from Asia.

FEATURES OF DOMESTICATION

What has happened to the ducks and geese listed in the previous pages during the long slow process of domestication? What features do they have in common, and do the four species differ from their wild ancestors in the same sort of way? (It must be remembered that nowadays many domestic ducks and geese are bred for show purposes (2), and to 'standards' of appearance that may bear little relation to the main utility reason behind their initial selection.)

First, all mature quickly and are capable of producing and fertilizing eggs the year after they themselves were hatched (44); even the juvenile plumage of the wild Muscovy seems to have been lost in captivity, and is often replaced by the dark melanistic down and feathering that is associated with good egg production. Maturity still comes sooner in ducks than in geese – the Pekin will lay when it is six months old, while the Chinese Goose, although it can lay at twelve months of age, produces more eggs in its second, third and later years (7,29).

Secondly, all domestic wildfowl have long breeding seasons. Seasonal changes in daylength affect the cycle of display, egg-laying, fat deposition and moult in all temperate and arctic birds (38). Ducks and geese from these regions have similar patterns of springtime breeding; they start to lay on a characteristic, species-specific daylength and are able to breed until nearly mid-summer. The long days of May and June cause their hormone levels to change so that laying ceases, the bird starts to moult, and it cannot nest again until the following spring. Short days cause the storage of body fat against the cold winter (thus the Greeks sewed up the eyes of swans so that they fattened faster while being forced fed). Domestication, to a greater or lesser extent, has freed the animal from these constraints (44). The ducks and geese that have been domesticated all naturally start to lay on a short day because they originated from rather low latitudes and, after selective breeding over many generations, lay earlier still and may produce eggs again in the autumn. Larger clutches are also typical and, in the Runner of Asia and in all modern, egg-laying breeds, the clutch system has collapsed completely, with long sequences of eggs appearing – nearly one a day for two or three years.

The early evolution of egg-producing ducks needed the parallel development of artificial incubation, since continual production of eggs is only possible if the female never goes broody. (In the *Tale of Jemima Puddle-duck* published in 1908, Beatrix Potter used a notorious bird at Hill Top farm in the English Lake District that had difficulty hatching ducklings because she was a 'bad sitter' – see Chapter 9). The quite recognisable Runners that appear on the Javan temple ruins at Borobudur were carved between AD 778 and 842; local techniques for artificial incubation must be equally old or older. Indeed, since the Zhou Dynasty more than 2,000 years ago, the southern Chinese have employed the sun, heated unhusked rice and the warmth produced by developing embryos during their last two weeks in the shell to hatch duck eggs (5,22). The Greeks and Egyptians used underground ovens beneath open fires; the hatchers were professionals, and returned two ducklings for every three eggs supplied. The excess, if any, was their commission – an arrangement that suggests that the system had a success rate of well over 60%.

Domestic geese are not prolific egg-layers, and are still much influenced by natural daylength changes. Those of the Greylag type are spring-time breeders and their gonads cease to be active before the long days of mid-summer. The Chinese female may lay for a second time in the autumn (29) when the day comes round again to the same stimulatory length that it was in the spring but, like the Embden and Toulouse, she too tends to produce clutches rather than a continuous supply. The sex hormones of Muscovies, because they originate from the tropics, are not inhibited by long days and the birds naturally lay over a longer period than wildfowl

Drake Muscovy Duck, showing the extensive areas of bare-facial skin that are associated with large body size. Both features are accentuated during the process of domestication. Photo by Joe Blossom.

domesticated from temperate species; in that, as in other features, they have not been greatly altered from the wild. Many farmyard Muscovies still produce clutches that contain no more eggs than they can sit on, and 'go broody' successfully; they are often used, therefore, to hatch the eggs of other waterfowl (2).

Obesity is a feature of most domestic animals (47,50). By selecting for longer breeding seasons, man has also manipulated other aspects of the seasonal response to daylight, such as the one that any migratory animal shows before migration – the laying down of fat to be used as fuel on the journey. Larger size is also typical, and with heavy mass goes difficulty in becoming airborne and in losing heat, so that flightlessness is normal, and many breeds have fewer wing and tail quills and looser feathering than their ancestors. Domestics often have knobs and wattles near their bills, plus dewlaps or gullets, especially in the males. These are also probably linked to large body size since all are sites of bare skin and thus of potential cooling; birds have no sweat glands and dissipate excess heat from unfeathered areas or from their mouths.

Surprisingly, the Mallard in captivity has not given rise to the great

Alexander Max Koester's beautiful painting entitled 'Ducks Resting' illustrates the habit common to domestic ducks of sitting close together even when adult. Their wild Mallard ancestors do this only as ducklings; fully-feathered birds will rest far enough apart to enable them to take flight quickly.

variety of coloured plumages and breeds that the Jungle Fowl has, although the hues of the cock and drake seem equally bright and elaborate.

Man tends to select and retain juvenile features in his farmed animals; that a bird breeds before it reaches the flying stage can be regarded as one example of 'neotony' – or reproduction in a state of immaturity. Another is that they tend to sit close together even when adult; the painting on this page shows a group of domestic Aylesburys resting as close as they would have done as ducklings. Wild Mallard would never be this intimate once they were fully feathered (15,16).

Polygamy (the choosing of more than one mate by a male bird) occurs naturally only in the wild Muscovy but is now usual behaviour in all domestic forms derived from the seasonally faithful Mallard, and the lifelong monogamous Greylag and Swan Goose (33); breeders do not need to keep more than one drake or one gander with four to six females. Aggression in wild Mallards is more obvious than it is in drake Aylesburys and, during the breeding season, Mallards show territorial behaviour while Aylesburys never do (16). The wild bird is more wary of man than the domesticated one, generally appearing much more alert, sleeping with eyes that open frequently, and resting while standing on one leg (15).

Hybrids between the Greylag and Swan Goose are completely fertile, a finding that initially caused Charles Darwin some concern since his early definition of a species was that it did not interbreed with any other (12,23). All the grey geese are similar genetically, and many fertile crosses have been produced (9). The Muscovy and the Mallard are not so far apart that crosses between them are impossible, but any progeny are sterile; nevertheless, their hybrids are useful in farming, and have considerable value in combining 'good' characters of both parents. 'Mulards' are more efficient food converters than pure Pekins, they can be killed at seven weeks, which is a week ahead of Muscovies, and the fat content of the

A painting of the hybrid Chinese/Grey Geese that figured in correspondence between Charles Darwin (who later acquired a pair of them) and the Rev. F. B. Goodacre about the definition of a species. Courtesy of Myrtle Ashmole.

carcass is significantly lower than in the Pekin. Crosses between Muscovy drakes and Pekin females are usually preferred because the Pekin lays more eggs and there is a smaller sex difference in the eventual size of the offspring (39).

REFERENCES

1. Adair, J. 1982. *Founding Fathers*. London: Dent.
2. Bartlett, T. 1986. *Ducks and Geese, a Guide to Management*. Marlborough: Crowood Press.
3. Beeton, I. M. 1861. *Book of Household Management*. London: S. O. Beeton.
4. Bonser, K. J. 1970. *The Drovers*. London: Macmillan.
5. Burgos, C. X. 1924. The duck industry in the Philippines. *Philippines Agric. Rev.* 17:87–99.
6. Charles-Picard, G. 1972. *Larousse Encyclopedia of Archaeology*. London: Hamlyn.
7. Clayton, G. A. 1984. Common duck, in Mason, I. L. (ed). *Evolution of Domesticated Animals*. London: Longman.
8. Clayton, G. A. 1984. Muscovy duck, in Mason, I. L. (ed). *Evolution of Domesticated Animals*. London: Longman.
9. Crawford, R. D. 1984. Goose, in Mason, I. L. (ed). *Evolution of Domesticated Animals*. London: Longman.
10. Coutts, J. A. Undated, about 1929. The Indian Runner Duck. The Feathered World.
11. Darwin, C. 1868. *The Variation of Animals and Plants under Domestication*. London: John Murray.
12. Darwin, C. 1880. Fertility of hybrids from the common and chinese goose. *Nature* 21:207.
13. David, E. 1960. *French Provincial Cooking*. London: Michael Joseph.
14. Defoe, D. 1727. *A Tour through the Whole Island of Great Britain*. Re-issued in 1975 by Everyman University Library.
15. Desforges, M. F. & Wood-Gush, D. G. M. 1975. A behavioural comparison of domestic and mallard ducks. Habituation and flight reactions. *Anim.Behav.* 23:692–697.

16. Desforges, M. F. & Wood-Gush, D. G. M. 1975. A behavioural comparison of domestic and mallard ducks. Spatial relationships in small flocks. *Anim.Behav.* 23:698–705.

17. Dickens, C. 1843. *A Christmas Carol.*

18. Donkin, R. A. 1989. *The Muscovy Duck, Cairina moschata domestica.* Rotterdam: Balkema.

19. Ekwall, E. 1954. *Street-names of the City of London.* OUP.

20. Felix, B., Auffray, P. & Marcilloux, J. C. 1980. Effect of induced hypothalamic hyperphagia and forced-feeding on organ weight and tissular development in Landes geese. *Repro.Nutr.Develop.* 20:709–717.

21. Forty, G. & A. 1979. *They Also Served.* Speldhurst, Kent: Midas.

22. Fuan, L. 1980 The parched rice incubation technique for hatching duck eggs, in Farrell, D. J. & Stapleton, P. (ed). *Duck Production and World Practice.* University of New England.

23. Goodacre, F. B. 1879. On the question of the identity of species of the Common Domestic and the Chinese Goose. *Proc. zoo. Soc.Lond.* 46:1–3.

24. Greenoak, F. 1979. *All the Birds of the Air.* London: André Deutsch.

25. Hartley, D. 1954. *Food in England.* London: MacDonald.

26. Heath, E. G. 1971. *The Grey Goose Wing.* Osprey.

27. Hughes, P. G. 1943. *Wales and the Drovers.* Foyle's Welsh Co.

28. Ives, P. P. 1951. *Domestic Geese and Ducks.* New York: Orange Judd Publishing Company.

29. Johnson, A. A. Undated, about 1951. *Chinese Geese.* Printed by Underhill (Plymouth).

30. Jones, P. E. 1965. *The Worshipful Company of Poulters of the City of London.* OUP.

31. Lawrence, D. H. 1934. Goose Fair, in *The Tales of D. H. Lawrence.* London: Martin Secker.

32. Lewer, S. H. Undated, about 1914. *Wright's Book of Poultry.* London: Waverley.

33. McFarland, D. 1981. (ed.) *The Oxford Companion to Animal Behaviour.* OUP

34. MAFF. 1973. *Ducks and Geese.* London: HMSO.

35. Morris, F. O. 1897. *History of British Birds.*

36. Moubray, B. 1842. *Ornamental Domestic Poultry.* London.

37. Muncy, R. W. 1935. *Our Old English Fairs.* London: Sheldon Press.

38. Murton, R. K. & Kear, J. 1973. The nature and evolution of the photoperiodic control of reproduction in wildfowl of the family Anatidae. *J.Reprod.Fert.,* Suppl.19:67–84

39. Olver, M. D. *et al.* 1977. The carcass composition and growth of the 'mule' duckling compared to purebred ducklings. *Agroanimalia* 9:7–12.

40. Pullar, P. 1970. *Consuming Passions.* London: Hamilton.

41. Purseglove, J. 1988. *Taming the Flood.* OUP.

42. Rowley, G. D. 1876–1878. *Ornithological Miscellany.* Vols 1 & 3. London: Trubner.

43. Soames, B. 1980. *Keeping Domestic Geese.* Poole: Blandford Press.

44. Sossinka, R. 1982. Domestication in birds. *Avian Biology* 6:373–403. London: Academic Press.

45. Stow, J. 1598. *A Survey of London*. Reprinted in 1912 by Dent: London.

46. Trusler, J. 1786. *The London Adviser and Guide*.

47. Ucko, P. J. & Dimbleby, G. W. (eds) 1969. *The Domestication and Exploitation of Plants and Animals*. London: Duckworth.

48. Whalley, J. I. 1980. *The Pen's Excellence: Calligraphy of Western Europe and America*. Speldhurst, Kent: Midas.

49. Wood-Gush, D. G. M. 1985. Domestication, in *A Dictionary of Birds*. Calton: Poyser.

50. Zeuner, F. E. 1963. *A History of Domesticated Animals*. London: Hutchinson.

3: Decoys

In England the first devices to be called decoys (a contraction of two Dutch words meaning duck and cage) were used for catching moulting ducks that could not fly. The swimming birds were rounded up and driven into netted traps and, so long as wetlands remained undrained and large numbers of wildfowl bred there, the system supplied some lean meat during two summer months. But as the East Anglian Fens were reduced in extent, the taking of flightless adults and their unfledged young year after year became unproductive because breeding stock was drastically reduced. The practice was banned in England on a number of occasions as being excessively destructive and, in 1710, 'the driving or taking of wild fowl in ye Moulting Season between 1st July and 1st September' was prohibited for good (26).

THE DUTCH DECOY AND HOW IT WORKED

The sophisticated technique of catching some of the larger numbers of migratory wildfowl in good autumn and winter condition seems to have been a Dutch development of the 16th Century. The new decoy was a modification of a shallow pool, not more than an acre or two in extent and surrounded by woodland, from which radiated up to eight ditches or 'pipes' – curved tapering extensions of the pools that were covered with netting hung over semi-circular hoops (9,26).

Successful decoys could vary in layout and operation; the curving pipes might be 50–70 m (55–75 yards) long, 5–8 m (16–26 ft) wide at the mouth with the top of the tallest hoop perhaps 5 m (16 ft) above the surface of the water. Along the outside of the curve was a range of 2 m (6 ft 6 in) high screens set in overlapping form which, in the manner of a venetian blind, hid the decoyman from birds on the main pool but enabled those

De Eend.

A duck from a Dutch child's alphabet book: 'decoy' is a contraction of the Dutch words *eende* meaning duck and *kooi* a cage. Redrawn by Sue Hazeldine.

in the 'pipes' under the netting to see him if he wished. Connecting these high screens at ground level, and making in plan a zig-zag pattern, might be screens about 50 cm (20 in) high known as 'dog-leaps'. Considerable skill and a knowledge of animal behaviour were required to operate the system. Wild flying creatures had to be persuaded to use the pond and then enticed along the netted pipes so that they could be caught.

Someone must have noticed that ducks and geese on water will swim towards and follow certain mammals moving on land; indeed, most country people were familiar with the phenomenon although they may not have understood its significance. The common medieval story that is depicted in church carvings of a fox dressed as a cleric 'preaching' to a flock of geese (38) must have its roots in observations of the fox's power of attraction. It was a decidedly clever human who worked out a strategy for putting the bird's behaviour to use. Ducks will not react like this to all mammals but they do respond to quite a variety; stoats, squirrels, ferrets, foxes and dogs all produce the desired effect. Only one of these could be trained to work at a distance, and that was the domestic dog. Traditionally, the decoy dog (called Pijper in Holland, where a special, fox-like *kooikerhonge* breed has been developed, and Piper in English because it worked in the decoy pipes – not in reference to the Pied Piper) was fox-like, reddish in colour, small, with a bushy tail and a lively gait. In fact, so far as eliciting a following response from the ducks, no very precise shape or colour seems to be necessary. A stuffed fox mounted on a long pole has been used successfully at Slimbridge, as well as a stuffed stoat bounced along the tops of the screens. Sir Ralph Payne-Gallwey, who in 1886 wrote the first book in English about duck decoys, tried a cat, a ferret and a rabbit at various times: 'they all attract, but are next to impossible to manage (26). I once bribed an organ-grinder to lend me his monkey'; the ducks rushed towards the monkey when it first appeared but flew in the opposite direction when the animal turned round, faced

This owl, being shouted at by four small mobbing birds, is on a misericord in Gloucester Cathedral. The fox (below), dressed as a friar and decoying a flock of geese, appears on a bench-end in Padstow Church, Cornwall. 'Reynard' can be found preaching to the geese on many English church carvings of the 15th and 16th Centuries; other fine examples are in Bristol Cathedral, Ludlow Parish Church, East Brent Church in Somerset and Beverley Minster. Photographs by Joe Blossom.

An ice-borne fox at Kilcolman Wildfowl Reserve, County Cork in Ireland. The fox has attracted a trio of swimming swans, one Whooper and two young Mutes, and a group of Coot. The necks of all the swans appear thicker than usual because their feathers are erect – a sign of mild threat and dominance. Photograph by R. T. Mills. See also the wood engraving, that heads this chapter, from the school of Thomas Bewick published in *Select Fables* (1820), courtesy of Newcastle upon Tyne City Libraries.

them and grinned. In that position it presumably looked too human!

The tendency to swim towards a dog is related to the collective 'mobbing' response of many birds to a potential predator – finches to an owl, titmice to a cat – or of large mammals to small somewhat dangerous ones, such as bullocks to a terrier. Dogs have been used elsewhere for their power to influence swimming wildfowl and to draw them within reach of a shotgun or of a camera. One reason why Wildfowl and Wetlands Trust Centres do not allow dogs into their reserves is that this attractiveness can be keenly upsetting for a well-trained family pet; perhaps the fox feels some of the same emotion and prefers to go away rather than endure the embarrassing attentions of the mob.

The birds' actions must have survival value (that is, individuals who show mobbing behaviour, on average, outlive those who do not and so leave more offspring) and the instinct seems as entrenched today as ever. An essential feature of the performance is that the participants are not in any perceived peril: small birds 'mob' an owl because, in daylight, the owl is a poor hunter who can be driven from the area; close pursuit of ducks by a fox or dog is impossible, as mammals do not fly and are relatively inefficient swimmers, and thus the real hazard is the possibility of being surprised – of not realising that the predator is there. Mobbing ensures that all members of the group are aware of the danger, teaches the inexperienced what an enemy looks like, and perhaps gets rid of the problem. As we saw in Chapter 2, geese can persuade a snake to leave their vicinity by the commotion they produce.

A successful duck decoy did not rely merely on a well-schooled dog; clever construction and siting maximised the chances of catching some of the birds. Absolute quiet seems to have been essential – every path was spread with sawdust to deaden footfalls – as also was a shortage of open water nearby since, if there were many other ponds available, the birds might disperse. Small ponds were more efficient because the ducks only react to the sight of the dog when quite close. The main pool had steep sides so that the birds found it difficult to rest on the banks; instead, loafing sites were provided just beneath the nets near the entrance to the pipes. A

A group of Call Ducks, bred especially small, white and noisy for service in decoys. Drawn by Joe Blossom.

'lead' of semi-resident ducks was desirable since birds flying over might not land on a totally empty water surface; many decoys used Call Ducks or 'coy ducks' to give the necessary impression of ease and friendliness. These were domesticated Mallard selectively bred for small size that did not need much feeding, were often noisier than wild birds and preferably white (see Chapter 2) so that they could be distinguished and spared when the slaughter began. If they were of normal, wild-type plumage, then a notch cut in the webbing of one foot would distinguish them, and clipping their wing feathers during their first year of life usually meant that they remained faithful to their decoyman's patch. In Denmark, at least, it was the custom for marked Call Ducks to be safe from killing in all neighbouring decoys (24). Here, wild ducks might be caught, feather-clipped, tamed and used to lure others into the pipes for a season before regaining their freedom the following summer. As many as 200 Call Ducks might be in service at every decoy, larger numbers being considered necessary if the pond were near any source of sudden sound such as a farmyard.

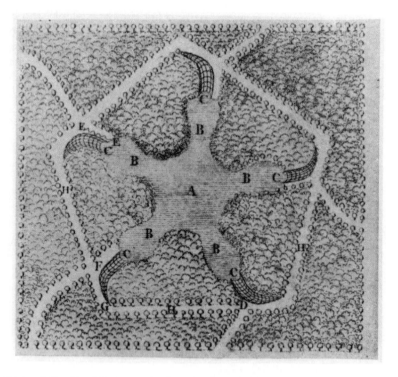

Richard Bradley FRS was the first Professor of Botany at Cambridge; his scheme for a five-sided decoy, published in 1726 in *Bradley on Gardening* (A and B are water, C the netted pipes and H the paths), was the master plan for Hale Decoy and probably for that at Martin Mere. Courtesy of Cambridge University Library.

One of Bradley's pipes showing the decoyman and his dog; the screens are of board with holes through which the dog vanishes from view of the ducks. These boards were still in use at Hale when J. Whitaker visited in 1917. Courtesy of Cambridge University Library.

In some decoys, food was also provided beneath the nets in order to entice the ducks into the right position. This might be grain, hempseed, or more recently, potatoes. In a few decoys, the Call Ducks were whistled at feeding time (an exception to the rule of silence) and the wild ones swam in under the pipes in their wake. Food as bait is usually used when decoys are operated to catch birds so that an identification ring can be put on their legs, and the same individuals may be trapped repeatedly. In past centuries, most decoy pools were essentially daytime roosts from which the birds would fly in the evening to feed in the surrounding fields. Disturbance from predators, such as foxes, otters, Herons *Ardea cinerea* and pike, was controlled by trapping and poisoning.

How did the system work? The first thing that the decoyman did was to test the breeze. Birds will take off only into a wind, so disturbance near a pipe into which the wind was blowing meant that all the birds turned back towards the pond and flew from under the nets. That was why the decoy pool needed more than one pipe if it were to operate in all weather conditions. Payne-Gallwey (26) thought five pipes to be optimal in places where duck were numerous, and three to be plenty where they were relatively scarce. To be correct for catching, the wind had to be blowing along the pipe from its narrow end towards the pond. Some decoymen, believing that ducks can smell, carried a piece of burning peat to mask any obvious human odours – peat smoke was apparently considered to be the familiar atmosphere of the countryside! (Ducks probably can smell a little but there is no evidence that they use this sense in alerting themselves to the presence of man, or associate his scent with danger.)

To operate the decoy the dog has to be shown to the ducks at one of the dog-leaps; it has then to walk quickly alongside the pipe away from the ducks and the pool, disappear behind the next screen, and reappear at the next leap, and so on until most of the birds have reacted and have swum under the nets. The person in charge of the dog must, of course, remain hidden until the right moment. When as many birds as possible have been drawn in, the 'coyman' appears at the outermost gap in the screen. The duck's retreat to the open pond seems to be cut off, they fly into the wind down the narrowing pipe with the decoyman in pursuit, visible to them but not to those on the pond, until he has them in a tunnel net at the end, which can be shut or twisted closed.

THE DECLINE OF THE DECOYS

Hundreds of decoys were constructed in Holland during and after the 16th Century (8,15,19,39). Sir William Wodehouse apparently built the first one in England 'known by the foreign name of Koye' at Waxham, Norfolk in about 1620. The earliest decoy of which we have a description of costs and materials was made for King Charles in 1665 in St James's Park by a Dutchman, Sydrach Hilcus, who was paid £30 and brought over especially for the job (26). Daniel Defoe, in his *Tour* published in 1727, wrote of an abundance of 'Duckoys' in the fens (6). Many early ones in East Anglia consisted of single decoy pipes built into a corner of a large lake (26,39). It was mainly 'old' George Skelton who spread the more efficient Dutch technique, of small ponds with several pipes, from Lincolnshire to Norfolk, starting with Winterton in 1807 (14,17,25). Payne-Gallwey listed 200 decoys in 1886 (26); by 1918, J. Whitaker found only 19 in use (41), and in 1936 the number had dwindled to just four in regular full-time commercial use (13).

Two hundred years ago, decoys were equally common in many parts of Europe and Asia over which there was a flight of migratory ducks, for instance, in Ireland (10,11,12,27), Bohemia, France, Denmark (24), Germany and the Netherlands (8,15,19,26). Modifications of the system are known in Iran (30), Pakistan (31) and in Japan (36). Now few European examples remain except in Holland. The decline involved several factors including the number of birds available to catch, the prices obtained and the cost of maintenance. Decoys were obviously only worth developing in regions with a good migratory passage of wildfowl in autumn and

'Piper' jumping the dog leap at Borough Fen while the decoyman parts the reeds of the screen to watch the reactions of the ducks on the pond. Photograph by Anne Cook.

winter, as well as plenty of locally bred birds. They were inefficient where guns were cheap, as a gun discharged nearby could mean that the birds deserted the pool for that day, so they went out of use in places where the decoyman could not control firearms under special legislation protecting the decoy's immediate neighbourhood (22). A rising human population also meant that there were more people working the land, with further possibilities for local disturbance. The upkeep of a decoy was labour-intensive and relatively expensive. The family who operated one had to have security over a few acres of land, and capital. The osier willow or wych-elm hoops, handspun hemp nets and reed screens needed constant care, and the weight of a heavy snowfall could cause the collapse of the whole device and its profitability. From 1688, in order to control monopolies, no-one could be both a decoy owner and a member of the Company of Poulters (16), which suggests that, only 68 years after the first one was built in England, decoys were supplying a good part of the London market.

Some English decoys, called house or sporting decoys, were built as an asset to an estate, providing a reliable larder of food rather as a rabbit warren, fish pond or dovecote did (indeed squab pigeons, available between May and September, conveniently filled a gap when the duck trap was not in use). The decoyman was one of many staff and could command help when needed from other servants. The break-up of the large estates must have hastened the loss of such decoys.

The selling price of birds taken in commercial or market decoys fluctuated with demand, the customer's preference for other foods, and the cost of alternatives. The requirement of large towns for wildfowl in the 18th Century seems to have been enormous; Daniel Defoe in 1727 mentioned the quantities sent to London 'twice a week in waggon loads at a time' (6). In 1790, a statistical survey of the capital published in the third edition of *Encyclopaedia Britannica* calculated that its million inhabitants consumed weekly '700 Dozen of wild-fowl, of several sorts, for six months'; that adds up to over 200,000 in a season lasting from September to February (many decoys operated a little longer, from August to March). The average catch at that time is not easy to guess. Accurate records were seldom kept, and non-Mallards were classed as 'half-ducks', but suppose an annual take of 165 dozen per establishment (41), then the complete harvest of 100 decoys would be needed to satisfy the London order alone. Of course, some birds would have been shot and others imported, and the proportion in each of these categories was to increase. By the 1850s, the decoys of Holland were competing only too successfully with those of the Fens, and reliable guns suitable for wildfowling were in common use. An account from Leadenhall Market addressed to Mr J. Williams of Borough Fen Decoy in February 1870 states that 'owing to the large supply of Dutch wildfowl, prices have again lowered'. In 1790, Londoners were paying £250 per week for 700 dozen wildfowl, or about 7d each (by contrast, a domestic duck cost 9d). The decoyman might receive $2\frac{1}{2}$d to 5d.

An increase in price coincided with the Napoleonic wars and a blockade of English ports (5). Food was short because ships, including Dutch ones, could not get through; thus an annual 165 dozen would have made about £330 in 1818. This had fallen to £144 in 1830, and to less than £139 by 1840. The price remained low until the 1914–18 war (5) but, by then, almost all the commercial decoys had gone, starved of sufficient income. H. A. Gilbert, writing in 1938 (13), calculated that an annual catch of 3,500 birds was needed for a British decoy to be profitable; few had ever reached that number. Another important factor in their demise was a shortage of home-bred ducks, particularly of the Mallard that brought the highest prices; migratory Teal *Anas crecca*, Pintail *A.acuta* and Wigeon *A.penelope*, all classified as 'half-ducks', could not make up the deficit that had come about through numerous fenland drainage projects. Prior to 1809, for instance, and the drainage of the great East and West Fen, ten decoys around Wainfleet sent a total of 31,200 ducks a season to the London market. The effect of drying out the land was immediate and devastating: by 1829 only three of those decoys were still in business (26).

Decoys in Holland remained relatively successful for much longer (8,15). Peter Scott, visiting that country in 1947, was shown 22 in a week, several of them with annual takes of more than 10,000 ducks (34). However, in Holland the number of pipe decoys had also declined, from 220 in 1830 to 120 by 1948 (22). Agricultural improvements had destroyed

'Piper', the decoy dog of Borough Fen, with her master Tony Cook beside the funnel end of the pipe. Photograph by Anne Cook. Folkard described such a dog thus:

> *Tho' gay and winning in my gait*
> *I'm deadly as the viper*
> *Follow me and sure as fate*
> *You'll have to pay the piper*

the isolation and tranquillity of many of them and profitability was shaky. In the mid-1950s it was calculated that 3,300 marketable ducks were needed to keep a Dutch decoy in credit although the average catch was nearer 2,250; thus many were being run on a part-time basis by decoymen whose main income was derived from farming. The overall annual take was thought to be 300,000 of which 73% were Mallard, 15% Teal, 8% Wigeon and 4% Pintail (8,22). About two-fifths of the Mallard were locally bred, encouraged by the placement of nesting baskets in the decoys, and most of those caught were juveniles. Strict rules stopped any shooting in the vicinity of a decoy, although wildfowling in the English sense did not exist in the Netherlands – in the mid-1950s, only about 20,000 shooting licences were issued compared to 300,000 annually in Britain – a country that is admittedly rather larger. The number of Dutch wildfowlers has now increased. In 1949, Britain was still the main market for wildfowl killed commercially in the Netherlands: in that year we imported 100,000 or a third of the catch (22). Today, we *export* shot wild duck to the Continent: in 1986, the figure was 13,500, and in 1987, 17,850 (see Chapter 4).

Why did the Dutch, who crossed the Atlantic in some numbers to settle around New Amsterdam (later called New York), not build a few decoys once they got there? Guns were probably too common and were certainly cheap. Capital may have been short, and the summertime was needed for farming. There are records of an Englishman from Ipswich, Emmanuel Downing, who installed a 'duckcoy' in Salem, Massachusetts, at the very early date of 1638, having brought the equipment with him from England at great expense (33). He is presumed to have used the decoy until his return to England in 1652 (Downing Street, the home of the British Prime Minister, is named after his son, and Downing College, Cambridge, after his great-grandson). The best-known pipe decoy in North America was started in 1949 at Delta Waterfowl Research Station in Manitoba, Canada, at the suggestion of Peter Scott (37). It was operated by a Dutchman and, in its first season, caught 1,400 ducks for ringing (20).

Decoys in England, Wales and Ireland (there were none completed in Scotland) were often 'set out' following visits by Dutch experts carrying out wetland reclamation projects. Some drainage of the site was usually essential, as the decoy only worked when most other pools close by had been removed. Decoys certainly did not go out of fashion because the ducks stopped following the dog. After centuries of eliminating birds that did so, the habit is as strong as ever. Successive waves of juveniles on their first autumn migration could, and still can be, decoyed on a pond with the use of live Call Ducks and a dog, day after day. At Borough Fen it has been noted that juvenile birds do not learn to ignore a predator so readily as older ones do (5). Decoys perhaps do not 'work' so well now because captured birds who have been 'fooled' are not killed. They are released (after a ring has been put on one leg) having learnt something of the procedure. Similarly, the shooting of ducks coming into a roost eventually proves unsuccessful, because enough birds escape to lead the others elsewhere.

DECOY DUCKS

Neither Dutch nor English decoymen thought it worthwhile to employ model ducks to attract birds flying overhead or under the pipes. Tame live ducks were common but not wooden models. And they seem never to have bothered with imitated calls, whether their own voices or manu-

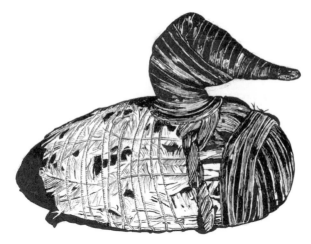

A Canvasback decoy, perhaps a thousand years old, from Love Lock Caves, Nevada, now in the museum of the American Indian, New York City. Drawn by Sue Hazeldine.

factured 'duck-calls'. Silence, apart from the whistle at feeding time, was golden.

Model ducks to attract wild ones were mainly an invention of the North American Indian (crude 'decoys' of clay and stones are reported from Chitral in Northwest Pakistan (31)) who used them to bring flying birds within reach of a throwing stick or bow and arrows. He did not make his models of wood, since he lacked the metal tools necessary for carving; woven reeds, feathers, bird skins and painted basket work which float well were utilised instead (and did not survive for long, so that aboriginal examples are very rare indeed). The oldest known rush models represent Canvasbacks *Aythya valisineria* and were found in 1924 in a Nevada cave (2,29). Their exact age is uncertain, but perhaps a thousand years is a fair estimate. The North American Indian had no need to tame the Mallard, nor yet the Canada Goose, and did not use live birds to bring in wild ones. They domesticated almost no birds or mammals and few plants, remaining largely as hunter-gatherers until the 19th Century. The dog was brought from the Old World, but there are no records of this animal companion being used by Indians for attracting wildfowl. In any case, diving ducks such as Canvasback, Redhead *Aythya americana* and Scaup *A. affinis*, which are common Eastern American quarry, do not follow a dog so consistently as the surface-feeding Mallard, Teal and Pintail (20). The Indian's models are not exploiting a mobbing response but a related behaviour pattern common to all migratory ducks, which is their extreme gregariousness. This instinct to congregate causes them to join others of their kind already on the water in preference to landing on an empty pond. Again, the behaviour must have survival value: birds that

North American wooden decoy ducks are worth a lot of money; these examples on postage stamps show work from the early part of this century. Note that the French word for a decoy is *appelant* or 'caller'.

are social leave more young than those that are not. Man has not yet changed the balance by killing a large proportion of those that respond to imitation models.

So the live Call Duck was a European concept and the inanimate 'stool duck' was American, perhaps a thousand years old. Tethered ducks and geese were used occasionally by shooters in Europe (especially in France, and by Dutch goose-netters) in the early 19th Century but the practice was not widespread and was eventually outlawed through Bird Protection Legislation. The original 'stool pigeon' was also a live bird tethered to a pole and used as a lure to the wild kind. After the Europeans with their guns settled in the New World, they seized with enthusiasm upon the notion of an artificial duck to draw in their prey. Carvers of floating wildfowl, called 'stool-makers', became skilled artisans although their creations were utilitarian long before becoming classified as folk art. They used native woods instead of reeds, fixed weights beneath so that the models bobbed realistically, and fastenings so that the decoys could be secured to the shore and re-used (2,7). A few carvings resembled the back half of an up-ending dabbler, but otherwise the birds were seldom depicted feeding, or fashioned in sleeping poses. The majority were of drakes in breeding plumage since these were thought to catch more easily the eye of any passing fowl. American experience was that ducks, geese and swans could all be decoyed and models were made accordingly (2). Whistling Swans *Cygnus columbianus* were attracted readily, 'particularly the tender-fleshed young birds', and appropriate dummies were produced until swan-shooting was prohibited in 1913 (it has since re-opened in parts of the west – see Chapter 4). Blue-winged *Anas discors* and Green-winged Teal models were always rare; do teal not respond, or do they react to models of other ducks so well that specific artefacts are not needed? Or are they so much smaller that they are not worth the shot? Brent Geese *Branta bernicla* apparently responded to decoys in the spring but not in the fall, so Brant decoys (in North America, Brent Geese are called Brant) ceased to be common when spring hunting was banned (2). While Brant hunting was allowed, model gulls were often used to float among the stool geese at sea, in order to give the scene a more natural look. Was this a whim, or was the hunter responding to an observation of real goose behaviour? Size was interestingly variable; American decoy ducks are often more than life-size, apparently because they are designed to attract birds passing high overhead. The Englishman's Call Duck could be small because their task was rather different – it was mostly to draw birds into the pipes after they had landed.

The American wooden models became known as 'decoys'. There were no real pipe decoys around to cause confusion, and it was live Call Ducks that the dummies were likened to. The word's meaning has changed completely; four centuries ago it was a trap into which flightless ducks were driven, now it means someone who, innocently or knowingly, lures another into danger.

Ducks and goose calls, to attract birds within reach of the gun, seem also to be American in inspiration and most hunters combine their dummy ducks with mechanical calls – 'the call catches the attention of the birds. They then see the decoys, and if everything looks right they drop in for a visit' (3). In Britain, model decoys at evening flight are said to have limited value: only the first birds will see them, and they are a nuisance to pick up in the dark. They are more often employed at early morning flight, especially in inland marshes, but the use of large numbers of decoys is frowned upon. British wildfowling books convey the impression that the art is to get within range of the birds, rather than to persuade the quarry to come within range of the gun. As for 'calling', most beginners are warned against the attempt – 'all too often their quacking will scare away every fowl within hearing, and they risk being peppered in the growing darkness by shooters even less experienced than themselves!' (32).

There is a difference between Britain and North America in the time of day that most duck are shot. Night shooting is illegal in the USA, while most wildfowling in Britain (as we shall see in Chapter 4) is done at dusk and dawn. So any difference in the tools of the trade may not necessarily reflect a divergence in the behaviour of the birds. However, there seems to be a real enough difference in the way passerines respond

Blue-winged Teal, drawn by Robert Gillmor (from *Rare Birds in Britain and Ireland.*)

to 'pishing' or 'squeaking' (3). These are techniques used by American and Canadian bird-watchers to bring wild birds into view, and involve sounds produced either by forcing air through the teeth or by sucking air through lips held against the back of the hand. A variety of birds, such as woodpeckers, warblers and nuthatches, will come from cover apparently to take a look at the performer. In Europe, bird-watchers agree in general that such simple tactics do not work. Perhaps the wildfowl of the New World are as innocent as the woodpeckers. It is also remarkable how much tamer are the shore birds of the west Atlantic than the same species of wader on British coasts – perhaps in part because all American shore birds are now protected. Migrating American ducks, geese and swans seem to be peculiarly susceptible to attraction by decoy models, and the application of this phenomenon has influenced hunting in the United States to a great extent – almost no-one shoots except over decoys.

In the past 20 years, a new decorative form has gripped the imagination of North America (29). Decoy carving is now a major hobby; a good carving can be a work of art (it must still float upright and level in a tank of water in order to win a prize among 2,500 entries in the Annual Championships). The fashion has reached England ('ducks have taken to the mainstream as objects of design' to quote from a recent magazine article) and a pair of wooden model Teal can cost over £600. An antique decoy, made and painted in Great South Bay or Chesapeake a hundred years ago, on the other hand, is incredibly expensive: a pair of wooden Common Mergansers *Mergus mergus*, dated 1860 and fashioned by P. Lathrop in Massachusetts, sold in 1985 for $93,500 at Christie's East in New York. British collectors are buying decorative wildfowl carved locally, and educational courses that teach the techniques are over-subscribed. Will the Dutch be the next to follow the trend, one wonders?

DECOYS IN MODERN TIMES

In 1907, a decoy in western Denmark was used as a trap to catch ducks for ringing in order to study their migratory behaviour. H. C. C. Mortensen ringed Teal in decoys at Fanø and subsequently received news of them from as far afield as Ireland and Spain (24). Between 1908 and 1910 he ringed 320 Pintails, and recovered 67 or 20%, some in decoys in Holland. The Dutch were the next to use decoys for marking birds for research and, in November 1912, a Teal was taken in Abbotsbury Decoy in England that had been ringed in the Netherlands. More of Mortensen's pioneer research is described in Chapter 5.

The earliest British stations to study duck migration were also decoys (40) and the majority of ducks ringed in Britain have been caught in them. The results obtained over 50 years or so have been immensely valuable, and our knowledge of wildfowl movements, and breeding and wintering grounds, would be far less advanced had decoys not become available (in

Bob Ridges demonstrating the first stages of carving a decorative wooden duck to visitors at Slimbridge. Photograph by Joe Blossom.

1934, Orielton in Wales (21) was the first to be used in Britain). At Borough Fen, where over 41,000 ducks have been ringed since 1947, 20% of the Mallard caught are later recovered outside the decoy (4,5). About 3.7% are found abroad and these recoveries suggest a movement from Russia and the Baltic regions. Mallard caught in the autumn move little in the year of ringing; 22% of first year recoveries are within ten miles and 90% within 80 miles. Few Mallard survive more than five years, but two did live to reach the ages of 20 and 21 years. One female ringed at Borough Fen in September 1962 was shot in Alberta three years later.

Teal recoveries show a more northerly breeding range and, in hard weather, birds fly on to Ireland, southern France and Iberia or, rarely, into Greece and Turkey. One remarkable Teal ringed at Borough Fen in November 1952 was shot by a Newfoundland hunter 27 days later. Wigeon breed further east and a number have been recovered from beyond 95° longitude, a quarter of the way around the world.

Even bird-ringing in decoys has declined, along with market catching, and they are hardly used today for any purpose. A list of those still in repair that can be visited will be found in Appendix 2. A brief history of those associated with The Wildfowl and Wetlands Trust, and of a few others restored for ringing purposes, is given here.

Borough Fen, near Peakirk, Cambridgeshire, is the only one remaining that has eight pipes set in a 'starfish' pattern and, in 1976, was designated by the Department of the Environment as an Ancient Monument. The decoy was operated by one family for 300 years until the lease was taken over as a ringing station by The Severn Wildfowl Trust in 1951, and records of its catches, with few breaks, exist since 1776 (4,5). Peter Scott had lived and painted there during the winter of 1932; the decoyman Billy Williams died in 1957, and his widow, the last of a famous line (Billy had married his cousin Annie Williams), at the end of 1986, aged 96 years (Chapter 10). Until the coming of the train in the middle of the last century, birds had been sent to London via the Great North Road, meeting the 'stage' at Norman Cross 16 miles away, to which point they were carried by horse. Birds caught in the afternoon at Borough Fen would be on the stalls in the capital's Leadenhall Market the next morning. They were packed in hampers probably made from osiers grown in the village of Peakirk, now the site of The Wildfowl and Wetlands Trust's smallest Centre. With their necks expertly dislocated, birds were in better condition for market than those that had been shot, and were preferred by London cooks as looking neater and keeping fresh longer – important before the advantages of refrigeration. In Mrs Beeton's day in the 1850s, it was largely from decoys (she mentions particularly those in Lincolnshire) that the London market was supplied. The effects of Dutch competition were, however, already becoming apparent and depressing prices. They were not to rise again until the years of the first world war (5,40).

Berkeley New Decoy, Slimbridge, Gloucestershire, is of the more typical crab-type or 'skate's egg' shape, with two pipes at each end of the pool, curving inwards at their points. It was built in 1843 to replace one thought to be too close to the disturbance of the recently dug Gloucester-Sharpness Ship Canal. Both were 'house decoys' for Berkeley Castle. Peter Scott acquired the site of the new Slimbridge one in 1946, when The Severn Wildfowl Trust was formed, and refurbished the decoy over the following three years (34,35,37). A dog was used from the second season and, later, ducks were lured by food alone. In 1961 and again in 1962, over 2,000 birds were ringed, the majority of them Mallard with a few Teal and the occasional Pintail and Shoveler *Anas clypeata*. These totals

A plan of an eight-pipe decoy, as at Borough Fen near the Peakirk Centre and, on the right, the plan used for the Berkeley New Decoy at the Slimbridge Centre of The Wildfowl and Wetlands Trust. Drawn by Sir Ralph Payne-Gallwey who thought that five pipes where duck were numerous, and three where they were not, were more efficient systems.

were encouraging, as the maximum killed in any season under the previous regime had been 1,410 in 1853–54. Over 27,000 ducks have now been ringed at Slimbridge. The Wildfowl and Wetlands Trust still operates Borough Fen and Berkeley New Decoys, but their effectiveness has declined and costs have escalated. Fixed cage traps on nearby waters (also man-made), such as Deeping Lake, Lincolnshire, and Swan Lake at Slimbridge, are found to be more productive, and labour is concentrated there.

The Delta Decoy in Manitoba, Canada, had its origins in two visits made by Peter Scott to the Waterfowl Research Station in 1948 and 1949 (37). He drew up the plans and helped early excavation. Aluminium tubing was used for the hoops and fish seine for the netting. A dog and a Dutch decoyman caught 211 ducks between 1951 and 1960, mostly in early autumn since the water freezes from the end of October. Blue-winged Teal and Mallard made up 60% of the catch, with Redheads (which responded better to bait than to the dog) about 20%. Over 800 ringed birds had been recovered by 1961 (20), but the use of the decoy dwindled and today it is no longer in service.

Nacton Decoy, Suffolk (also called Orwell Park), was the last decoy in

The frontispiece of Payne-Gallwey's *Book of Duck Decoys* is a lithograph of
the second George Skelton, a famous builder of decoys. The caption reads
'Arriving with the first fruits of South Acre Decoy, Nov. 1854'.

Britain to be employed commercially and was built only in 1830 having,
unusually, two working ponds (23). The main one was adapted from a
mill reservoir and has the traditional skate's egg, four pipe shape; a fifth
pipe, designed for catching Teal, leads from a smaller pond in a secluded
part of the wood. Nacton was a most successful venture (40) and was
operated by one man, Tom Baker, for 52 years. The total of 9,303 ducks
taken during the season of 1925–26 is the highest authenticated catch for
any British decoy, while the average was 3,903 for the fifty years up to
1969 (23). A lease was acquired by The Wildfowl Trust in 1968 and
subsequently 15,631 birds were trapped and ringed (using a dog and many
Call Ducks) including a high proportion of Wigeon, Teal and Pintail.
Over 50% of all the Pintail ringed in Britain were taken at Nacton. They
have been recovered in their Russian breeding grounds, in Romania,
France, Italy and Morocco. The first British-ringed duck of any species
to be recovered south of the Sahara was a young female Pintail, killed in
January 1969 in Senegal. However, the catch declined here as elsewhere
and The Trust's lease was given up in 1982, since when this beautiful
decoy has fallen into disrepair.

Abbotsbury Decoy in Dorset was built soon after 1655 and is therefore one of the oldest in England (28). It is another example of a house decoy, supplying winter food for an estate, and has been owned by the Strangeways family (sometime Earls of Ilchester) throughout its existence. It is small and lies at the edge of the tidal Fleet amongst a reed bed. In comparison with eastern decoys it was not particularly productive, the best catches being 2,564 duck during three seasons in the 1920s. Ringing started in 1937 (although ducks were again taken for food during the war years of the 1940s) using two pipes. Since 1976, it has caught some 1,400 birds for ringing, of which 74% were Teal and 11% Pintail.

Dersingham Decoy in Norfolk was built with five pipes by the second George Skelton in 1818, and he died there in February 1857 aged 67 years. The decoy was not used commercially after 1870; a single pipe was reconstructed in 1965 and nearly 5,000 ducks caught for ringing before operation ceased in 1970. About three-quarters of the catch were Teal and the rest Mallard (18).

Boarstall Decoy, near Brill in Buckinghamshire, is run as a ringing point and museum by the Berks., Bucks. and Oxfordshire Naturalist's Trust. It has no complete history but appears on a 1697 map of the Manor of Boarstall, and was a house decoy for the Aubrey family (41). The Wildfowlers' Association of Great Britain and Ireland used it for a while

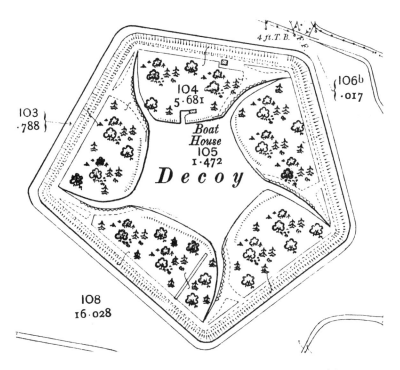

An early map of the five-sided decoy at Hale in Lancashire.

An 18th Century sketch-map showing the vanished five-sided decoy at Martin Mere in Lancashire; the left-hand edge of the map was bounded by Langley's Brook which is still visible as the Ring Ditch, the right-hand edge is a private road known as Long Meanygate, while the bottom edge (the Geldhey Bank) is today the northwest boundary of The Wildfowl and Wetlands Centre. Redrawn by John Turner who has added North.

with one reconstructed pipe restored in the late 1960s (32). It catches and rings about 300 ducks, mostly Teal, during October and November.

Orielton Decoy, in Pembroke, has the distinction of being the first British decoy to become a ringing station for migratory ducks, catching Teal wintering in Wales and breeding abroad (21,40). At the beginning of this century, Orielton was being operated by Herbert Williams of the same family that ran Borough Fen. It went out of use but, on the instigation of Peter Scott, it was reconditioned in 1934 with the object of marking wild ducks. Before the war, nearly 6,000 birds were ringed, and after 1945 another 5,166 were caught when the International Wildfowl Inquiry, and later The Severn Wildfowl Trust, paid for ducks to be ringed (Chapter 5). The decoy was, however, damaged by storms and disturbed by local farming, and it ceased operations after the 1959–60 season.

Hale Decoy, 14.5 km (9 miles) from Liverpool, was possibly constructed about 1730. It had five pipes and a moat around it that still fills during high tide on the River Mersey which is 400 m (440 yd) to the south (26,41). The Lancashire Trust for Nature Conservation with the Cheshire Conservation Trust care for it and a few ducks are trapped. Its distinctive pentagonal shape led indirectly to the rediscovery of an unsuspected decoy site on Wholesome Brow, an island of peat and boulder clay that appeared from the bed of Martin Mere in southwest Lancashire after initial drainage around 1700. Aerial photographs by Professor W. G. Hale in 1985 show the Hale-type five-sided form still apparent in the soil and, indeed, the decoy appears on Christopher Greenwood's map of Lancashire published in December 1818 (1). Fields in the area are called 'Coy hey' and 'Coy croft' to this day. The decoy seems to have been owned by Lord Derby and may have operated for as much as a hundred years but was no longer in use, totally forgotten, when Payne-Gallwey listed in 1886 all the decoys of which he could find evidence. It was the same size as Hale and probably an exact copy.

REFERENCES

1. Bagley, J. J. & Hodgkissing, A. G. 1985. *Lancashire: a history of the County Palatine in early maps.* Manchester: Richardson.

2. Barber, J. 1934. *Wild Fowl Decoys.* Windward House (re-issued in 1954 by Dover: New York).

3. Boswall, J. & Barton, B. 1983. *Human imitation of bird sounds.* London: BLOWS.

4. Cook, W. A. 1960. The numbers of ducks caught in Borough Fen Decoy, 1776–1959. *Wildfowl* 11: 118–22

5. Cook, W. A. & Pilcher, R. E. 1982. *The history of Borough Fen Decoy.* Ely: Providence Press.

6. Defoe, D. 1727. *A Tour through the Whole Island of Great Britain, 1724–5.* Vol.II, Letter 7. Re-issued in 1975 by Everyman University Library.

7. Earnest, A. 1982. *The Art of the Decoy. American Bird Carvings.* Pennsylvania: Schiffer.

8. Eygenraam, J. A. & van Troostwijk, W. J. D. 1964. Analysis of the catches of Dutch duck decoys. *Proc. 1st European Meeting on Wildfowl Conservation*: 77–86.

9. Folkard, H. C. 1859. *The Wild fowler.* London: Piper, Stephenson, & Spence.

10. Fox, J. B. 1982. Duck Decoys in Ireland. *Irish Wildbird Cons. News* 32: 6–7.

11. Fox, J. 1984. Duck decoys in north Co. Cork. *Mallow Field Club J.* 2: 111–120.

12. Fox, J. B. 1986. Kellyville decoy and its catches. *Irish Birds* 3: 245–254.

13. Gilbert, H. A. 1941. British Decoys, in 'Factors affecting the General Status of Wild Goose and Wild Duck': 50–56. Cambridge: *Intern. Wildfowl Inquiry* Vol 1.

14. Glegg, W. E. 1943/44. The duck decoys of Essex. *Essex Naturalist* 27: 191–207, 211–225.

15. Haverschmidt, F. 1931. Vangsteijfers van eenige Nederlandsche eendenkooien. *Ardea* 20: 152–169.

16. Jones, P. E. 1965. *The Worshipful Company of Poulters of the City of London.* OUP.

17. Key, H. A. S. 1955. The Tempsford duck decoy and reports of recorders. *Beds. Nat.* 9: 24–40.

18. Lambert, J. E. A. & Cook, W. A. 1967. Dersingham Decoy. *Wildfowl* 18: 22–23.

19. McAtee, W. L. 1932. 'Duck ponds' in Holland. *Auk* 49: 346–347.

20. McCabe, R. A. & Mulder, N. 1961. A history of the Delta Decoy. *Trans.N.Amer.Wildlife Conf.* 26: 80–98.

21. Mackworth-Praed, C. W. 1936. The Orielton Decoy – past and present. *Brit.Birds* 29: 167–171.

22. Matthews, G. V. T. 1958. Wildfowl conservation in the Netherlands. *Wildfowl* 9: 142–153.

23. Matthews, G. V. T. 1969 Nacton Decoy and its catches. *Wildfowl* 20: 131–137.

24. Mortensen, H. C. C. 1950. *Studies in Bird Migration.* DOF: Munksgaard, Copenhagen.

25. Owen, D. 1988. Decoy champion. *Country Life.* Sept: 192–193.

26. Payne-Gallwey, R. 1886. *The Book of Decoys: Their Construction, Management and History.* London: Van Voorst.

27. Pentland, G. H. 1915. Notes on a decoy in the County of Louth. *Irish Nat.* 24: 209–211

28. Prendergast, E. D. V. 1987. Dorset Decoys: Abbotsbury & Morden. Dorset Nat. Hist. & Arch. Soc.

29. Ridges, B. 1988. *The Decoy Duck: from Folk Art to Fine Art*. Limpsfield: Dragon's World.

30. Savage, C. 1963. Wildfowling in northern Iran. *Wildfowl* 14: 30–46.

31. Savage, C. 1966. Wildfowl survey in south-west Asia: progress in 1965. *Wildfowl* 17: 45–48.

32. Sedgewick, H. M. *et al.* 1961. *The New Wildfowler*. London: Jenkins.

33. Schorger, A. W. 1968. An early colonial duck decoy. *Can. Field Nat.* 82: 223.

34. Scott, P. 1948. The Decoy. *Wildfowl* 1: 52–55.

35. Scott, P. 1950. The Decoy. *Wildfowl* 2: 10–18.

36. Scott, P. 1965. Shinhama – the Imperial Duck Decoy. *Wildfowl* 16: 129–131.

37. Scott, P. 1961. *The Eye of the Wind*. London: Hodder.

38. Smith, J. C. D. 1974. *A Guide to Church Wood-carvings*. London: David & Charles.

39. Southwell, T. 1904. On some early Dutch and English decoys. *Norfolk & Norwich Nats. Soc.* 7: 606–17.

40. Thomson, A. L. & Mackworth-Praed, C. W. 1941. Ringing of duck at British decoys for the Wildfowl Inquiry Committee, in 'Factors affecting the General Status of Wild Goose and Wild Duck': 64–83. Cambridge: *Intern. Wildfowl Inquiry* Vol. 1.

41. Whitaker, J. 1918. *British Duck Decoys of To-Day*. London: Burlington.

4: Wildfowling

This Chapter continues the theme of providing man with food. After the practicalities of domestication and the subterfuges of decoying, we come to wildfowling – the killing of ducks and geese with weapons. There is, at least nowadays, a substantial difference of approach in that wildfowling is considered a sport (mass destruction not being the object, and many of the quarry getting away) and most recent writing on the subject (12,13,26,28) conveys an impression of pleasurable, almost romantic, activity – of 'old instincts running strong'. The lonely wildfowler of the coast, up to his waist in mud and cold water, does seem to find the experience exhilarating even if he takes home nothing for the pot.

There is a tradition of fine literature on wildfowling, and Hawker (9), Folkard (6) and Payne-Gallwey (17,18) are classic authors on the subject. Peter Scott's beautifully illustrated *Morning Flight* (23), published in 1935, has been called one of the great wildfowling books of the 20th Century or of any other (13). Lawrence Durrell's description of a duck shoot in the Nile delta near Alexandria (5) is another expression of the magic of water, wilderness and the early morning flight of birds. I have used extensively, in the early part of this Chapter, John Marchington's *History of Wildfowling* (13); he makes the point that it was the gun that created a sport of what had previously been work, although the change of attitude occurred slowly over several centuries. There were elements of 'games-manship' before firearms, but it was not until the era of Peter Hawker that coastal wildfowling became acceptable among the wealthy classes with time on their hands. Gunpowder was introduced into Britain in the 14th Century but the flintlock musket, whereby the gun was fired by sparks from a flint, not until the 17th. This most significant change enabled the quarry to be pursued with the weapon 'at the ready' instead of being ignited with a slow match while the bird got up and flew away!

WILDFOWLING BEFORE THE GUN

Wildfowl became quarry many thousands of years ago. As ducks, geese and swans were large birds, they must have been especially prized and many were the ingenious ways of catching them, rather seldom on the wing but often at night and sometimes under water. Bolas are a New World weapon of the chase consisting of two or three stones united by rope to a common centre. The hunter whirls the bolas round his head and sends it, revolving through the air, to wind around the object to be brought down. Fish hooks, nooses, pitfall traps, snares, loops, birdlime, drugs and flightnets were all employed on wildfowl somewhere. In China and India, hunters approached their prey swimming beneath large calabashes (the hard shells of a fruit, which originated in tropical America, made into a vessel) that covered their heads and necks, and presumably seemed like part of the natural scene. Treading water, they would reach

A 'stalking-horse' on Whittlesea Mere in 1835, when the landscape looked remarkably like Holland. The weapon is a very large shoulder-gun. From G. D. Rowley's *Ornithological Miscellany*.

slowly for the bird's legs and drown them by holding them beneath the surface. 'Stalking horses' (which were sometimes bullocks or even ostriches), were originally ridden into the unsuspecting flocks but later were skinned and remodelled to contain the fowler himself as a modern hide or blind does, and therefore became more usual after guns were invented (2,3). The name 'stalking horse' was also applied to the floating hides that commonly concealed guns on inland waters during the last Century.

The driving and netting of moulting wildfowl has been referred to in Chapter 3. Some methods of catching wildfowl without the use of firearms have persisted well into this Century. At the end of the 1950s, it was estimated that 1,200,000 ducks were killed in an average winter season in the marshes around the Caspian Sea of northern Iran; shooting accounted for only 9% of them (22). The principle manner of capture is by net, gong and flare at night. The fowlers go in two boats; in the bow of the first burns a weak, flaring flame screened from the rest of the vessel by a large hood. Behind this stands a man with an elongated hand-net and behind him a companion who does the paddling. The second boat travels

'Catching ducks at night with a flare on a Caspian lagoon', an oil painting from *Wild Chorus* by Peter Scott.

A fowling scene painted about 1400 BC on the wall of a tomb at Thebes. The hunter, dressed in a linen kilt, holds his throwing stick aloft while his tame Egyptian Goose stands in the prow of the boat, perhaps acting as a decoy.

close and contains one man beating a brass gong incessantly and another who paddles. Mallard are the species most susceptible to this method of hunting; they wait for the boats to approach within three or four yards and are caught as they leap into the air. The shape, brightness and sound of the boats clearly evoke no 'predator response' in the ducks; the effect is dazzling and bewildering and resembles nothing that they have cause to fear. One team, in ideal conditions, might take six hundred in a night.

The Egyptians have left pictorial evidence of their marsh hunts and here it was the throwing stick that was aimed most skilfully at the neck of the duck. We can see in royal Egyptian carvings and paintings the first depictions in the ancient world of the thrill and enjoyment of the fowling party, with a sporting aspect to the whole thing. The Greeks and Romans reserved their enthusiasm for the hunting of stags and wild boar while leaving the trapping of wildfowl to ordinary folk.

Hawking, as a method of catching flying birds, has occurred since the time of Aristotle (340 BC). In the 13th Century, members of the court of Kublai Khan flew Goshawks *Accipiter gentilis* at ducks, and Peregrines (the falcon that the Americans called the 'Duck Hawk' *Falco peregrinus anatum*) at wild geese (3). This was again mainly for sport rather than for food. Hawking was indulged in only by the wealthy – King John issued an edict in 1209 that forbad the taking of wildfowl by any method so that he could hunt them with falcons. Maybe the ducks had had a poor breeding season that year; generally, there must have been a vast supply of migratory and locally-bred birds and no such restriction would have been necessary.

A few sporting wildfowlers may have used bows, both long-bows and cross-bow, and arrows or bolts (the longbow was around in 3000 BC but, as noted in Chapter 2, we have little idea when the feathered arrow was first employed, although it goes back at least to Upper Palaeolithic times). Food cannot have been the main motive for using an arrow against a flying duck or goose since, for the purpose, it was relatively inefficient and costly to lose.

THE HISTORY OF THE GUN

To begin with, guns did not do much to improve man's success in killing birds. A projected missile, aided by something other than the arm, came with the sling, the arrow and the cross-bow bolt; the invention of

A detail from the 'Alphonse Psalter' painted in England in the 14th Century.

Sir Ralph Payne-Gallwey in his gun-room at Thirkleby Hall.

gunpowder to move the missile was, nevertheless, crucial to the development of firearms (13). Gunpowder arrived in Europe around AD 200 as 'shooting powder' although it had been used much earlier in India and China. The recipe was six parts saltpetre or potassium nitrate and two parts each of powdered charcoal and sulphur. It was employed in European warfare around AD 1000, and introduced into England for guns during the 14th Century. The English had firearms at the Battle of Crecy in 1346 and, by 1373, Chaucer was writing of 'gonnes' as if they were familiar objects.

The earliest personal guns were simple metal tubes, closed at one end, into which gunpowder and projectile were placed, and which had a hole where the powder was exploded by being 'touched' with fire from a match. The closed end of the tube was set in a stock, and the whole device rested against the shoulder. Only details (albeit important ones of comfort and safety) have changed this arrangement since.

Matchlock firing, whereby a slow-burning match could be brought into contact with the touch-hole by means of a trigger, was one advance; then in the 16th Century came the wheel-lock and, in the 17th, the flintlock both of which worked on the principle of firing the gunpowder, not with a match, but with a spark produced by the clash of flint on steel. The tedious business of muzzle-loading, shoving the powder and projectile down the tube or barrel with a ramrod, ceased with the invention of the breech-loading gun which broke at a hinge and could be loaded at a point near the ignition system. This happened during the first part of the 19th Century. Ignition by percussion with a hammer rather than by fire also came at the beginning of the 19th, and the once-prized, old flintlock guns were slowly discarded. Finally, the cartridge consisting of a charge of powder plus a bullet in a thick paper (called 'cartridge paper') container and, later, a detonating cap were invented and marketed by Eley in the 1860s. Pelletted lead shot arrived at about the same time, although the plastic cartridge case did not appear until 1965 (13).

Developments in the philosophy of wildfowling gradually produced the idea that the surest way of killing 'clean', the hardest and therefore the 'best' and most sportsmanlike way, was to aim at flying quarry. Obviously this was possible only after the flintlock gun became available.

THE HISTORY OF WILDFOWLING

The modern definition of wildfowling is precise: it is the pursuit of legally taken ducks and geese below high-water mark with shotguns (13,26). Dogs to retrieve the dead and wounded game, especially after dark, are an essential part of this tidal-zone shooting and were on the scene by the 16th Century. Their possession, like much else to do with guns, was then restricted to the landed gentry. Spaniels (their name meaning 'spanish' from *español*) were the first dogs developed for finding and retrieving birds, probably by the Romans; they were trained to quarter the ground ahead of the hunter and to scent and pick up anything killed or injured, originally by falcons. For the coastal shooter, they had the disadvantage of being relatively small and not strong in water. The wildfowlers' favourite breeds – labrador, Chesapeake Bay and golden

A wood-engraving by Johnstone, an apprentice of Thomas Bewick, showing two gentlemen out with guns on the seashore. Their small dog is probably a spaniel.

More scenes of wildfowling engraved by Thomas Bewick and (right) Clennell. Here the dogs look like terriers.

retrievers, poodle ('puddle hound') and Irish water spaniel – were developed in the 19th Century. They sit by the hunter's side while the ducks and geese are shot, and are sent out to collect and return with the bird, often travelling across creeks.

The labrador, like other wildfowling dogs, reached Europe from North America, specifically from the cod-banks of Newfoundland, where it was used as a working colleague by fishermen; it could swim with ropes in its mouth even sometimes to ships in distress, its short, water-repellent coat shedding any ice. Peter Hawker seems to have obtained the first labradors, or St John's dogs, in England, from sailors plying between Poole in Dorset and Newfoundland (9). The breed is thought to have been derived from the Spanish black pointer ('labrador' comes from the Portuguese, meaning 'the worker') crossed with hounds belonging to the native Indians. Undoubtedly, the companionship of a well-trained dog has become part of the pleasure of wildfowling (26). The next greatest invention to improve the enjoyment of the wetland sport must have been the rubber 'wellington' boot which was put on the market in about 1860; however, even this boon was slow to catch on since diehards preferred leather, that had to be treated with oil or wax after each outing but was reasonably porous and warm – presumably a servant did the 'treating' not the exhausted hunter!

Colonel Peter Hawker (1786–1853) of the Light Dragoons published *Instructions to Young Sportsmen in all that relates to Guns and Shooting* in 1814 (9). Until then, coastal fowling was confined to those 'who sought wildfowl for the poulterers and were actuated solely by the love of gain'! The techniques of marine duck-hunting were already well known, but his writing introduced the sport to a wider public and, in particular, made it a respectable pursuit for gentlemen and so set a pattern for the future. His book has been called a milestone in the history of wildfowling: 'the textbook and the Koran of the fowler afloat' (13).

Hawker was wounded in 1809 in the Peninsular War and left the Army in 1813 to run an estate centred on Longparish House in Hampshire. Enormously energetic if there were any opportunity for sport, he was nevertheless an hypochondriac and cross enough with his fellow man to be involved often in litigation. His diary appeared in 1893 edited by Payne-Gallwey and, from it, Marchington (13) deduces that he was both a pessimist and a complainer.

His famous *Instructions* (9) are not, in fact, primarily about wildfowling; the subject of wildfowl shooting is not reached until page 319, and he then quickly moves through shoulder-gunning for duck before coming to the real love of his life which was punt-gunning. The book deals mostly with technical matters, and not at all with the beauties of the coastline and countryside; he shows little concern for his quarry and the crippled birds that he left behind. Between 1802 and 1852, he recorded that he shot 4,488 wildfowl and he appears generally to have been an excellent marksman. He lived in the days of the muzzle-loader and flintlock – the first English breech-loader was put on the market in 1853, the year he died (13). With Hawker, it was the game of numbers and anything unusual (in 1823, he killed two Egyptian Geese in Norfolk and three at Longparish), and he often sent his servant out punt-gunning if he could not go himself. He never felt, or at least never wrote about, the exhilaration of the storm, or the thrill of seeing geese and swans in flight along the tide's edge: that was for unborn generations to experience.

John Marchington (13) places the golden age of wildfowling in the 19th Century. It started when guns were efficient enough to kill flying birds with ease, and dogs had been bred to retrieve from water with skill, and ended, like the age of duck decoys, with the drainage of the wetlands and the loss of coastal habitats. He also suggests that as many birds are killed now as then, although today it is by many more shooters – the golden days were for the few; however, during that time the seeds of conservation were sown. Transport was the major problem for the ordinary man; coastal areas within walking distance of towns and villages were shot over by everyone, while numerous remote spots were not.

The first book to deal entirely with wildfowling was H. C. Folkard's *The Wild Fowler* (6) and here at last was an author who expressed kindly feelings for the natural world and for his quarry. He shows sympathy for

'The tedious business of muzzle-loading' engraved by Bewick.

Sir Ralph Payne-Gallwey, Bart., standing in front of his punt, with a gun in one hand and a dead Brent Goose in the other.

the many cripples of his favourite sport which was punt-gunning. (Punt-gunning was, indeed, the ultimate enjoyment for most wildfowlers of that period). He also described, for the first time, shooting over model decoy ducks imported from America.

Sir Ralph Payne-Gallwey has been mentioned before because he wrote the first book on duck decoys (although Folkard had already dealt with the subject in a number of chapters of *The Wild Fowler*) and he edited Hawker's diaries. As an exponent of the art of shooting, Payne-Gallwey had no equal. He was to the second half of the golden age of wildfowling what Hawker had been to the first. He was an inventor (he invented a double-barrelled breech-loading punt gun) and champion archer, had a three-pipe decoy built at Thorkleby Hall near Thirsk by Thomas Skelton and, above all, he wrote. *The Fowler in Ireland* (17) and *Letters to Young Shooters* (18) were lavishly illustrated and much praised and, again, we read that punt-gunning was his passion. It was a totally masculine pursuit: the gun was very large indeed, and the combination of boat, sea, stealth and romance gave a special pleasure. The 'bag' *could* be huge, up to 300

'Among 'em at last!' the frontispiece to Payne-Gallwey's *The Fowler in Ireland*. The caption to this scene of punt-gunning continues 'on Retrieving cripples; the result of placing $2\frac{1}{2}$ lbs of BB! NICELY! into a company of several thousand Wigeon, after three weeks without a shot, owing to unfavourable weather and the wildness of the birds'.

Brent killed by the firing of a double-barrel, but these numbers were rare. Punts were excitingly dangerous too; the lower the boat was made to float in the water (so that the birds would not notice its approach) the more likely it was to swamp in rough seas, and the weight of the gun did not help stability. The recoil of the immense weapon sometimes caused injury to the gunners while the smaller guns, used to stop crippled ducks or geese, were occasionally fired by mistake through the vessel's floor. There was always the horrible chance that another punter would fail to see you through the sea mist and, in winter, ice was yet another hazard!

The eelgrass disease of the 1930s, by removing their main food supply, put an end to the large flocks of Wigeon and Brent grazing in British coastal regions (1), and the decline of the classes who had no need to work for a living was equally significant. Only five professional punters were alive just before the last war. The war itself put an end to most punting, as official coastal defence did not look with favour on small armed craft that crept about at night.

The 1954 Wild Birds Protection Act restricted the maximum bore or diameter of the gun barrel to $1\frac{3}{4}$ inches (4.5 cm), and various unsuccessful attempts have been made since then to ban punt-gunning in the UK altogether, as it has been in most other countries. Current opinion seems to be that this expensive sport can be allowed to die naturally for want of anyone who can afford or would wish to carry on.

Plenty of attempts to create and then lengthen a close season during which British wildfowl could not be killed have been made in the past. Spring shooting threatens the potential breeding stock, so the 1881 Wild Birds Protection Act gave protection to all British birds between 1 March and 31 July; regulations were occasionally waived, as after the end of the 1918 war when the season was extended to the end of March and the selling of dead wildfowl until 15 April, partly to ease the food shortage and partly to give the returning soldiers some sport. An anecdote (16) in *The Norfolk Naturalist*, describing a night in the trenches in France 1917, suggests however that the ordinary soldier was not an experienced wildfowler:

'The guns have ceased roaring for a brief period. Gradually there grows upon our ears sounds that make our flesh creep. "Is that Jerry coming over?" whispers many a Tommy. "He's trying to put the wind up us with that hellish noise, I'll bet." Presently star-shells are put up, and we can clearly discern a large flock of geese, flying fairly low, approaching our lines. Machine-guns on both sides opened on them, but neither Fritz nor our gunners apparently scored a hit'.

Legislation was slow to be implemented and, until the 1950s, was mainly in the hands of the County Councils rather than decreed at National level. An act passed in 1939, entitled the Duck and Goose Act, protected wildfowl from 1 February to 11 August, although tidal shooting was permitted up to 20 February. The 1954 Act safeguarded all wild birds at all times except where specified, and Brent and Barnacle Geese *Branta leucopsis* (in most places) were removed entirely as species that could be shot. The Act was strengthened in 1967 by the banning of market-shooting of geese, and again in 1981 as the Wildlife and Countryside Act (15).

The months before the 1954 Bird Protection Act were full of sound and fury. Relationships between conservationists (The Severn Wildfowl Trust had been founded in 1946 and had an Honorary Director who was not only a national figure but known to have given up shooting) and wildfowlers touched bottom. Two years later, Max Nicholson's 'tea parties' at the Nature Conservancy broke the ice and, in 1957, the Wildfowlers' Association of Great Britain and Ireland (WAGBI) and the newly renamed Wildfowl Trust formed sub-committees that slowly managed to convince the majority of wildfowlers that Peter Scott's young Trust was not fundamentally opposed to their activities.

The establishment of refuges for quarry species of wildfowl was what Max Nicholson (then Director of the Nature Conservancy) was after, and the Humber Wildfowl Refuge was the first to be set up in 1955 with the Southport Sanctuary in Lancashire a close second. The wildfowlers themselves were enthusiastic members of these refuge committees, so that the shooter of the 20th Century was often no longer just a hunter, but had become something of a conservationist (26). The incentives of food for his family and financial gain had gone. The professional wildfowler of the past had an unglamorous, uncertain and dangerous life – if he exists today it is as a guide for a new generation of amateur wildfowlers out for enjoyment.

Of the 160,000 individuals who shot wildfowl in 1980, 60,000 were members of WAGBI, or the British Association for Shooting and Conservation (BASC) as it had become (7). In sociological terms they did not differ from the population as a whole, except that very few were female and more wildfowlers came from the country than the towns. The 874,000 birds that they shot were no longer predominately living on the sea-shore, three-quarters of the 'bag' was taken inland and consisted mostly of Mallard.

Many wildfowlers joined the National Wildfowl Counts scheme before and after it was organised by The Severn Wildfowl Trust in 1954 (see Chapter 5) and helped to produce the first mammoth survey of populations and distribution published in 1963 by the Nature Conservancy as *Wildfowl in Great Britain* (1). The need for this book was evident from the deep disagreements about the number of ducks and geese that had created such bitterness during the preparation of the 1954 Act. A second edition, perhaps The Wildfowl Trust's greatest achievement of the 1980s, appeared in 1986 (15).

John Marchington (13) said in 1980, at the end of his book *The History of Wildfowling*, that the main threat to British wildfowling in the future was legal rather than physical; he felt that habitats were being watched and their safety ensured by the conservationists and it was unlikely that any duck or goose species would be eliminated or much reduced; but the need to catch votes at parliamentary elections, and Britain's membership of the European Economic Community, were seen by him and by fellow wildfowlers to bring dangers to field sports.

To be seen to be leaving the major responsibility for the well-being of the environment to others was probably not, in the end, a good idea. It enabled Ian Prestt, Director of the Royal Society for the Protection of Birds (RSPB), to argue in 1985 (19) that wildfowlers had failed to appreciate or protest about the tremendous loss of habitat that had occurred through the agricultural revolution which, in his opinion, had had a far greater impact on sporting prospects than anything else, including the anti-sports lobby: 'BASC played no part whatsoever in the fight to get stronger provisions to save habitat' through the 1981 Wildlife and Countryside Act. Wildfowlers served on refuge committees, established reserves on parts of rented shoots or made new ones out of excavated gravel-pits (26) but, unlike the RSBP, Wildfowl Trust and other local and national conservation bodies, BASC had had no programme for land purchase. The granting of crown foreshore access (see later) had perhaps created a feeling of invulnerability that came to be regretted by some members, and a land acquisition fund has now been set up. Wildfowler's lead shot is also a major pollutant of the environment (21), and many conservationists feel that shooters have a duty, not only to ensure that their activities are not detrimental to wildfowl populations, but to convince others of this. The subject of lead poisoning is further examined in Chapter 8, and the future of wildfowling in the UK in Chapter 10.

THE EFFECT OF SHOOTING ON WILDFOWL POPULATIONS

There is a fairly generally held misconception about the hunting of wild animals by humans, and that is that it helps keep the hunted population healthy by eliminating the old and the weak. In North America, for instance, where duck shooting in autumn and winter is closely controlled, it had been assumed that this control ensures a consistently fit breeding population during the following season. The data on Mallard, at least, do not support the assumption (15). The evidence suggests that, unless shooting pressure is excessive, natural mortality quickly compensates for that caused by wildfowling, and that the removal of some birds early in the winter merely means that fewer will die of other causes later. The hunting pressure in North America is lower than that in Europe, where between 40% and 45% of the late summer duck populations may be shot. This European level is thought to be around the threshold for some species; in other words, it is close to being 'excessive' (27). Nevertheless, most British quarry ducks are, at the moment, rising slightly in numbers. They are limited by the amount of usable habitat available to them in mid or late winter rather than by wildfowling and, in the main, conservation measures are best aimed at the creation and management of a series of refuges that contain their preferred habitats (15).

The second edition of *Wildfowl in Great Britain* (15) points out that we badly need more figures on the shooting kill of duck and goose populations at all stages of their migration, and that the better collection of 'bag' statistics is critically important. In addition, continued intensive ringing or marking of individuals is required so that life histories may be followed and understood (see Chapter 5). Wildfowl counts over the past two or three decades have increased greatly our knowledge of what is there to be shot, but the monitoring of the 'harvest', rather than the numbers sitting on a pond, has been far less efficient because modern wildfowlers (unlike Peter Hawker) are notoriously reluctant to give precise facts about their kill. BASC has been carrying out a National Shooting Survey since 1979 and some results have been mentioned already (7). The Survey established that an estimated 874,000 ducks are killed and retrieved by wildfowlers annually. This, if we include those taken by 'rough shooters', means an annual 'bag' of around a million birds. Losses of cripples (ducks hit but not retrieved and which subsequently die as a result of their wounds) are unknown, but data from North America suggest that these could be an additional 20–35% of the figures for retrieved birds. Sixty percent of ducks shot by BASC members were Mallard, 20% Teal and 14% Wigeon with the other quarry species making up the rest (7,15).

If we try to extrapolate from these figures to a national estimated shooting mortality for ducks we arrive at 700–750,000 Mallard, 150,000 Teal and 50–100,000 Wigeon (excluding crippled birds). Do these numbers seem credible? For Wigeon, which peak in Britain at about 200,000, a loss of 60–120,000 ducks (including a further 20–35% of cripples) seems not unlikely. For Teal, the suggested kill of 180,000 (again including ducks both retrieved and lost) is considerably higher than the counted peak population of 100,000. The Teal is a small secretive duck that is difficult to census accurately, and the National Wildfowl Counts may miss large numbers; or the birds killed may be replaced during the season with further recruits from the Continent. Similarly, the 600,000 Mallard estimated to fall to wildfowlers equals the peak numbers counted in Britain during the winter. Here the picture is complicated by the fact that most Mallard are shot at the beginning of the season before the winter counts are underway, and that wildfowlers add an estimated 400,000 which they rear themselves and release; about 60% of the total Mallard bag is taken by the end of November, at which time migratory foreign-bred duck are still arriving (15). All these factors make it difficult to guess what proportion of the population really is being shot.

This lack of information is unsatisfactory and worrying. We are far from being able to assess the importance of shooting mortality for British ducks (for geese, see later). Much better estimates are needed of the numbers and species of wildfowl shot, season by season, and also of cripples. Otherwise, as total populations seem to be limited by habitat, conservationists can continue to manage duck populations only by preserving their breeding and wintering grounds, hoping that population trends will not be downwards and that hunting kill will not increase.

Some effort has been made in Britain to collect statistics about the age and sex of shot ducks. A Sevenoaks general practitioner called Jeffery Harrison (he was, I am happy to record, once my family doctor), managed also to be an enthusiastic naturalist and wildfowler, and became an inspiration to both camps. He persuaded fellow wildfowlers to co-operate in a duck production survey in which they were asked to send in a wing from each of their dead birds; these were examined by experts and classified according to species, sex and whether they had hatched that year or were fully adult. To begin with, the majority of wings came from Kent but, by the 1970s, over 4,000, mostly from Mallard, Wigeon and Teal, were being sent annually to BASC from the whole country (8,26). Adult males occur as often as females in the total Mallard kill (46% are drakes), but are more common in Teal (57%) and Wigeon (70%). Unfortunately, 4,000 is insufficient to give a good indication of the 'mix' of ducks

Dr Jeffery Harrison receives a retrieved bird from his gun-dog. Photograph by Pamela Harrison.

available; although juveniles are more vulnerable to shooting than adults, the National Wildfowl Counts in most years do not correlate with the percentage of young in the BASC sample (15).

The situation for geese is somewhat different from that known, or guessed, for ducks (14,15). Most geese are shot later in the winter, mainly in December and January. Greylag and Pinkfeet make up the largest part of the bag, but about 15% of the total are Canada Geese and a smaller number are Barnacles. Unlike the situation with the ducks, the quantity of winter habitat does not appear to be limiting any British goose species at the moment and wildfowling does add to their total mortality. Protection from market-shooting, imposed at the wildfowlers' instigation in 1967, has, it seems, allowed an increase in numbers of all species (see Chapter 8).

WHY PROTECTION IS IMPOSED

Bird preservation has many roots, including sentiment. In Europe, for instance, swans are protected in every country, often with special penalties; however, this has more to do with feelings than a knowledge that their populations could not be sustained if an open season were allowed. In the United States, Whistling Swans have been shot legally in certain western states in recent years although, interestingly, during the 1969 Whistling Swan season, a few Nevada hunters purchased permits merely to prevent the birds being killed by others; they thought it wrong to destroy swans

(25). Introduced Black Swans *Cygnus atratus*, on the other hand, have been shot in New Zealand with rather less resistance. If the only consideration were the amount of meat obtained, then a swan will feed more people than a Teal; but it would take many more years to replace the larger bird. Plenty of migratory wildfowl of the northern hemisphere do produce a regular surplus of juveniles which can be eliminated before the next breeding season without affecting the replacement of the stock (15). In some cases, however, shooting restrictions are imposed because a species has been found (or is guessed) not to fit that pattern, being unable to stand the pressure of added mortality due to hunting. To take an extreme example of the now very rare and tame Hawaiian Goose: an open season from 15 September to 1 February was permitted until 1907, although the birds nested through the winter (10). Its current status is that of a few hundred individuals living in marginal habitat, half of the potential breeders failing to nest every year, and most of the goslings dying before they are reared (Chapter 6). It is clear why no-one wants to add to their existing troubles.

A not quite so clear-cut case is that of the northern Eider *Somateria mollissima*. This bird also appears ill-suited to hunting since it takes two to four years to reach breeding age and because success, as measured by young birds fledged, is low in most years. It had a special place in the hearts of those who signed the Migratory Birds Convention in 1916 between the USA and Great Britain (on behalf of Canada); the Eider and the Carolina Wood Duck were given special protection as overexploitation had greatly depleted their numbers and extinction was feared. The Eider is protected in most of its European range (it is shot in Denmark), and in many parts is increasing in numbers, although not in Iceland where that protection is perhaps most rigid. In West Greenland, where thousands are killed every year, numbers are declining, and in parts of Canada they are still, or again, under severe threat because of aboriginal hunting (20). The view of most researchers is that some hunting can be sustained, but not in the spring, nor in combination with down and egg collection.

The Brent Goose is not shot in Britain at present, although it is very numerous (at times 200,000 birds), and there are great pressures from wildfowlers to have it restored to the shooting schedules. This goose was given full protection in 1954 because the world population of the dark-bellied race was then alarmingly low at 16,500, partly through the lingering effects of the eelgrass disease of the early 1930s, and partly because it is an erratic breeder, failing on average to raise any young every other year. Numbers rose slowly at first, and then rapidly; geese started to feed over the sea-wall on agricultural fields, and farmers had to be licensed to shoot them in support of scaring devices. Why not, then, return the bird to the general quarry list? One reason is that 35 years of comparative peace have made the Brent, already a fairly confiding beast, even tamer, and some preservationists fear great slaughter. Sir Peter Scott suggested a compromise: shooting should be allowed, but only inland of the sea-walls.

This system, which would be under annual review, would allow some increase in sport, help farmers protect their crops, and might drive the birds back to their natural setting. BASC, while welcoming the climate of reasonableness, felt obliged to state that wildfowlers want the Brent restored as a sporting quarry species, not as a pest to be controlled. *Impasse* for the moment.

Sometimes the status of a bird has to be safeguarded because it resembles another, uncommon kind. In places, the Whistling Swan and occasionally even the Snow Goose have to be protected because, in poor light, the rare Trumpeter Swan may be mistaken for either species (25). The Aleutian Canada Geese *B.c.leucopareia* wintering in California were effectively saved from extinction only by closing the hunting of all Canada Geese before the Aleutians arrived every fall (see Chapter 6); this race has recovered so remarkably that it is to be reclassified as no longer Endangered in the official listings of the world's rarest animals and plants that were another of Peter Scott's inventions – the *Red Data Books* of the IUCN.

In the UK, ducks and geese may be temporarily protected by a closure of the shooting season in prolonged severe weather, when food becomes difficult to find and the birds lose condition. BASC gave a lead in reaching a consensus with The Wildfowl Trust and the Nature Conservancy Council about the need for restraint, but statutory control by Government was necessary to make the system work.

The morality or otherwise of shooting in order to profit from the sale of the bird has exercised the minds of wildfowlers and non-wildfowlers alike. The shooter for the market is interested in maximum numbers for the least effort and cost, and sitting targets are easiest to kill. Market shooting ceased in North America in 1918; in Britain, the sale of dead geese ended over two decades ago, and that move is thought to have been partly responsible for the great increase in numbers; the Pinkfoot, for instance, rose from 35,000 in 1957 to nearly 170,000 in 1988. The sale of quarry species of ducks (except for Gadwall and Goldeneye) is still permitted between 1 September and 27 February; indeed, the UK exported 13,514 dead wild ducks 'in feather' in 1986 and another 17,848 in 1987, no statistics being kept on those sent out plucked and 'oven-ready'. Presumably many thousands are sold to the home market; in October 1988, wild Mallard could be bought at the game suppliers in Lytham, on the Ribble Estuary in Lancashire, for £3.20 each, Teal for only £1.40 and Wigeon for £1.60 – the same 'half-duck' values that we saw in decoy 'takes'. (The coastal county of Lancashire, having large numbers of ducks and plenty of people to shoot them, is responsible for a very high proportion of the national bag (7)).

Undoubtedly some protection measures are imposed because it is felt that killing wild birds for any purpose is unethical. Only one person can kill a duck while many bird-watchers can enjoy its flight. Peter Scott's feelings on giving up wildfowling are probably typical (24) and are explained in his autobiography *The Eye of the Wind*. He was out fowling with six or seven friends who were standing together when a single goose flew over; every man fired two barrels. The bird staggered in the air and flew on losing height; it came to rest by crash-landing, quivered to a halt, and put its head up. It was on some inaccessible quicksand, 500 yards out, and its legs were broken; there was nothing that could be done. After lunch, it was still there with its head up, and so it was next morning. Peter wrote: 'What right have we men to do this to a bird for our fun – to impose this kind of suffering? I should not want this for a sworn enemy, and that goose was not my enemy when I shot at him – although I was his'.

DIFFERENCES IN LEGAL RESTRICTIONS ON WILDFOWLING

There are considerable differences in the laws under which hunters operate in Europe, particularly the UK, and North America. In the USA and Canada much of the land is publicly owned and access is free; in Britain most land is private and shooting on it is permitted only to the owner, or his agents. There is an exception to this general rule and that is on the coastal strip below ordinary high tides known as 'crown foreshore'. Although no member of the public has the right to shoot on the seaward side of sea-walls in England and Wales, WAGBI negotiated in the 1960s an authority entitling its members to be on the foreshore with a gun without fear of prosecution (26). This move did no harm to membership recruitment! In Scotland, incidentally, the foreshore remains open to public recreation, including wildfowling, by all and sundry, and shooting below high-water even on nature reserves can only be prevented by special bye-laws.

In the USA until recently, restrictions on the length of the season were imposed at Federal level, depending on the birds' breeding success that year, and each state decided on opening and closing dates appropriate to the time that migratory wildfowl arrive (11). Since varying the season was found to vary the bag but not the population, seasons are now fixed. Birds roosting on open water must not be disturbed; shooting is permitted only from half-an-hour before dawn to sunset, and no feeding of flight ponds is allowed. Bag limits vary between two to ten for ducks and one to six for geese. Some systems allocate different points to different species or sexes; for example, male Canvasback outnumber females two to one and are scored lower, so a hunter is allowed to take more of them.

In Britain, it is typically peer-pressure that stops ungentlemanly excesses. Americans are frequently amazed to discover that there are no limits to the number of birds that an Englishman may shoot, and that the open season hardly ever varies in length, no matter whether the quarry have reproduced well or not: or that dusk and night-shooting, when it is more difficult to distinguish what is being shot, is not only permitted but is the usual practice. The monitoring of wildfowl numbers is in the main done by private Trusts in Britain (often funded by the government indirectly) while in North America such research is partly paid for by 'duck stamps' which every hunter must purchase, and is carried out by government agencies; these funds also go towards habitat purchase. British wildfowlers see much to envy in the North American situation, mainly perhaps because it is governments that protect the sport. With only three countries involved from nesting to wintering grounds (Mexico was added to the Migratory Birds Convention in 1936), things are easier to organise than they are in Europe; but all has not necessarily been better than in the UK.

John Lynch of the US Fish and Wildlife Service wrote some years ago a funny but very serious paper (11), published posthumously, and entitled 'Escape from mediocrity'; in it he says that 'fine tuning' of waterfowl hunting regulations is unnecessary and, indeed, unenforceable. Rules, based on reports of duck numbers and expected output, were drafted in August and varied, often elaborately, from year to year and state to state. Lynch believed that the hunters in general take no notice, and all that was needed to guess the likely harvest is an assessment of spring rainfall in those regions of potentially good duck productivity. Firm requests to stop shooting should follow summers of drought but, in years of really high duck numbers, there was no point in bag limits because the surplus is going to die of some cause anyway and taking a high proportion of them makes little difference to next season's breeding stock. Changes have now been made, at least as far as variable seasons are concerned.

REFERENCES

1. Atkinson-Willes, G. L.(ed). 1963. *Wildfowl in Great Britain*. HMSO.
2. Barber, J. 1934. *Wildfowl Decoys*. Windward House (re-issued in 1954 by Dover: New York).
3. Clark, G. 1948. Fowling in Prehistoric Europe. *Antiquity* 22: 116–130.
4. Delacour, J. 1964. *The Waterfowl of the World*. Vol 4. London: Country Life.
5. Durrell, L. 1957. *Justine*. London: Faber.
6. Folkard, H. C. 1859. *The Wild Fowler*. London: Piper, Stevenson & Spence.
7. Harradine, J. 1985. Duck shooting in the United Kingdom. *Wildfowl* 36: 81–94.

8. Harrison, J. G. & Boyd, H. 1968. A duck production survey in Britain. Report of the pilot scheme 1965–68. *WAGBI Ann.Rep. & Year Book* 1967–68: 29–33.

9. Hawker, P. 1816. (2nd Ed) *Instructions to Young Sportsmen*. London: Hunter.

10. Kear, J & Berger, A. J. 1980. *The Hawaiian Goose*. Berkhamsted: Poyser.

11. Lynch, J. 1984. Escape from mediocrity: a new approach to American waterfowl hunting regulations. *Wildfowl* 35: 5–13.

12. McPhail, R. 1987. *Open Season*. Airlife.

13. Marchington, J. 1980. *The History of Wildfowling*. London: Black.

14. Owen, M. 1980. *Wild Geese of the World*. London: Batsford.

15. Owen, M. Atkinson-Willes, G. L. & Salmon, D. 1986. (2nd Ed) *Wildfowl in Great Britain*. CUP.

16. Paterson, A. H. 1930. *A Norfolk Naturalist*. London: Methuen.

17. Payne-Gallwey, R. 1882. *The Fowler in Ireland*. London: Van Voorst.

18. Payne-Gallwey, R. 1896. *Letters to Young Shooters*. London: Longmans.

19. Prestt, I. 1985. Interview. *Shooting Times* August 29, No.4356: 10–11.

20. Raveling, D. G. 1984. Geese and hunters of Alaska's Yukon Delta: Management Problems and Political Dilemmas. *Trans. N. Amer. Wildl.Conf.*. 49: 555–575.

21. Sanderson, G. C. & Bellrose, F. C. 1986. A review of the problem of lead poisoning in waterfowl. *Illinois Nat. Hist. Surv. Spec. Publ.* No.4.

22. Savage, C. 1963. Wildfowling in Northern Iran. *Wildfowl* 14: 30–46.

23. Scott, P. 1935. *Morning Flight*. London: Country Life.

24. Scott, P. 1961. *The Eye of the Wind*. London: Hodder & Stoughton.

25. Scott, P. & The Wildfowl Trust. 1971. *The Swans*. London: Michael Joseph.

26. Sedgwick, N. S., Whitaker P. & Harrison, J. 1970. *The New Wildfowler in the 1970s*. London: Barrie & Jenkins.

27. Tamisier, A. 1985. Hunting as a key environmental parameter for the Western Palearctic duck populations. *Wildfowl* 36: 95–103.

28. Willock, C. 1966. *The Bedside Wildfowler*. London: André Deutsch.

5: Conservation, research and education

Sir Peter Scott founded the precursor of today's Wildfowl and Wetlands Trust, The Severn Wildfowl Trust, in 1946 with three aims: conservation, research and education, and it is with these aspects of man's interaction with wildfowl that Chapter 5 deals. The whole subject cannot be covered, but I have picked out some topics that particularly interest me, and have given aviculture a Chapter to itself. In 1982, the Council and members of The Trust decided to add a fourth aim – recreation or leisure – and I hope that the whole of this book comes into this category.

WILDFOWL COUNTS AND SURVEYS

The longest continuous activity of the Research Department of The Trust, and the one involving the most people, started in 1947. The National Wildfowl Counts were initiated by the London-based International Wildfowl Inquiry following concern at an apparent decline in the numbers of ducks and geese in Europe. Obviously, to know whether conservation measures were needed it was first necessary to find out where the birds were and in what numbers. The Trust took over responsibility for the counts in 1954 when George Atkinson-Willes, who organised them until 1981, moved from the Natural History Museum to Slimbridge. The plan behind the scheme was to use amateur counters to census ducks, geese and swans month after month on the same waters, and to compare their totals so that any trends in the population, upward or downward, could be noted.

Certain groups of waters that were thought to contain a large proportion of British wintering wildfowl were given priority, thus ensuring that information from them would be analysed quickly. Counters of these 170 waters sent stamped postcards to Slimbridge the day after the priority count had been made – usually on a Monday. A monthly index of abundance for the six commonest ducks was then calculated and, eventually, all the indices in every season were combined to give an annual figure which, in its turn, could be compared with a 'master' year to reveal any population movements. This priority scheme had a number of drawbacks, was rather costly and ended with the winter season of 1979–80 when the Research Department acquired a computer.

Work began by 'keying in' all the count data collected since 1960 – an exercise that took an entire year. Today, the counts are processed fairly soon after the end of the season, analyses are made for every species counted, using censuses taken once a month from September to March at about 2,000 waters. Every one of the 1,500 counters, as well as major ornithological organisations, receives a 60-page annual booklet called *Wildfowl and Wader Counts* produced by The Trust under contract from the Nature Conservancy Council (a contract that also covers the organisation of the counts). This publication also includes the British Trust for Ornithology's report on their monthly counts from the Birds of Estuaries Enquiry. The majority of contributors to this vast undertaking are still amateurs, carrying out the counts during winter week-ends, in their own time and travelling at their own expense. Their findings indicate that almost all species of British wildfowl are stable or even increasing their numbers.

One of the most commonly asked questions is how do they estimate the number of birds they are looking at and, frequently, the comical answer is that they count their legs and divide by two. But it *is* important to establish the reliability of the information. Some years ago, Dr Geoffrey Matthews, the then Director of Research at The Trust, did an experiment with a number of black-and-white photographs of flocks of Pink-footed Geese, and three groups of people divided according to their expertise (17). The first group was of counters, the second were birdwatchers who had spent some time observing birds but had never tried to count them, and the last group was of laymen with no particular interest in natural history. He asked them to look at the photographs for half a minute, and then write down the number of birds that they thought were in the pictures. Surprisingly, the first and second groups were found to be about equal in counting ability and were both able to calculate to within 10% accuracy; the third group, with some spectacular exceptions, including three errors of 100%, were only slightly less good, although not everyone was consistent at scoring high or low. The conclusion was that the errors of a number of different observers tended to cancel themselves out. The counters – that is those who had already had some experience – as one might have hoped, were more consistent than the other two groups.

The amateur involvement in the National Wildfowl Counts is unique to Britain as to size and commitment (17). Obviously, the figures that they collect cannot provide the whole story, and some surveys, especially of geese on Scottish islands, have been done using professional counters travelling over the flocks in aircraft. Britain is a small part of the northwest

European flyway for migratory wildfowl, and a change in the number of ducks and geese in Lancashire, say, may not mean anything more than a shift of the population within that flyway. On the other hand, it might indicate a much more significant alteration in breeding success; only by studying the whole of the range can the difference be told. In 1967, the first European midwinter count was organised by the International Wildfowl Research Bureau (the successors of the International Wildfowl Inquiry), covering waters in Europe, North Africa and the western half of Asia. By 1983, 16,800 wetland sites had been visited at least once. Again, so far as the northern ducks, geese and swans are concerned, the general picture is not one of decline; Scaup *Aythya marila* and Pochard *A. ferina* in Great Britain have gone down somewhat, probably mainly due to the clean-up of sewage outfalls in our estuaries but, even now, Scaup are showing an upward trend again (6,23). We assume that increases in most arctic and near-arctic nesting wildfowl are due to protection and to a continuing mild climate on the breeding grounds.

The value of long-term studies of this type is immense (24). The facts assembled on the computer at Slimbridge are used by many conservation organisations setting-up refuges or opposing developments, as well as by planners and developers themselves. The attempt to put the third London Airport at Foulness showed that figures for wildfowl alone may not have had an unequivocal effect on those who decide our future, since it was the poor economic situation at the time that caused the cancellation of those plans, not the number of geese that might be displaced. Nevertheless, it cannot be claimed that anyone is unaware of the importance to birds of sites such as Foulness when they are determined to take them over for other uses. The count data are also in demand by those who need to know, for instance, the likely effects on duck numbers of recreational activities such as fishing, boating, wildfowling and windsurfing. And in 1986, the second edition of *Wildfowl in Great Britain*, which is a massive synthesis of the counts made between 1960 and 1983 (the first had appeared in 1963), was published to coincide with The Wildfowl Trust's 40th anniversary.

WETLAND RESERVES; THEIR PROVISIONING AND MANAGEMENT

Wildfowl counts are used, most importantly, in siting reserves in the right places – where the maximum number of birds will obtain the benefit of good feeding, a safe roost during the entire winter, or a suitable staging post while they are on route to destinations north and south. It is a fact that, although British wildfowl are not at the moment declining, a greater number and higher proportion of them are depending on the protection of National Nature Reserves or on refuges managed by The Trust, the Royal Society for the Protection of Birds and other conservation organisations.

Conservation measures may also involve areas that initially do not hold

A gravel pit reserve under construction at Sevenoaks by Dr Jeffery Harrison (left), a famous wildfowler and conservationist. Photograph by Pamela Harrison.

large numbers of wildfowl; the use of gravel-pit reserves by local naturalist groups, once extraction has ceased and the hole can be flooded, is a case in point. This imaginative creation of instant wetland was pioneered by a wildfowler, Dr Jeffery Harrison, who was involved in the surveys mentioned in Chapter 4. Some of The Trust's best reserves (it now manages nearly 1,600 ha (4,000 acres)) are man-made, and Sir Peter Scott's early efforts at landscape design went into recreated wetland habitat. The New Grounds at Slimbridge, where the Whitefronts *Anser albifrons* graze, exist because a series of sea-walls gradually won back land from the tidal Severn. The Trust's Welney reserve covers 340 ha (850 acres) that lie between the Old and New Bedford Rivers created in the 17th Century; in times of winter flood, the surplus water from the Fens overspills from the Old Bedford to create a huge shallow reservoir prized by Bewick's Swans *Cygnus bewickii* and Wigeon.

The new Martin Mere started from very unpromising beginnings. It was once the largest lake in Lancashire, teeming with wildlife, and set in the midst of hostile mossy wetlands that even that intrepid traveller, Celia Fiennes, took care to avoid in 1698 (5); in fact, drainage to allow cultivation of its rich peat soil had started six years earlier in 1692. Eventually, nothing remained but a patch of wet farmland, dry enough for summer grazing, but too damp for the plough. After The Trust purchased 145 ha (360 acres) in 1972, 6 ha (15 acres) were dug out to provide a permanent lake once more, and another 8 ha (20 acres) of pasture were set aside as a duck marsh. The latter area was embanked, and pipes were laid so that water could be pumped on and drained off. The effects of flooding the land from October to March, and drying it in the summer, became obvious fairly soon. Most of the pasture vegetation was killed by being drowned; the only plants to survive the harsh treatment were annuals that germinated from seeds once the water was removed, and those perennials with tough

Part of the Hundred Foot Washes between the Bedford Levels now owned by The Wildfowl and Wetlands Trust at Welney. Photo from AOAS Aerial Photography Unit, Cambridge. Crown Copyright Reserved.

Miller's Bridge Hide at Martin Mere is a favourite place for birdwatchers. The need for screening banks on either side of the approach has created a shallow pool now stocked with water plants, frogs and toads. The ramp on the right allows access for wheelchairs and was paid for with a grant from Greater Manchester Council; support by the local community has been among Martin Mere's greatest strengths. Photograph by Barry Greenwood.

rootstocks. Where there was once grass there is now spikerush, bistorts and golden dock which have one feature in common – that they flower and fruit prodigiously, as if immediate and massive reproduction were the only thing that mattered. Then, after a late hay-cut has shaken the ripe seeds to the ground in September, the tap is turned on, water floods across the surface of the land, and the ducks descend to devour the quantities of seeds that float within reach. Pintail, Teal, Mallard and Gadwall *Anas strepera* find the liberal meals much to their liking.

Obviously, although skilled management is involved, Martin Mere's duck marsh provides winter food in a fairly natural way. Some other cold-weather feeding of wildfowl may be totally artificial and has more in common with the creation of an immense bird-table. At all Trust centres where wild swans occur in winter, they are taking grain put out for them. The Pink-footed Geese at Martin Mere, in addition, consume annually many hundreds of tonnes of waste potatoes brought in and spread on one of the fields. Winter provisioning of this type is likely to become increasingly necessary as natural habitat is reduced in extent and, in particular at Martin Mere, it has helped keep birds off crops that they might otherwise damage. The exercise is, however, not without its critics; the situation at The Trust's Welney reserve, where floodlights enable the paying public to get a breathtaking view of Mute, Whooper *Cygnus cygnus* and Bewick's Swans being fed early in the evening, has been dubbed disparagingly *swan et lumière* (27). It has been suggested (10) that the creation of 'honey-pots' for birds given 'extra' food induces a taste for unnatural diets, such as wheat, and encourages later damage to sown wheat. The creatures are said to become 'dependent on hand-outs', to 'hang around waiting for service' and to be more susceptible to disease (10). Although the last of these charges is worth investigation, the others seem exaggerated, in view of the general artificiality of the diets of most common garden, forestry and farmland birds.

To use the example of the Pinkfoot again; in winter it feeds entirely on a diet provided and manipulated by man – sprouting winter-wheat and barley, potatoes (neither native nor natural), sown pastures, stubbles and the occasional carrot – and yet surely it remains a truly wild bird, and the skeins of calling geese strung across the evening sky are among the greatest wildlife spectacles left in Britain. St James's Park in the heart of London is a haven for two populations of Tufted Duck *Aythya fuligula*, resident and migratory, both of which eat a great deal of food given by a 'doting

*Anas Fuligula
prima Gesn.*

A Tufted Duck from St James's Park, figured in Francis Willughby's *Ornithologia* of 1676–8.

Crispin Fisher's Tufted Ducks, from *The Atlas of Wintering Birds in Britain and Ireland.*

public' (8); the provision of bread and grain occurs throughout the year, and the appealing nature of 'the lovable little diving ducks' guarantees that the situation continues. The resident Tufties were first put there in King Charles' time; more recently, they have increased from a dozen breeding pairs in the 1950s to just under 70 pairs by 1984, mostly laying in boxes. The migratory birds had risen in numbers from 400 before 1950 to nearly 800 by the winter of 1986–87. All are, to some extent, being nourished by hand (8). It is difficult to know without an experimental stop to all feeding for a period – and that is unlikely to be tried since no-one is going to starve a public animal for science – just how significant is the supply, but it is probable that a high proportion of these wild birds is there just because of it. Are they therefore to be considered pets or – even worse – pests?

As every feeder of garden birds is told, it is important to continue the regular provisioning of animals once the system has been established if they are not to become frustrated and stressed, and this is just as significant for Bewick's Swans as for Robins *Erithacus rubecula*. In North America, refuge managers often sow agricultural food crops, such as maize, for wildfowl and leave them unharvested in order to keep the birds off nearby farmland. In Britain, regulations about quotas, harvesting, marketing and disease control make these schemes much more difficult to arrange.

As well as providing food, humans also interfere by giving assistance at nesting time. Swans may have nesting material supplied; indeed, the colony of Mute Swans at Abbotsbury (see Chapter 6) is dependent on supplies of food for their young and handouts of reeds for nests. The extension of the range of certain ducks has been made possible by the provision of artificial sites in which the female can lay her eggs in greater safety. Originally, these were provided so that part of the clutch laid in them could be taken for food; the Laplanders built Goldeneye *Bucephala clangula* boxes for this purpose. The early 19th Century saw the first 'altruistic' interventions although, even here, many boxes were placed to encourage insectivorous birds in much the same way that one provides a cat with a home in the hope that it will catch mice. There is a long history of wild Mallards using baskets around decoys in Holland 400 years ago, for instance, and in St James's Park where they were installed by King Charles's decoyman (8). The baskets are placed quite low as the Mallard is commonly a ground-nester, likewise the stone-houses constructed for Eiders in Iceland (Chapter 6); however, most artificial structures are for wildfowl that use real cavities, either burrows or tree-holes. In modern times, the spread of Carolina Wood Ducks in North America, Goosanders *Mergus mergus*, Goldeneye and Mandarins in Britain and, in New Zealand, of the Grey Teal *Anas gibberifrons*, has been made possible by boxes erected high on tree-trunks which, from the birds' point of view, are as handy as natural tree-holes and protect them just as adequately from predators that hunt by sight. There is a tendency for female ducks to choose to lay in sites that resemble those in which they were hatched; thus the habit of box-nesting spreads through a population.

STUDYING THE CLIENT

In order to find out what birds like to eat at various times of the year, or prefer to nest in and why, scientific investigation is necessary. Research is a uniquely human activity and, for a few people, becomes a passion.

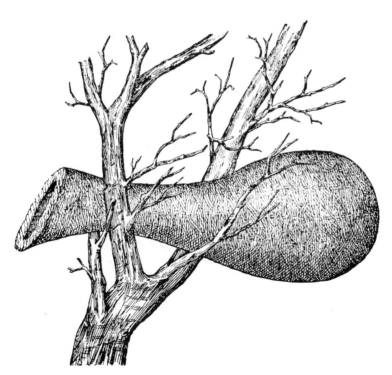

A woven reed basket for nesting Mallard used a hundred years ago in the decoys of Holland. From Payne-Gallwey's *Book of Duck Decoys*.

The pleasure of discovery is always special, but exploration into animal behaviour can provide some of life's greatest thrills. Wildfowl have been involved in basic and far-reaching research, and have engaged many gifted and inquiring minds in the pursuit of knowledge. I have again selected, from the vast number of potential projects, a few that appeal to me and seem to fit within the scope of a volume entitled *Man and Wildfowl*.

WILDFOWL-RINGING

We tend to forget how recently bird-ringing began and how little we knew previously of the travels of the ducks and geese wintering around our coasts. Wildfowl figured in the pioneer days of ringing, and much of the joy of revelation comes through in the writings, already referred to in Chapter 3, of H. C. C. Mortensen of Denmark (19). He was the first ornithologist to mark birds extensively for science. He began large-scale migration research in 1899 with Starlings *Sturnus vulgaris*, fitting their legs with strips of aluminium stamped with numbers and letters and bent into the required shape. However, of over 1,500 Starlings ringed, he was disappointed to have news of only three. In 1898, he had marked his first duck, a Red-breasted Merganser *Mergus serrator* and, since this was recaptured soon afterwards, he was encouraged in his belief that he now had a key for studying wildfowl movements.

He describes the long journey by train, steamer and coach to the decoys

The Red-breasted Merganser became, in 1898, the first wild duck to carry a leg-ring. This drawing of a pair (the female in the foreground is searching beneath the surface for fish) is by John Busby, from C. D. Hutchinson's *Birds in Ireland*.

An upending Bewick's Swan showing a new darvic ring on one leg and a standard metal BTO ring on the other. A strip of transparent tape is used to hold the plastic in place while the adhesive sets and, eventually, this will wash off; it is visible here because mud is lodging around the edge. The use of Slimbridge's large rings has revolutionised research on individual life histories of many birds. Photograph by John Beer.

on the island of Fanø with his secretary (whom he was later to marry) through the torrential rains of autumn. The decoy was found in a tangled thicket of weather-beaten trees close to the coast and among the sand dunes; the gate carried the message 'Entry forbidden'! Fifteen Teal were in a sack on the floor of the decoyman's house, waiting to be purchased, plus one dead one whose foot he could measure to confirm that his rings were of suitable size. He remarked upon the chestnut-coloured eyes of the Teal that looked wonderingly up at him when he pulled them from the sack. None made any noise when he held them, nor made any attempt to peck him; everything went smoothly and in silence and, on release, they sped away like arrows – what 'had been disturbed was set right'. A hundred rings were eased around small cold legs and, although this seemed very few, his purse was the lighter (19). A month later came the news that a Teal had met its end in Holland at Philipsland; then came a still more interesting report – one had been shot in France, and this was followed by news of five more from the same country.

Mortensen's rings could only be recovered if the ducks were caught

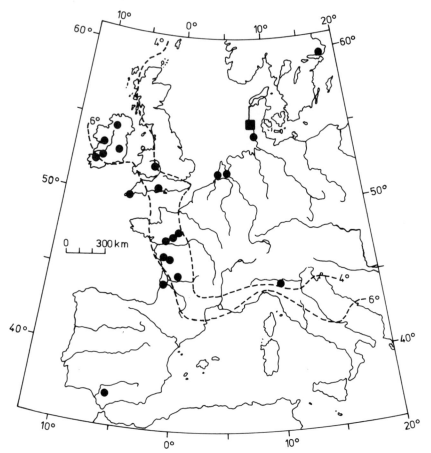

A map showing, as black dots, where 21 of Mortensen's Teal had been recovered by December 1908; the island of Fanø, where the ducks were ringed, is indicated by a black square. Redrawn by John Turner.

again or dead, usually shot. A major advance in the long-term study of larger birds, such as swans and geese, came with the production by The Wildfowl Trust of plastic rings that could be deciphered at a distance on the living animal (20). The rings are made of coloured laminated PVC called 'darvic' with individual letter and number codes engraved on them so that it is possible to recognise individual birds in the field. There had been a number of attempts to develop such marks before the 1960s, and flat engraved wing-tags had been used on shags and eiders. Then in 1967, Malcolm Ogilvie obtained some darvic direct from ICI and experimented at Slimbridge with making rings of the material. The engraving, through the top coloured layer down to the middle black strip, was done with the sheets of plastic laid flat, and the breakthrough came when he learnt to shape the plastic into circles after softening it in boiling water (20). A few tame Mute Swans were ringed during the summer of 1967 and the first wild Bewick's in November of that year. The first darvic goose rings were put on Barnacles *Branta leucopsis* in the summer of 1973 during a Trust expedition to Spitsbergen and, later, they were worn by Brent Geese. Since then, darvic rings have been supplied for use on flamingos, pelicans, penguins, vultures, Coot *Fulica atra*, shelducks, sheldgeese in the Falklands, Wigeon, White-headed Duck *Oxyura leucocephala*, ospreys, shags and gulls, so that Slimbridge's technique (20) has revolutionised research into the lives of individual birds. Neck-collars of darvic have also been made for migratory swans and geese, although they are not used frequently in Britain and not at all, so far, on swans caught by The Wildfowl and Wetlands Trust which is wary of an adverse public reaction to such conspicuous 'decoration' of a wild animal.

About a quarter of a million wildfowl were ringed by The Trust in the first 40 years of its existence, and between 5,000 and 6,000 are still marked every year. The majority are ducks; in 1987, for instance, only 317 were geese and 50 swans. Can continued ringing be justified? Are we ever going

A captive Pink-footed Goose under test with a darvic neck-collar; the device has not yet been used on wild Pinkfeet. Photograph by Peter Wallis.

to know enough? Perhaps we are, but certainly not yet (7). Because so many wildfowl are hunted, we have a particular reason to investigate their 'turnover' and we need to continue to monitor the level of kill so long as the sport of wildfowling continues.

Much can be discovered from bird-ringing in addition to information about migratory behaviour and mortality rates. The breeding success of any bird and the chances of it dying change with age, but only by studying individuals, marked as juveniles, over their whole life-span can we discover at what stage they are most likely to breed well or to die. Further, it has been shown that the long-term success of any pair of Bewick's Swans is influenced most strongly by the size and weight of the male parent; so while a swan is in the hand being ringed, it can also be weighed and measured (24). Other research has suggested that ultimate adult weight and size are strongly affected by the growth pattern during the first year of life. Certain individual swans that, for some reason such as severe weather, grow slowly during their fist winter are unlikely, therefore, to prosper throughout the whole of their breeding lives. We can also explore aspects of natural selection using ringed birds, because individual differences in lifetime breeding success are the most important components of evolutionary change.

Occasionally it is possible to distinguish familiar individuals without having to ring them – just as a good shepherd knows his sheep. Peter Scott was not the first person to realise that Bewick's Swans had different face-patterns (25), but he was the first to notice that the pattern was 'fixed' for the life of the bird, and to grasp the great potential for study that this natural variation allowed (25). His talent for telling them apart has been surpassed by that of his daughter, Dafila, who recognises hundreds of swans and is likely to be confused only by a likeness to an individual's parent, suggesting that the patterning of black-and-yellow on the bill is inherited (1).

Of course, to get a plastic ring on a swan or a goose you have first to catch it. Ducks can be trapped but most of the ringing of geese, at least, has been done either with nets fired over the feeding flocks, or by rounding up the moulting birds on the breeding grounds (26) – both techniques pioneered by Peter Scott after he had given up chasing wildfowl with a gun. Migratory swans are also taken while flightless and, in winter, are often caught in specially designed large 'decoy' pipes, well supplied with food, which operate at the Slimbridge, Caerlaverock and Welney Wildfowl and Wetlands Trust Centres. Since 1967, 1,347 different Bewick's have been caught and ringed at Slimbridge, and a further 474 Whoopers and 183 Bewick's Swans at Welney and Caerlaverock.

Migration studies are made easier when a few ringed swans are dyed with harmless picric acid applied to small patches of their white plumage. The yellow-dyed feathers, which are lost at the next moult, draw attention to the fact that the bird is wearing a leg-ring the number of which can be read with binoculars or a telescope.

The logo of the 'adopt-a-duck' scheme.

We now know the routes taken by both kinds of migrant British swan, and 20 years ago we discovered the height at which they travel. Radar screens can detect large flocks of flying birds in the same way that they pick up aircraft. An excellent example is that of a 'blip' located over the Inner Hebrides in December 1967 moving south at an altitude of 8,200 metres or 27,000 feet, 2,000 feet less than the height of Everest (4). A plane was sent up and identified a party of swans at the edge of the jet stream; the birds were assumed to have started their journey from Iceland in a ridge of high pressure at dawn, and it was calculated that they would reach their destination in the north of Ireland in a flight-time of seven hours, travelling at the amazingly low temperature of − 48°C (4).

Much of the funding for The Trust's duck-ringing activities over the years has come from further public involvement in an extremely successful 'adopt-a-duck' scheme launched in 1948, only two years after The Trust's birth. In fact, the idea originated at the Natural History Museum with the International Wildfowl Inquiry, and The Trust did not take over its running until 1954 when the National Wildfowl Counts came to Slimbridge. On payment of five shillings, the subscriber was allotted a wild duck and told its species, ring number and the date and place of ringing; if the bird were later recovered, then he or she would be notified of how, why and where (most would have been shot).

The press treated the notion of having one's own duck with great enthusiasm – 'Ducks for Dinner at 5s.' was one headline, and *The Times* editor wrote a humorous fourth leader on the subject. Indeed, it was probably a newspaper reporter that thought up the catch-phrase 'adopt-a-duck' and the media are still inspired enough to give the matter publicity every Christmas when folk are searching for that slightly different present to give to a child or the friend-who-has-everything. The first Adoption Scheme Annual Report of 1949 records that 1,700 ducks had been adopted by over 1,000 'owners' and that the money raised was being used to repair wartime dilapidations at Orielton Decoy which the Inquiry committee, of which Peter Scott was a member, was operating as a ringing station (Chapter 3). The 'best' return during that first year was a young Wigeon drake, carrying ring number 906499 and owned by Mrs Hurley of Virginia Water; the bird had reached Ekaterinberg (now called Sverdlovsk) east of the Russian Urals where, like the Tzar and his family 30 years earlier, it had been shot. Occasionally rings get as far as a restaurant customer before being 'recovered': a Teal was cooked and served with the ring still round its leg; and an unattached ring, put on a Mallard some weeks earlier, once turned up in a pork pie. Today, there are about 5,500 duck adopters, and swans and geese have been added to the list of wildfowl that may be supported; the scheme still helps to finance the investigations of The Trust into wildfowl distribution and numbers and, in 1988, produced a gross income of £49,000.

IMPRINTING

Someone who had a real duck of his own as a child and was much influenced by the experience was Konrad Lorenz (13,15,16). He was a Nobel Prize Winner, born in Austria in 1903, and one of the great students of animal behaviour. After the war there was an attempt to obtain a post for him with Peter Scott at Slimbridge, but this fell through when he received an offer from the Austrian government. The public know him as the naturalist who wrote a witty and engaging book called *King Solomon's Ring*, published in German in 1949 and in English translation in 1952 (14), about the animals that he and his wife kept in and around their house at Altenberg. He described how his Greylag goslings became 'imprinted' and accepted him as their parent, walking after him every-

'The Hen has brought out four Ducklings. The old proverb says "if you put another man's child in your bosom, it will creep out at your sleeve."' The quotation is from Thomas Bewick, who made this engraving of a hen watching her imprinted foster-children take their first swim.

Three Greylag Geese follow Konrad Lorenz. Photograph by H. Kacher.

where 'with all the dignity characteristic of their kind'. In investigating the process whereby a goose or a duck learns its identity and the species to which it belongs, he discovered that it does not hatch with an instinctive recognition of its parent but, instead, will imprint on and follow the first moving thing that it sees after hatching. Of course, this is usually the mother, but it can be a member of another family or of another kind entirely, such as a hen or a man or, occasionally, some inanimate object.

The term 'imprinting' is a translation of a German word that means to stamp an image on a coin. Something of its nature has been known for centuries. Pliny, the First Century Roman writer on natural history, tells us that the philosopher Lacydes was continually accompanied by a tame goose; wherever he went, into the streets or in his own house, the bird forced itself into his presence. The philosopher seems to have felt that the animal had some religious feeling for him and, when it died, paid for a magnificent funeral. Other authors have commented on the fact that young wildfowl, deprived of companions, follow humans with apparent affection. There is a Cape Barren Goose *Cereopsis novaehollandiae* at Martin Mere that was reared by hand, without brothers or sisters, and does not now relate to her own kind. She greets every visitor and is locally so well known that on her tenth birthday she received over 900 cards of congratulation! Edward Lear's poem 'The Duck and the Kangaroo' may illustrate a real incident observed in the menagerie of his patron, Lord Derby, in which a drake Mallard (to judge by Lear's charming sketches) attached itself to and followed 'his own dear true love of a kangaroo'.

Konrad Lorenz was not an experimenter in the usual way; instead, he kept at free-range a flock of treasured geese who treated him as one of them, and he watched and recorded their behaviour year after year. As a result of his observations, he came to regard the learning process whereby an animal recognises its parent as unique – it happens at an early stage and is very rapid – and he felt that, once the relationship is formed, the process differs from other learnt behaviour in that it is irreversible. In other words, a goose reared by humans seeks human companionship all its life, including the time of mate selection. Recent research has suggested that 'imprinting' is not necessarily so drastic in its effects; a Slimbridge Snow Goose hand-reared for a film (see Chapter 9) is now fully integrated with his own kind after 20 years, but still greets humans.

'Cynthia', the Cape Barren Goose at Martin Mere, is unusual in that

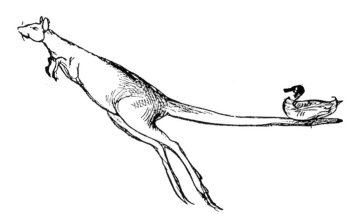

'The Duck and the Kangaroo', a drawing by Edward Lear that illustrated his poem of the same title; he was perhaps depicting real animals that he had known in the park at Knowsley.

Cynthia, the imprinted Cape Barren Goose at Martin Mere, greets visitors with a characteristic stretched-neck display. She identifies with humans because she was hand-reared without other companions until she was fully-grown. Photograph by Ray Greenhalgh.

she was in human company for many months after hatching, and had no other family. In general, it appears that the parent companion gradually loses its importance to the bird and that it is siblings that provide the template for choosing a later sexual partner. Male birds tend to select mates that are not exactly like their sisters but are not entirely unlike them either, so that distant relatives are often preferred. We find that Bewick's Swans do not usually pair with birds from the same brood as themselves, so that the chance of inbreeding is reduced. Perhaps incest between siblings is avoided in humans too, not mainly because of social taboos, but by a similar learnt disinclination to find sexual desirability in the brothers and sisters with whom we were reared.

THE CASE OF THE DRAKE'S TAIL

Another apt piece of wildfowl research was carried out by Charles Darwin in the 1850s when he studied, among other things, the inheritance of characteristics altered during domestication (2). In particular, he set out to discover the origin of the remarkable domestic Runner Duck (see

Chapter 2). When he started work on *Variation of Animals Under Dom-estication*, he did not realise that the Runner descended from the Mallard (its ancestry was still being disputed 60 years later). He was puzzled because the wild Mallard is unknown in the Malay Archipelago where the natives farm the Runner; so he begged for skins from Bali and Lombok to be sent to him by Alfred Russel Wallace, who independently conceived the idea of evolution by natural selection, and by Sir James Brooke, the rajah of Sarawak.

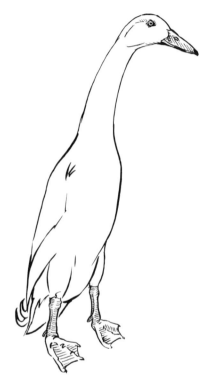

An Indian Runner drake with curly tail. Drawing by Joe Blossom.

He found that the Runner has 18 tail feathers instead of the Mallard's 20, and that the bones of the leg are greatly elongated as one might expect in a duck that walks to and from the fields every day and finds most of its food 'on the hoof' like a goose; but his most significant discovery was that the four middle tail-feathers of the male in breeding plumage curve upwards as in the Mallard, the Rouen, Aylesbury and Call Duck, but in no other dabbling duck (2). 'In all domestic breeds these curled feathers exist and on the supposition that they descended from distinct species, we must assume that man formerly hit upon species all of which had this now

A duckling on the visual-cliff apparatus and (below) a little duckling using a parachute. Drawings by Robert Gillmor.

unique character'. Selection by humans had changed much, but the curly tail of the drake remains unaltered, and that for Darwin clinched the argument. The Runner was a Mallard selected by man as an egg-layer that walked in search of food rather than flew or swam: 'in the great duck family, one species alone, the male of *A. boschas* has its four middle tail feathers curled upwardly. I am not much surprised that some writers should maintain that this breed must be descended from an unknown and distinct species; but it seems to me far more probable that it is the descendant, much modified by domestication under an unnatural climate, of *Anas boschas*'. (In those days, the Mallard was known scientifically as *Anas boschas* – the 'wild duck', rather than *Anas platyrhynchos* – the 'duck with the flat nose').

DO DUCKLINGS HATCH WITH A FEAR OF HEIGHTS?

At Slimbridge in the early 1960s, a research project started that would investigate the manner in which ducklings that hatch high up in holes in trees, such as Mandarins, reached the ground (11). How does a newly-hatched bird, that cannot fly, react when it sees the 10 m (33 ft) drop beyond the entrance to the nest? We have all been impressed by the self-confidence of ducklings taking their first swim; are they equally positive

when contemplating the long descent to the ground? The possibility that they might just jump had often been doubted; there are many tales of young ducks being carried in their parents' bills, on their backs, or between their legs. In fact, they do leap into the unknown and, being light in weight and covered with down, tend to bounce and come to no harm. So do they hatch without any fear of heights?

An apparatus had been designed in North America to discover whether human babies at the crawling stage avoid what looks like a cliff edge (the finding was that, like many young animals, they do stay clear of a drop); it was modified for wildfowl mainly by making it smaller. It consisted of a central board laid across a rectangular piece of heavy glass supported about 50 cm (18 in) from the ground. On one side of the board, a sheet of chequered cloth was placed directly against the underside of the glass thus giving it the appearance of, as well as actual, solidity. On the other side, the sheet of chequered material was laid on the floor thereby producing what looked like an edge and a sharp drop. The piece of glass was surrounded by upright edging to prevent the ducklings or goslings from leaving. Ten individuals of a number of species were taken directly from the nest where they had hatched, so that they had had less than 24 hours experience of the world. Each young bird was placed singly on the board at the centre of the glass and watched to see what direction it took. As soon as it had demonstrated a clear decision, it was put back with its family.

The finding (11) was that there were differences in behaviour between youngsters on the brink that made sense if they were related to the position in which the birds normally hatched. Species that hatch on the ground, like young geese, left the central board on the shallow side of the apparatus, while those that are laid in holes in trees, such as Goldeneye, Mandarin and Carolinas, chose either side at random. However, hole-hatching ducklings did not react as if they could not tell the difference between deep and shallow; they ran off on the shallow side and launched themselves with a little jump on the deep one – just as they must when leaving a tree-hole. In general, the ability to see and avoid a sharp drop aids survival but, clearly, it would be unhelpful if a Mandarin hatched with a dis-inclination to jump into a chasm and therefore failed to join its mother at the bottom of the tree. It does not positively prefer the drop; if it did it might hurl itself over every cliff it met. Further experiments showed that a fear of heights is acquired gradually even by ducklings of hole-nesting parents and that, by two weeks of age, they too avoid the deep end.

EDUCATION, INTERPRETATION AND COMMUNICATION

Almost no human endeavour is worth pursuing unless others can partake of the experience, and teaching the young about animals and the natural world brings special rewards. The process of learning is frequently divided into three stages: romance, precision and generalisation. In the romantic element we include the emotion that we feel when birds approach us with confidence and inspire admiration of their beauty; during the precision stage, we take in facts and, at the generalisation stage, a good teacher will show us how to extrapolate from those facts and discover for ourselves such things as evolutionary similarities and adaptations.

Wildfowl are particularly well adapted for this educational sequence. It takes time to build a relationship with an individual animal – Lorenz gave a beautiful description (15) of the process in 'Why Waterfowl' – but the fact that tame ducks and geese will move towards people and 'ask' to be fed from the hand seems all-important (the fact that they do not overeat is likewise all-important to the avicultural staff who care for them). A questionnaire directed at children showed that the nibble of a small beak on the palm of the hand and the closeness of the bird was what they had most enjoyed on a visit to Martin Mere. Many adults find it equally agreeable.

The child's second favourite activity was going into a hide. Quite why this was we did not discover – was it because 'teacher' could no longer see them in the darkness, or was it to do with the wild world beyond the windows? Birdwatching does give a great deal of pleasure to a lot of people. It was Peter Scott who realised that the sea-wall at Slimbridge, which kept back the Severn tide and created the New Grounds, also acted as a screen bank behind which humans could walk and enter viewing points without disturbing the birds. It was part of his philosophy that Trust reserves exist so that wildfowl can be attracted, and that the public are to be shown them with minimum discomfort. In achieving this aim, Peter Scott and The Trust were again occasionally at odds with peer opinion. The centrally-heated hide at Welney, overlooking fed and floodlit swans, seems to some to be 'the ultimate in dubious sophistication', and to pass beyond the realm of countryside interpretation into that of the safari park or zoo (27). Stephen Goodall, once The Trust's Comptroller, tells a story that must silence some of the criticism: he came upon a retired doctor in the Welney observatory who had been struck down by a stroke just before retirement and would spend the rest of his life in a wheelchair; only in that hide was he able to continue his hobby of birdwatching in the depths of winter.

The floodlights at Welney and Slimbridge may be thrilling for the public, but convey something more to the birds. The annual cycle of all temperate wildfowl is tied to daylength and, if their winter day is extended artificially, they receive the prophecy of an early spring. Powerful lights left on until 10 o'clock on winter evenings around the Rushy Pen at Slimbridge meant that the captive Hawaiian and Cape Barren Geese moulted their flight feathers in January and February and failed to nest. The wild Bewick's Swans were less drastically affected, since they were often out on the river, but the majority fattened and departed on their northeastern journey to Siberia up to a month earlier than they did elsewhere (22) – hardly the result that Peter Scott was trying to achieve. The floodlights now stay on for a shorter period that is calculated to have a minimal effect.

Visitors to Wildfowl and Wetlands Trust Centres mainly come in summer, despite the attractions of winter floodlit swans, masses of wild-fowl and waders, and spacious hides. Most arrive in August when migratory birds are scarce and many of the captive ducks 'eclipsed' and not looking their best. In 1969, the Countryside Commission published a Slimbridge Visitor Survey which was important in setting The Trust on the course of opening further 'Slimbridges' throughout Britain – at Martin Mere, Arundel and Washington – in order to take its message to a wider market (18). Its findings have not changed much during 20 years: more visitors were in their middle years than was expected, both the young (16 to 24 years) and pensioners (over 65) being under-represented and, surprisingly, fewer than half the visitors were accompanied by children. The proportion in the top social groups (AB) was far above that for the population as a whole. Three-quarters were on their first visit 'to a pleasant location for a day out'. Most had come by car, travelling over 80 km (50 miles) and, of the 68% that had seen advertisements, television was mentioned as the usual source.

A child feeding a Snow Goose at Slimbridge.

Her Majesty the Queen feeding a pair of Hawaiian Geese at Slimbridge.
Photograph by Jonathan Leach.

Films and television bring wildfowl to man in a very immediate way.
Peter Scott's programmes in the *Look* series, that started in 1953 and gained
him the Television Society Award in 1955, were the first to make a major
conservation impact; they were transmitted from Bristol where the BBC's
Natural History Unit was set up in 1957, its location largely determined
by the fact that Peter Scott had chosen Slimbridge as his home (21). The
Trust's film *Wild Wings* won an Oscar as the best Live Action Short
Subject in April 1967, and brought the organisation further to public
attention as it went round the Rank cinema circuit with Frank Sinatra
starring in *Von Ryan's Express*.

Some film subjects are almost guaranteed to succeed. The story of a
goose-drive from rural East Anglia to London called *Laughterhouse* was
one of the funnier films of 1985. Directed by Richard Eyre, it starred Ian
Holm and Bill Owen who, because of a union boycott, stubbornly walk
the 100-odd miles with their birds through modern traffic, biting cold
and 'the nosey buggers of Suffolk' to the big city. The BBC's *Private Life*

of the Swan, shown during 1973, was one of a TV series of five produced by Jeffery Boswall including the Atlantic Grey Seal, Jackass Penguin, Japanese Monkey, and Herring Gull, as well as the Mute Swan (21). *The Swan* was the most highly praised of the group: 'beautifully done', 'interesting', 'exciting', 'superb photography' and 'well written' were typical comments obtained by market researchers. The sequences filmed by Maurice Tibbles of cygnets, slow motion flying and landing, and swimming birds in fading light as closing scenes received lavish compliments. Only 7% of those reporting made any negative comment – two viewers, inevitably, were uncomfortable with footage of the birds copulating. One indication of the success of a programme is the degree to which its audience is willing to watch through to the end – it is rare that no-one reports trying a bit and then giving up, but this did happen to *The Private Life of the Swan*.

Journalists frequently file springtime reports of ducklings and their mothers being escorted across busy roads, and these stories can be certain of sympathetic attention. In Japan, a famous Spot-billed Duck *Anas poecilorhyncha* has, since 1983, hatched her brood on a man-made pond outside the headquarters of the Mitsui Trading Company in Tokyo. In the full glare of media coverage, and with police protection, she takes them across an eight-lane thoroughfare to a much larger water body – the moat of the Emperor's palace. In 1985, the birds gained celebrity status in a television programme that recorded their development and final flight away on migration. The following year, 25,000 spectators showed up on a single day, and an average of 5,000 office workers ate their lunchtime sandwiches watching the youngsters and their mother. One daily paper ran a picture of the ducks sharing their bread with sparrows: 'they get along with other kinds of birds' was the comment, 'if only humans were just a little more like ducks'. The British newspaper, *The Independent*, carried the story and, a few days later, a correspondent felt obliged to point out that, although duck fever might grip the Japanese once in a while, they shoot thousands of wildfowl annually. In a smaller way, the final non-return from Siberia to Slimbridge of an old and much-travelled Bewick's Swan that had been named 'Lancelot' by Peter Scott 20 years earlier, in 1963, and had arrived every year since, was made much of in the media, and brought many a lamenting letter.

Books that tell of a personal relationship with ducks, geese or swans were mentioned in Chapter 1; fictional ones with a wildfowl theme are covered in Chapter 9. Books about the science of ducks, geese and swans have had, in some cases, a profound impact on our understanding of biology. Mortensen (19), Lorenz (14,15,16) and Darwin (2) have already been discussed, and I find their original works worth re-reading. *The Swans* by Peter Scott and The Wildfowl Trust (25) is still the best book on the subject, and a particularly beautiful one. David Lack's *Evolution Illustrated by Wildfowl* does just what the title says: answers questions about the 'why' of taxonomy in an understandable way (12). Jean Delacour's

Waterfowl of the World, illustrated by Peter Scott, remains a masterpiece (3), and *A Thousand Geese* by Peter Scott and James Fisher (26) is a thrilling account of the discovery of the Pinkfoot's breeding ground in the remote centre of Iceland; it tells of a research programme (that continues today) which started with the capture and ringing of 1,000 birds. Al Hochbaum's *Travels and Traditions of Waterfowl*, written at the Delta Waterfowl Research Station in Canada (9), is also recommended for an explanation of migration that does not ignore its magic.

The UK Department of Transport's road-sign for a 'duck-crossing'. Redrawn by John Turner.

REFERENCES

1. Bateson, P. P. G. 1977. Testing an observer's ability to identify individual animals. *Anim.Behav.* 25: 63–64.
2. Darwin, C. 1868. *The Variation of Animals and Plants under Domestication.* London: John Murray.
3. Delacour, J. 1954–64. *The Waterfowl of the World.* London: Country Life.
4. Elkins, N. 1983. *Weather and Bird Behaviour.* Calton: Poyser.
5. Fiennes, C. 1949. *Illustrated Journeys 1685–1712.* Edited by C. Morris. London: MacDonald.
6. Fox, A. D. & Salmon, D. G. 1988. Changes in non-breeding distribution and habitat of Pochard *Aythya ferina* in Britain. *Biol. Conserv.* 46: 303–316.
7. Fox, A. D., Gitay, H. & Owen, M. 1988. A preliminary assessment of the use of ringing to estimate survival rates and proposals for the future organisation of wildfowl marking programmes. *Unpublished Wildfowl Trust report.*
8. Gillham, E. 1987. *Tufted Ducks in a Royal Park.* Romney Marsh: E. Gillham.
9. Hochbaum, H. A. 1955. *Travels and Traditions of Waterfowl.* Minnesota: University Press.

10. Humphries, P. N. 1980. The use and abuse of nature reserves. *Country Gentlemen's Mag.* June: 276–277.

11. Kear, J. 1967. Experiments with young nidifugous birds on a visual cliff. *Wildfowl* 18: 122–124.

12. Lack, D. 1975. *Evolution Illustrated by Wildfowl.* Oxford: Blackwell.

13. Lorenz, K. 1952. The scientific value of a group collection of live animals. *Wildfowl* 4: 47–50.

14. Lorenz, K. Z, 1952. *King Solomon's Ring.* London: Methuen.

15. Lorenz, K. 1973. Why Waterfowl? *Int. Zoo Yb.* 13: 1–6.

16. Lorenz, K. 1979. *The Year of the Greylag Goose.* London: Methuen.

17. Matthews, G. V. T. 1960. An examination of basic data from wildfowl counts. *Int.Ornith.Cong.* 12: 483–491 (Helsinki, 1958).

18. Matthews, G. V. T. 1971. A visitor survey at Slimbridge. *Wildfowl* 22: 126–132.

19. Mortensen, H. C. C. 1950. *Studies in Bird Migration.* DOF: Munksgaard, Copenhagen.

20. Ogilvie, M. A. 1972. Large numbered leg bands for individual identification of swans. *J.Wild.Mngt.* 36: 1261–1265.

21. Parsons, C. 1982. *True to Nature.* Cambridge: Stevens.

22. Rees, E. C. 1982. The effect of photoperiod on the timing of spring migration in the Bewick's Swan. *Wildfowl* 33: 119–132.

23. Salmon, D. G. 1988. The numbers and distribution of Scaup *Aythya marila* in Britain and Ireland. *Biol. Conserv.* 43: 267–278.

24. Scott, D. K. 1987. The importance of long term studies. *Wildfowl World* (The Wildfowl Trust Magazine) 96: 16–17

25. Scott, P. & The Wildfowl Trust. 1972. *The Swans.* London: Michael Joseph.

26. Scott, P. & Fisher, J. 1953. *A Thousand Geese.* London: Collins.

27. Tubbs, C. R. 1979. Poor substitute for wilderness. *Birds* 7(6): 26–27.

6: Aviculture

Wildfowl in captivity look better than other birds – indeed, better than any other animal group (29). A cage is usually unnecessary and a pond appears so much their natural element that, even when rendered flightless by feather-cutting or pinioning, they need be neither obviously unhappy nor unsightly. Their surroundings can be made to look almost normal, and they provide excellent subjects for behavioural studies (17,25,26). They give great pleasure with their attractiveness and confidence, and collections of pinioned ducks, geese and swans have played an important role in informing the general public about the needs of conservation, thus ultimately ensuring the safety of wetlands on which their wild relatives depend (38).

Habitat destruction, especially the draining of wet areas, and the introduction of predators and disease, have resulted in a few (mostly non-European) wildfowl reaching the point of extinction in historic times (24). Many adapt well to captivity and are being bred in numbers that may ensure future survival, even after they have died out in their natural state (22,29,32). Potentially, aviculture allows the release of some of the offspring into the original habitat (if it still exists) and this Chapter will examine a number of such programmes. It also describes the 'farming' of swans and Eider Ducks under controlled conditions.

SOME CELEBRATED KEEPERS OF WILDFOWL

There have been some famous wildfowl aviculturalists who have clearly appreciated both the beauty and companionship of their birds. The 12th Century bishop of Lincoln, St Hugh, kept a tame Whooper Swan (see Chapter 9) that was aggressive and unmanageable to everyone else, but learnt to search the priest's pockets and sleeves for bread, and would follow him about, even entering the manor and climbing the stairs (39). The modern bishop of Wells has a pair of Mute Swans that swim in the palace moat and ring a bell set in the wall when they want food. Other swans have done this since 1850, when an individual (now stuffed and in the Wells museum) was taught by the bishop's daughter the trick of pulling with its bill at a rope-end attached to a bell. Every time the bird did the right thing, she rewarded it with bread. The original bell-ringing swan passed on its skill to successive generations of cygnets who learnt by observation and imitation. Regrettably, the swans now receive so much food from visitors that it is rare for them to bother to ring!

Other palace gardens have had their tame wildfowl. Her Majesty the Queen keeps a small flock of breeding Red-breasted Geese *Branta ruficollis* on the lawns at Buckingham Palace. An earlier monarch, King Charles II, established a wide variety of exotic ducks and geese in St James's Park, as well as a decoy (see Chapters 3 and 7) and a row of aviaries along Birdcage Walk. One of his favourite daily occupations was feeding his beloved ducks – so much so that in the 19th Century the suggestion was made that he had died of malaria caught from his birds (4,13). In fact, the malaria common in Europe in the 1680s was not of a fatal kind and the ducks, in addition to being incapable of infecting their patron, probably helped reduce the incidence of the disease by eating the real vectors – the larval mosquitoes that shared the ponds with them. Charles inherited his interest in animals from his grandfather James I who, in 1612, made improvements to the Park and established his own zoo there. His French contemporary, Louis XIV, had waterfowl on the ornamental watercourses at Versailles, and the Empress Josephine kept swans at La Malmaison near Paris. She chose them as her personal motif because they are always found in pairs and mate for life, so it is particularly sad that Napoleon thought her inability to give him children sufficient reason to divorce her. The same tendency, ironically, is found among wild Mute Swans; the divorce rate is low at 9%, but occurs mainly between pairs that have had no success at rearing cygnets (39).

THE HISTORY OF WILDFOWL AVICULTURE

Where and when did it all begin? Is there a history to wildfowl aviculture, or some aspect of it that is unique? I believe that there are features that make it rather special. Aviculture can be defined as the keeping and breeding of non-domesticated birds in captivity. The most popular kinds are parrots, finches, pheasants, 'softbills' (a variety of smallish birds that feed on insects, nectar and fruit) and waterfowl. Because birds can fly, most captives are confined to aviaries, but wildfowl are usually pinioned instead – that is, the bone at the tip of one wing is removed so that the primary feathers on that side never grow. Wildfowl go through

The bell-ringing Mute Swan at Wells.

a flightless period every year that lasts up to two months, and to prevent them flying altogether seems not to impose the same hardship that it might on other birds. Pinioning stops them from escaping but obviously means that they are vulnerable to land-based predators. Nowadays, tall fox-proof fencing surrounds any waterfowl collection; King Charles and members of the gentry employed gamekeepers to control such unwelcome visitors, or established lakes which acted as natural barriers. The successful keeping of ducks, geese and swans increased as estates were 'improved' in the 18th Century by landscape architects who set welcoming stretches of water in parkland, with informal pastoral charm. The grounds of Holkham Hall in Norfolk, including a lake that is a mile long, were laid out by Capability Brown in 1762; Canada and Egyptian Geese were introduced and, ultimately, their offspring flew away to populate the surrounding countryside (Chapter 7). Many garden designs, starting with Versailles, used large bodies of water and pinioned waterfowl as decoration, so that a number of prominent families became owners of swans and geese almost by accident; a very few went on to appreciate their birds as individuals and they or their heirs evolved into true wildfowl aviculturalists. The hobby eventually became so much a passion of the landed English that the majority of wildfowl species were first bred in captivity in England (7). Recently, Peter Scott has designed and created wetland vistas for wildfowl that are quite as elaborate as any of Capability Brown's.

It had started long before that; the ancient Egyptians kept pet geese, the Chinese treasured pairs of Mandarin Ducks, and the monks of Abbotsbury monastery, founded in the reign of Canute, had tamed (and eaten) their swans and turned them into a unique breeding colony of about 500 birds by the 14th Century (3,11,16). (In 1541, the swans passed with the monastery into the hands of Henry VIII and he granted them to 'Giles Strangwaies, Knight', whose family maintained the swannery and, one hundred years later, built a decoy nearby (Chapter 3)). These were among the first aviculturalists, using birds that were to hand. When the desire for

Edward Lear's drawing of an Orinoco Goose at Knowsley Hall; they are said to have displayed constantly, 'flapping their wings and attacking intruders'. From Gray's *Gleanings from Knowsley*, photographed by Iris Young.

Knowsley Hall, 'the seat of the Right Hon'ble the Earl of Derby' who built up his extensive private zoo using one hundred acres of land and seventy acres of water. Fifteen wildfowl species bred regularly including, for the first time in captivity, Ashy-headed Geese, Orinocos and Hawaiian Geese. Drawn by G. Pickering and engraved by W. Taylor in 1841.

the exotic arose, someone had to fetch it. A monarch such as Charles II was able to use an early equivalent of 'panda diplomacy' to obtain many of his rare birds; others sent agents on collecting trips, and eventually it was possible to buy birds through dealers – in the 1850s, live Black Swans could be bought at Leadenhall Market (21). Lord Derby obtained the first Black-necked Swans *Cygnus melanocoryphus* ever brought to Britain through the exertions of his brother-in-law, Admiral Phipps Hornby (36), who was Commander-in-Chief in the Pacific.

The 13th Earl of Derby (1775–1851) was perhaps the greatest private animal-keeper of all time (14,33). His menagerie cost him £15,000 a year, but included Carolina Parakeets *Conuropsis carolinensis* and quaggas (the beautiful wild striped ass of southern Africa), both of which creatures were extinct within one hundred years. Not the least of his considerable achievements was a large nesting colony of Passenger Pigeons *Ectopistes migratorius*, another bird that was doomed to extinction. Special attention was devoted to wildfowl; he maintained over 50 species, and in 1834 hatched the first captive Hawaiian Geese (23), keeping diligent notes of their behaviour and publishing his observations (40). He befriended Audubon and, from 1832 to 1836, employed Edward Lear to draw his

Edward, 13th Earl of Derby, a remarkable naturalist and aviculturalist, President of the Zoological Society of London until his death, and patron of Edward Lear. In 1946, the 17th Earl sold the land now owned by The Wildfowl and Wetlands Trust at Martin Mere. Photograph (of a painting at Knowsley Hall by William Derby) taken by Iris Young.

birds; in his spare time, Lear took to writing amusing verse for the children of the household. *A Book of Nonsense*, published in 1846, is dedicated to 'the great-grandchildren, grand-nephews and grand-nieces of Edward, thirteenth Earl of Derby, by the author, Edward Lear'. When the Earl died in July 1851 his son, a politician destined to become Prime Minister within seven months, presented a pair of Black-necked Swans to Queen Victoria at Windsor, and sold the other animals for £7,000 (33).

The Zoological Society of London, while regretting the dispersal of this splendid collection under the auctioneer's hammer, bought some of the 'more select' of the ducks, geese and swans and, happily, the remaining pair of Lord Derby's precious Black-necked Swans hatched cygnets in Regent's Park six years later (36,39). Wildfowl continued to be a speciality of the London Zoo (they were keen enough to have paid £70 for two pairs of Mandarins in the 1830s (35)) and, by 1880, 270 individuals of 53 species were being exhibited. Magellan Geese *Chloephaga picta*, received from the Falklands' Governor, bred first in 1863, and Ruddyheads *C. rubidiceps* from the same source in 1865. Dr Sclater, Secretary to the Zoological Society, published the records of many other successful first hatchings – of Trumpeter Swans on 6 June 1870, and of some parti-coloured hybrids whose father had been a Black Swan and mother a Mute (36). One of the Zoo's more prolific importations was a pair of New Zealand Shelducks *Tadorna variegata* that nested in captivity initially in 1865, and whose youngsters were distributed to most of the larger zoological gardens of Europe (36).

There was immense competition to be the first keeper and, later, the first breeder of some unusual creature, and the more learned of the aviculturalists exhibited skins, eggs and young at the meetings of the

Lord Grey, Foreign Secretary of Great Britain from December 1904 to July 1916, with his Pintail, Eider, Red-crested Pochard and Mandarin. He started his wildfowl collection in 1884 while still at Oxford and, despite failing eyesight, birdwatching remained his main hobby all his life. Photograph by Seton Gordon.

Linnean Society (founded in 1788) or the Zoological Society (founded by, among others, Lord Derby in 1828). The Avicultural Society itself was not started until 1894; its journal *The Avicultural Magazine* published between 1951 and 1953 (in English) the results of Konrad Lorenz's early investigations into the taxonomy of waterfowl as determined by their displays (25).

It is possible to put together a distinguished list of successful, wealthy and mostly English wildfowl keepers of the last Century and the period between the two world wars. It includes Mary Tribe, Duchess of Bedford (one of the first women to hold a pilot's licence) who, in 1926, bred captive Red-breasted Geese for the first time at Woburn Abbey (2); Whitaker's book (43) on duck decoys (Chapter 3) is dedicated to her. Viscount Grey of Fallodon (1862–1933), after whom the world-famous Edward Grey Institute for Field Ornithology at Oxford is named, demonstrated that not all politicians are philistines, since he found solace from his busy life as British Foreign Secretary among his ducks. In Alfred Ezra's collection at Foxwarren Park in Surrey the first nest of a captive White-backed Duck *Thalasssornis leuconotus* was recorded in 1931 (7), the last Pink-headed Duck *Rhodonessa caryophyllacea* died in 1936, and it is from here that most of the feral population of English Mandarins derives (see the following Chapter). J. Spedan Lewis, who died in 1963, set up both

A pair of Pink-headed Ducks painted by the talented American artist Louis Agassiz Fuertes for Phillips' *Natural History of the Ducks*. Fuertes died in 1927 before the birds became extinct; could he have seen them alive? It certainly appears that he did.

Peter Scott's lighthouse at Sutton Bridge, with a human figure feeding
the geese. Drawing by Peter Scott from *Wild Chorus*. This was the scene
which inspired Paul Gallico's *The Snow Goose*.

the John Lewis Partnership and his home at Leckford in Hampshire where,
beside the clear waters of the river Test, the Radjah Shelduck *Tadorna
radjah* bred for the first time in captivity in 1940 (7,8). Jean Delacour
assembled three extensive wildfowl collections in France during his long
lifetime (1890–1985), losing two to war; a Hawaiian Goose, said to be
very old and the last of the line that had bred at Knowsley in the 1830s,
vanished from Clères in 1940, apparently eaten by the invading forces (8).
Lord Lilford (1833–1896) wrote fine bird books and commissioned their
illustrators; he owned a splendid Jacobean house near Oundle in Northamptonshire with a garden full of birds, including the first Marbled
Teal *Marmaronetta angustirostris* ever seen in England. It was from Lilford
Hall that the Little Owl *Athene noctua* escaped to populate the English
countryside.

THE WILDFOWL AND WETLANDS TRUST'S COLLECTIONS

Peter Scott had visited Lilford Hall during school and Cambridge
university days (37), and many of his friends kept waterfowl. His own
collection of ducks and geese was assembled before the last war in about
three acres of fenced marsh or saltings around his lighthouse at Sutton

Bridge in East Anglia. These birds were not, on the whole, captive-bred but were shooting casualties used as models for his paintings. About a score were still alive and brought to Slimbridge when The Severn Wildfowl Trust opened, including a pair of Lesser White-fronted Geese *Anser erythropus* which had been kept by a Lincolnshire farmer friend Will Tinsley (who had also introduced Peter to Borough Fen Decoy). These, together with a flock of geese belonging to the writer Gavin Maxwell, were released into the Rushy Pen at Slimbridge on 20 September 1946 (37). It is seldom that the collection of a private individual survives him, but Peter Scott's has done that.

The first Annual Report of The Trust records that, by 1948, there were 400 birds of 67 species. Many had been imported from the wild but, since the early days, emphasis was placed on breeding in captivity those that were needed for exhibition. There was, and still is, a feeling that no animal should be deprived of its freedom in the wild without due reason and, since world-wide legislation has now reduced and in some cases forbidden the import of birds that are in danger of extinction, the only recourse is to produce them from pinioned stock already held (38). The Trust (18) has bred many for the first time in captivity, including Bewick's Swans (39), Spotted Whistling Duck *Dendrocygna guttata*, Hartlaub's Duck *Pteronetta hartlaubi*, Bronze-winged Duck *Anas specularis*, Cape Shoveler *A. smithi*, New Zealand Brown Teal *A.aucklandica*, New Zealand Scaup *Aythya novae-seelandiae*, Black-headed Duck *Heteronetta atricapilla*, and the Recherche Island Goose *Cereopsis n. giseus* (5) which was first described as recently as 1980 and of which only about 500 exist in the wild. By the end of 1987, the number of birds held by The Trust at its various centres was 7,100; not all of these are captive in the strict sense, since an increasing number of native wildfowl is full-winged.

The aims of the collection were scientific from the start: Konrad Lorenz wrote a piece (26) in an early Annual Report of The Trust on the value of these captive birds saying that 'the attempt to disentangle the course of

Lesser White-fronted Goose, drawn by Robert Gillmor (from *Rare Birds in Britain and Ireland*).

A Magpie Goose feeding its young. Drawing by Robert Gillmor.

Aboriginal drawing on rock, from the Northern Territory of Australia, showing a Magpie Goose about to feed two begging goslings. Photograph by S. F. F. Davies.

evolution by comparing the similarities and dissimilarities of living animals is among the most fascinating enterprises that the human mind can undertake'. Paul Johnsgard followed this advice and, after 18 months of study at Slimbridge, published his *Handbook of Waterfowl Behaviour* (17) which changed our view of the taxonomic relationships of, among others, the Cape Barren Goose or *Cereopsis* and the Crested Duck *Anas specularioides*. It was only when the Australian Magpie Goose *Anseranas semipalmata* bred at Slimbridge that it was noticed that it fed its young from the bill – something that the Aboriginals had apparently known all along, although Australian scientists had not believed them.

Wildfowl and Wetlands Trust staff have been responsible for the discovery and implementation of many important techniques which they have passed on to the veterinary and avicultural world. In the early 1950s, the realisation that running water through the duckery protected young birds from a gizzard-worm, caught from water-fleas, was a major step towards rearing success. Later, the provision of disused Coots' nests for stiff-tailed ducks was the breakthrough that persuaded many of this group to lay (30). Invention of effective portable incubators for the long-distance transport of hatching eggs, even from continent to continent, was a considerable advance (32). Adult birds are now hardly ever taken from the wild; if new genetic material is required, a clutch of eggs suffices. The ability to sex birds accurately at hatching is common to all The Trust's avicultural staff, although in the early days the necessary techniques were not understood even for adult birds, let alone for day-olds. Thus in 1950, when the then Curator John Yealland returned from Hawaii with two Nenes, thought to be a true pair, embarrassment followed when both laid a clutch of eggs the following spring (23). Exotic birds are now pinioned, with minimal trauma, at one day old – on the left wing of females and the right one of males; this enables wildfowl with similar plumage to be sexed visually without the need of being caught.

REINTRODUCTION PROGRAMMES

Captivity, even during the last century, had become a refuge for birds threatened in the wild, although a knowledge of what was happening in the natural state was sometimes fragmentary. Those 80 or so Passenger

The Carolina, known to Audubon, Lord Derby and Mrs Beeton as the Summer Duck, and now usually called the North American Wood Duck. Photograph by Brian Gadsby.

Hawaiian Geese were first hatched in captivity on 13 April 1834 at Knowsley Hall; a drawing by Peter Scott.

Pigeons at Knowsley probably bred successfully because Lord Derby had the sense to keep them in a large flock; at the auction in 1851 they were divided and never bred again. In September 1914 the last of this once numerous North American species died in Cincinnati Zoo. The Pink-headed Duck was held at the London Zoo in 1874, and later at Clères, Foxwarren and Lilford Hall at a time when the bird was already extremely rare; unfortunately it never nested and is now extinct (7,24). In 1918, there were probably more **Carolina Wood Ducks** (like Jean Delacour (7), I much prefer the name 'Carolina Wood Duck' or simply 'Carolina' to 'North American Wood Duck') in collections than in the wild; they were thought to be going the way of the Passenger Pigeon so, rather late in the day, hunting was forbidden and not again allowed until 1941. The duck had been taken to Europe from the state of Carolina – a title that honoured King Charles II – and had done well during 300 years of captivity. In 1922, an English gamekeeper was brought to Connecticut to look after a small flock that had been imported from Belgium and, by 1939, 2,579 of their offspring had been released (34). Ringing recoveries indicated that these captive-bred Carolinas had reached 15 States, and even Ontario in Canada, and that many groups, laying in artificial nest-boxes, were being successfully established; it showed that a captive-rearing and release pro-gramme could be a positive step towards the conservation of a wild bird.

The restoration of the **Hawaiian Goose** or **Nene** has become something of a conservation classic that is mentioned every time the value of reintroductions of zoo-bred stock is discussed (23). At the end of the 1940s, there were probably only 30 individuals in the wild and 13 in captivity. Usually nothing can be done when a population falls so low as 50; however, from the two females sent to Slimbridge in 1950 and a male in 1951, plus four more ganders added in the 1960s, nearly 2,000 birds have descended, all related to that original mis-sexed 'pair'. Two hundred of these have been returned to Hawaii to join 1,800 bred there in captivity plus a few raised at Litchfield, Connecticut, by Dillon Ripley; all have been released into sanctuaries either on Hawaii or the adjacent island of Maui. At first, this did increase the estimated wild population – on Hawaii to 450 in 1972 and to 650 by 1977, and on Maui from 150–200 in 1975 to between 225 and 325 by 1977. (All the Maui birds had been reared in captivity or were offspring of such birds, whereas some wild stock had still remained on the island of Hawaii). Because of the apparent breeding success of the geese that had been set free, and the increase in population size, releases of captive-reared Nene slowed after 1976.

Then, in the late 1970s, numbers on both islands declined; by 1980 only 300 geese were estimated to be present on Hawaii and between 100 and 150 on Maui. Today, the situation is probably somewhat worse, with only 350 birds in the wild. Half the adults are failing to breed every year, the goslings are suffering high mortality during adverse weather, and there is heavy loss of incubating females and their eggs to introduced predators. The goose now lays almost exclusively in the highlands, where the food supply may be deficient and the climate is poor compared to the lowlands where the birds used to breed but cannot any longer because most of the land there is used for agriculture. Inadequate nutrition may be the reason why only a small proportion of the potential breeding population attempts to nest, and could also contribute to low gosling survival.

A recovery plan drawn up in Hawaii recommends that the number of introduced predators, especially mongooses, is reduced; that research is carried out into the nutritional requirements of young and old; that release sites at lower altitudes be sought, release techniques improved, and that captive-reared Nene continue to be added to bolster the wild population. So the passage of nearly 40 years has not resulted in complete success. Some of the difficulties encountered occur in all captive breeding programmes, but the major problems in restoring the Nene have been related to a lack of understanding of exactly why it had become endangered in the first place – which of the many adverse factors were the most important – and to the absence of a suitable habitat in which to restore it. An 'unauthorised' release during the 1980s onto the mongoose-free island of Kauai resulted in a population of about 30 birds living at low elevations, and brought some criticism from 'purists' worried about an introduction into an environment that never had Nene. In fact, sub-fossil remains of the goose have been unearthed in the soil of many Hawaiian islands, and it was probably widely distributed until comparatively recently.

White-winged Wood Ducks in their rain-forest habitat. Drawn by Sam MacKenzie.

White-winged Wood Ducks spend much of their lives in the trees. Drawn by Sam MacKenzie.

The rare **White-winged Wood Ducks** *Cairina scutulata* from the disappearing rain-forests of southeast Asia did not nest freely in captivity until The Trust discovered the importance of keeping them under trees, out of direct sunshine, and it was at bosky Peakirk that the first second-generation breeding in captivity occurred (28,32). It seems obvious, but the possibility that the displays of a woodland duck might be suppressed on an open pond was not considered for many years; even Peter Scott was one of those who thought that wildfowl and trees do not mix! The White-winged Wood Duck is now well established in many zoos and The Trust has provided stock for breeding programmes within the birds' original range in Assam, in Aranchal Pradesh in India and in Thailand where forests reserves are being preserved or restored. Unfortunately, The Trust's stock numbered less than ten to begin with and records show that the genes of only two of those are effectively represented in the present captive birds. Equally unfortunately, the captive birds are peculiarly susceptible to avian tuberculosis (28) for which, ironically, the only disinfectant is bright sunlight; the search for a vaccine is underway.

The **White-headed Duck** *Oxyura leucocephala*, reduced in numbers because of over-shooting as well as loss of habitat, might become the hero of another re-introduction success story (30,32). Through a scheme organised by The Wildfowl and Wetlands Trust and the Hungarian Ornithological Union, some 70 White-headed Ducks have been raised in captivity in Hungary from eggs laid in Britain, and the first breeding was recorded in 1986. Five pairs of young White-headed Ducks were released into the wild in Kiskunsag National Park where the duck had become extinct as a breeding species 30 years earlier. The ducks proved hard to monitor, and two females are known to have died. A separate attempt is being made to restore the bird to Sardinia via eggs laid in England, and a rather different plan to save the duck by restoring its habitat is described in Chapter 10.

The **Brown Teal** of New Zealand is being bred and released, largely by aviculturalists and wildfowlers working in an organisation known as Ducks Unlimited (10,15,24). The Teal became increasingly rare following European settlement when drainage of swamps and naturalization of predatory mammals characterised the New Zealand scene. It remained on the shooting list until 1921, despite being amiably tame like many island birds, and the suggestion has been made that it was also infected with a disease caught from introduced domestic fowls. By the 1980s, a population of only 1,500 wild individuals was estimated, making it one of the rarest ducks in the world. The first reintroduction was to Kapiti Island in June 1968, and I recall my delight at finding a female Brown Teal with ducklings there four months later. Up to 1985, 670 birds had been raised in captivity by Ducks Unlimited and the Wildlife Service, and the majority liberated. Releases continue – 104 in 1986 and 45 in 1987 – and, as importantly, research into release techniques, survival rates and habitat assessment (the original environment having virtually disappeared) is being funded by the New Zealand Department of Conservation.

The 1,800 km (1,100 mile) chain of Aleutian, Commander and Kurile Islands that stretch south and west from Alaska was once the home of the little **Aleutian Canada Goose**. Genetic tests have shown it to be the most different of all the races of Canada Goose; it could once be found breeding in thousands and migrating, some to North America and others from the western part of the archipelago to Japan (20). Populations declined slowly during the late 19th and early 20th Centuries because of native hunting, but crashed when Alaskan residents, in an attempt to develop a fur industry during the 1920s, released blue foxes (a colour phase of the arctic fox) onto all the islands except the isolated 1,600 ha (4,000 acre) Buldir which lacked a harbour. The use of the islands for military purposes, the introduction of dogs and cats, and the accidental release of the black rat during the war, caused further reductions, with the result that after World War II just 300 birds remained. It was decided to clear some of the other islands of foxes and to breed goslings in captivity for restocking. Geese were trapped on Buldir in 1963 and, in 1966, the first generation of captive-bred youngsters was hatched at Patuxent Wildlife Research Center, Maryland. By 1977, 380 young had been produced, but their return presented particular problems; no-one had ever tried to restore a long-distance migrant before and, in this case, no-one was even sure where the geese spent the winter months.

Seventy-five captive-bred geese were released on Amchitka Island, after it had been cleared of foxes, to try to extend the numbers and range of the natural population. A later check revealed no trace – predation by

Bald Eagles *Haliaetus leucocephalus* was indicated. The next release onto another cleared island, Agatu, was made with some adult 'guide' geese from Buldir and did result in a sighting during the winter in California, but no return to the release site the following summer. In 1976, the propagation facilities were moved from Patuxent to Amchitka, 28 young birds were liberated but were lost almost immediately to the Eagles.

Ringing of the Buldir birds had meanwhile revealed that the whole population wintered with other geese around the Sacramento valley in California and, since 1975, hunting of all Canadas there has been banned. These restrictions have resulted in average annual increases in the population of 22%, so that 1,630 birds were counted in November 1977, 2,310 in January 1981 and 5,000 in 1987. It is hard to believe that aviculture has helped significantly to restore the numbers of Aleutian Geese, except in revealing where the birds spent the winter and what heavy losses they were suffering. They breed fairly readily in captivity, perhaps because they are not true inhabitants of the arctic – Buldir is at 52°N, almost the same latitude as Slimbridge. With hindsight, it might have been better to have tried to fill the available habitat on Buldir with captive-reared stock. The new birds would then have had companions with which to migrate and might eventually have searched of their own accord for less crowded nesting situations on islands from which the foxes had been eradicated. Meanwhile, two other small populations have been discovered, and one colony of 60 birds transplanted from Buldir to Agatu has begun to breed.

ARE CAPTIVE BREEDING PROGRAMMES NECESSARY?

Ever since the survival of species became an important concern for conservation organisations such as The Trust, a debate has waged on the desirability of bringing birds into zoos in order to save them from extinction in the wild (22,29,32). A number of committed aviculturalists argue that captive breeding programmes should be initiated, not only for threatened species, but as a precaution for those not yet on the critical list. Some go further in suggesting that the aim of all aviculture is the eventual release of offspring back into their natural state; indeed, this argument is used fairly indiscriminately to justify many institutions and individuals taking animals into captivity.

Sadly, there is a great gap between the theory and the practice of reintroduction, and there are still few examples of bird populations that have been successfully re-established in the wild through the release of captive-reared young. The breeding programme and the later field-work must be scientifically planned and supervised, and we need to know more about why species become rare; if due to habitat destruction, then there is no point in restoring the birds without first repairing their environment: to quote the Swan of Avon 'You take my life when you do take the means whereby I live'. If, as sometimes happens with ducks and geese, shooting was a major reason for a decline in numbers, then there may be virtue in adding further individuals, or in reintroducing the species where it has become extinct. But, as we saw in the case of the Aleutian Canada, a ban on hunting may achieve the same end. In reintroductions, we can predict from recent experience that large, long-lived birds do best, especially if they mature quickly, are polygamous and lay a large clutch. Sedentary birds are easier than migratory ones, and families with a varied age structure, in which the parents are not related, are to be preferred for release. Many wildfowl fit some of these criteria, but the chances of success are still small.

There are a few species, like the Laysan Teal *A. laysanensis* (Chapter 7), where a captive population may act as a reservoir for reintroduction in the event of a disaster, either natural or through the arrival of a predator. Laysan, like many coral islands, is slowly sinking and a period of inundation and re-emergence is not unlikely. The next cyclone may swamp the vegetation and destroy the animals. Should we then reintroduce some of our stock of teal? If a shipwreck allowed the escape of a pair of rats, would we remove the rodents and their progeny and then restore the birds? There are no certain answers, but probably we would (22).

Aviculture must, in most circumstances, be seen as existing for itself; often it will bring great pleasure, or provide research possibilities, or give the chance to show the public why their taxes are needed to protect the wild (29,38). Human beings seem to find great therapeutic value in having pets and in caring for young animals, especially when they are as attractive and responsive as cygnets, goslings and ducklings.

WHAT HAPPENS DURING CAPTIVE BREEDING?

Wildfowl respond well to captivity for many of the same reasons that they domesticate easily (see Chapter 2). Indeed there are only fine lines to be drawn between aviculture, farming and true domestication. The Mute Swan and the Eider are examples of wild birds that have been farmed for man's utilitarian purposes for hundreds of years, and will be considered later in this Chapter.

What happens to a wild species after many generations of breeding in captivity? Man will select, usually inadvertently, for traits that fit the bird to his particular environment — its climate, altitude, daylength cycles, food supply, noise levels, etc. (22,29). With the colonial Mute Swans of Abbotsbury the monks were able, eventually, to produce a lack of territorial aggression in the cobs, but only (we assume) by removing over and over again any males who insisted on fighting for a large space around themselves. This worked for two reasons: by natural variation there were individuals in the population that were slightly less territorial than the rest and could pass on this characteristic to their descendants, and because the cygnets were fed artificially, or were able to obtain an abundant supply

A Mandarin nest-box at Slimbridge with a female at the entrance and her mate half-way up the ramp. Photograph by K. Portman.

of eelgrass from the West Fleet nearby (the monks also had to provide nesting material – a practice that continues today). The function of territoriality in most Mute Swans seems to be to ensure adequate food during the rearing period by securing a wide space around the family unit. When food is not limited, such territoriality becomes redundant (3,11); indeed, colonial (non-territorial) Mute Swans do occur rarely elsewhere in Europe – in Denmark and Poland, for instance – where food is sufficient, and do so without much human intervention (39).

A crucial problem of all captive propagation is that, usually, the gene pool of the founders is small; rare species, therefore, often carry the seeds of their own destruction since inbreeding brings together harmful genes that larger pools would dilute (29). A drop in fertility is not unusual after many generations in captivity; this was probably the reason for the decline to extinction of the first importation to Europe of Hawaiian Goose stock. The second import to Slimbridge in the early 1950s was of three birds already closely related, and the fertility of their descendants' eggs fell, generation after generation, to only 40%. Four ganders of wild 'blood' arrived during the 1960s and viability was restored (23). The three pairs of New Zealand Brown Teal that came to Slimbridge in 1957 flourished initially but had dwindled to three males by 1979. In that year, Ducks Unlimited sent two females; in the next season 14 young were reared and 16 more followed in 1981. However, a few species quite unpredictably show no lack of vigour after similar inbreeding in captivity. Three pairs of New Zealand Scaup that travelled with the Brown Teal are the ancestors of most if not all of the numerous captive birds in Europe and North America. And the Laysan Teal seems not to have suffered genetically from a decline (at one time) to a world population of less than ten.

Husbandry in captivity can eliminate many characteristics that are useful in the normal habitat but undesirable in an aviary or a collection; indeed, to breed animals in captivity is often, with the best of intentions, to breed them *for* captivity (29). For instance, birds that have been captive for many generations may lay year after year in a nest-site from which their eggs are taken for artificial incubation. The wild ancestors of these females would always choose another site after a predator had removed their first clutch; only if the eggs had hatched would they use the same nest for a second or third time. Captive Carolinas and Mandarins are often said by aviculturalists to be quite unconcerned by the loss, and will lay repeatedly in an identical box despite forfeiting their eggs; a wild bird that took no precautions against egg-thieves and did not learn to search for a safe situation before breeding would leave no offspring to pass on that trait (22). There are obvious implications for current schemes to introduce hole-nesting Mandarins to Britain (see Chapter 7).

Another example is the laying of a clutch during a daylength that would be inappropriate in most of the natural range of the species concerned; here, selection chooses the unusual bird that will breed at the latitude where the flock is kept and excludes the majority of individuals that will not. For instance, Bewick's Swans from the high arctic do not normally breed in European zoos (39) because summer days are too short; only long days provoke the cobs to display, in turn triggering the females to ovulate. But one Slimbridge line, derived from a male who was presumably a natural variant and did respond to shorter days, does now breed (22). Theoretically, if his descendants were restored to the wild, they would either lay earlier or move to areas further south than evolution has so far determined is best for them.

Many more young survive in the hands of an aviculturalist than would in the wild; the mother duck typically loses eight of a brood of ten, and competition imposed by the presence of brothers and sisters tends to eliminate any weaklings. In captivity, that rate of success would hardly be applauded, and yet the sharp edge of natural selection is being dulled by caring for the less-than-healthy and by raising maximum numbers rather than by allowing only the more vigorous to survive (29).

Mute Swan. An engraving from Bewick's *A History of British Birds.*

FARMING THE MUTE SWAN IN BRITAIN

The Mute Swan in England has been tamed and partly, but not truly, domesticated for hundreds of years. Domestication implies that man decides upon the choice of mate, and thereby selects the genetic characteristics of the animal's descendants. For the swan, pinioning must have restricted the natural choice somewhat; however, man never seems to have stopped particular pairs breeding, never killed adult birds, and seldom selected between the cygnets that were taken to be fattened for the table.

Youngsters that grew on to become the parents of the next generation were left to cope with all the hazards of the natural environment and its selective pressures. So although tameness (the ability to nest in close proximity to humans) may distinguish British Mutes from most of their Continental relatives, they are typically robust and retain a high degree of territoriality, flocking only as non-breeders or in the winter. Almost all other domesticated animals can be herded throughout the year. The monks of Abbotsbury 'bred out' some of the Mute Swan's natural but undesirable quarrelsomeness; it worked, as has been pointed out, only because there was plenty of food for the young. (In 1917, while a war was on, the usual grain could not be fed, and a late cold spring meant that no cygnets were reared (43)).

Much has been written about the history of this royal swan (3,7,11,16,21,39,41). During the 12th and 13th Centuries, any wild birds gradually became 'owned' by persons with freehold land, and strays were pronounced to be the property of the Crown. Swans were seen as status symbols both alive and dead. No medieval feast was complete without a 16 lb, or so, roast swan (they were said to be best between All Souls Day – 2 November – and Lent) and, as Ticehurst (41) pointed out in *The Mute Swan in England*, their possession lent distinction to the owner and enabled him to make a glamorous gift or to profit by selling a prized commodity. Whether their flavour was particularly pleasant seems to have been a matter of opinion. Charles Darwin wrote (6) that 'the meat was pretty good, but tasted like neither flesh nor fowl, but something halfway like Venison with Wild duck'. Another more jaundiced writer (1) of 1738 compared the meat unfavourably with goose as 'blacker, harder and tougher, having grosser Fibres hard of Digestion, of a bad melancholic Juice; yet for its Rarity serves as a Dish to adorn great Men's Tables at Feasts and Entertainments, being else no desirable Dainty'. They had to be young birds to have any gastronomic value, and the practice was to take the cygnets from their parents at 'swan-upping' and put them in special fenced pits containing a 'stew' or pond, to be fattened on barley for Christmas and feasts such as weddings. Henry III's court had 125 young swans for Christmas dinner in 1251; and 400 were eaten when the Archbishop of York was installed in 1466.

Ownership necessitated a system of marking with a life-long label (41). The soft tissue of the upper bill was found to grow scar tissue that remained until death. Scars could also be made on the webbing of the foot; the 'Hive of Ilchester' is a mark made on the outer web of swans of the Abbotsbury 'royalty' (11,16). Pinioning was essential so that the birds would not fly but only swim away. It is extraordinary that Mute Swans – the world's largest flying birds – survived for many centuries as part of the English fauna without the power of flight and with further man-inflicted damage, albeit slight, to their bills and feet.

Legislation protected them from indiscriminate attacks by man, although not from foxes, nor their cygnets from underwater eels and pike.

The swan-pit or *cygnorum* owned by St Helen's Hospital, Norwich, where cygnets were fattened for Christmas. Photograph from the 1903 *Transactions of the Norfolk Naturalists' Society*, courtesy of the Norfolk Museums Service.

The system clearly functioned well – Mute Swans were commoner then than now. Celia Fiennes (12) had a nice description of the numbers that she noticed when travelling near Ely in 1698: 'here I see the many swans nests on little hillocks of earth in the wett ground that they look as if swimming with their nest, some were with their young signetts 3 or 4 in a troope with their damms hovering over them for their security'. The Mute was the only farmed animal where the offspring were shared between the owners of the parents, and the possessor of the father, rather than the mother or dam, had the first pick (41).

A Swan Master and numerous deputies throughout Britain were appointed by the King to oversee the division of the cygnets before any could fly away (3,41). The owners had to be present, so the Swan Master or his deputy was responsible for informing all interested parties, organising the boats and managing the swan-catching programme. The young birds were divided according to clearly laid-down and complex rules.

If the parents of the cygnets both belonged to the same landowner and they had nested on his property, then he could claim them all (3,41). If they had nested on someone else's land, then a single cygnet (called the 'ground bird') went to that person as land rent. If, however, he was a freeholder of insufficient property to own swans at all, then he was paid the value of the cygnet by someone who had the privilege of keeping swans and who added that bird to his collection. When the pen and cob belonged to different owners, the brood (after payment of the ground bird, if necessary) was split between them, and the owner of the male had the first choice. If the remaining cygnets were an odd number, then disposal of the extra bird seems to have been subject to local custom. In the Fens, it went to the owner of the cob as being 'the more worthy'. On the Thames, it was valued and whoever took it paid the owner of the other parent half the agreed amount. Sometimes two owners took it in turns annually to claim the odd cygnet.

Swan-keeping declined through the 18th Century as it was expensive, and luxury foods like the Turkey became more widely available. Mute Swans had two drawbacks as farmed animals. First, they were aggressive and so normally could not be maintained at a high density and, secondly, they had to have access to water. The performance of rounding them up was difficult and time-consuming compared to dealing with a flock of geese or Turkeys. Their value was correspondingly high: in 1315 a breeding pair and five other swans were said to be worth £10 – a goose would have cost perhaps 6d (see Chapter 2). The history of *The Worshipful Company of Poulters* (19) gives the price of swans over many years, starting in the 13th Century. Turkeys appear in their lists for the first time in 1559, and Company officials bought for two shillings a Turkey hen, presumably as a treat, for their Master's feast on 29 August 1563.

The swan mark of the Bishop of Ely in the 16th Century. Eight nicks were made, four on each side of the upper mandible, plus a band and circle across the centre.

The rising cost of swan as recorded in the Poulters Company price lists (19).

1274	3/– (£0.15)	
1370	4/– (£0.20)	
1521	3/4 (£0.17)	Easter to All Saints
	4/–	All Saints to Shrovetide
1537	5/4 (£0.26)	Midsummer to Allhallows
	6/4 (£0.33)	Allhallows to Shrovetide
1551	8/– (£0.40)	
1634	7/– (£0.35)	Cygnet until Allhallows
	9/– (£0.45)	Allhallows to Shrovetide

Swan-upping, when all swans are counted and the cygnets are pinioned and their bills marked, now takes place only on the river Thames in July, while the adults are in wing-moult and the youngsters have not yet fledged (in fact, the practice of pinioning was abandoned in 1978). Bill marks, like the large plastic rings described in Chapter 5, are conspicuous enough to be seen from a distance so that ownership can be confirmed without the need to catch the bird repeatedly. The marks result from cuts made with a sharp knife in the soft tissue of (usually) the bird's upper mandible. In the 16th and 17th Centuries, between one and eight notches might have been cut in one or both margins. More elaborate variations included initials and heraldic devices, and these were made across the centre of the bill. As many as 630 marks were in use between 1450 and 1600 (41). Apart from Abbotsbury (11,16), the only present day 'royalties' in swans confer a right to own birds on the Thames, and are those granted to the Dyers' and the Vintners' Livery Companies of the City of London (39). The bills of the cygnets still receive one notch for the Dyers', two notches, one on each side, for the Vintners' (an anomalous situation under the Wildlife and Countryside Act of 1981), while any royal birds are left unmarked. 'Swan feasts' have been held at the Vintner's Hall, London EC4, for over 400 years; they used to occur in February just before Lent or Shrovetide, but in 1987, at least, the banquet took place in the presence of the Duke and Duchess of Gloucester on 26 November.

THE FARMED EIDER DUCK

If the farming of Mute Swans is peripheral 'aviculture', then the situation to be considered next is more so. The northern Eider is another wildfowl that has been protected extensively in its wild state, and tamed by man for its utilitarian qualities (7). Again, the process of farming has not resulted in true domestication – no selection of mates and progeny is involved – but the choice of breeding sites is extended and predators are controlled.

Feather-down, plucked from their breasts by laying females to line their nests, is unique to wildfowl, although it is not found in any quantity in the few species where both sexes incubate and the eggs are never uncovered, or

Eiders nesting around an up-turned boat on Helgeland, Norway. Photograph by Myrfyn Owen.

where the eggs are very large. Its function is to insulate the clutch from the cold and from dehydration, and to camouflage the site while the parent is away. The natural colour of the breast-down is white, and female ducks that lay in the open grow special brownish down at the start of the breeding season so that the nest can be rendered more inconspicuous.

In northern Europe, mainly Iceland and the islands off the coast of Norway, Eider colonies are protected from foxes, mink, dogs and gulls that might disturb or kill the sitting females or take their eggs (7). Artificial cavities and boxes are constructed as nest sites and, in Iceland, flags are erected to flutter in the wind and indicate the position of the protected area (9). The suggestion is that the flags resemble the wings of gulls in whose colonies wild Eiders often choose to nest because their eggs suffer less predation if they incubate among a mass of other birds. (Some Eiders in East Greenland have even taken to breeding close to tethered husky dogs, with a result that their nests increased from two in 1955 to 1,292 by 1975 (31). The Eiders seem to regard the dogs not as predators but as providing a 'fox-free island'!) In return, farmers gather the down for sale. The first collection of quality material is removed soon after incubation has begun; this the duck replaces over the next few days, and the second collection takes place after the eggs have hatched and the ducklings departed with their mother. The down left behind is often soiled and mixed with bits of vegetation, and requires careful cleaning before it can be used in quilts.

The tradition of collecting down in Iceland is very old, as old as the State itself (9). The practice was economically so important that the taking of the birds or their clutches for food had to be prohibited. Attempts at protection are thus almost as ancient – dating at least from the 13th Century; the law gradually became more and more severe against hunters and those who traded in eggs, which suggests that it was not always observed. After the volcanic eruption of Hekla in 1783, the government tried to increase the down trade so that the farmers whose land had been devastated could have some income. Complete protection of the Eider was achieved only in about 1900.

The amount of down obtained then increased. Between 1909 and 1917, more than 250 farms supplied 2,500 kg (5,500 lb) annually and a record 4,294 kg (9,500 lb) was gathered in 1915, representing the production of about 280,000 female Eiders (9). However, down exports from Iceland have steadily decreased since the 1940s. This is not because of lower demand – the price indeed remains high. Many suggestions have been made to account for the decline: an increased standard of living brings more sewage outfalls and rubbish dumps and a consequent increase in the number of gulls preying on the ducklings; mink from fur farms have escaped and many ground-nesting birds have been killed; the lumpfish industry has flourished and Eiders drown in nets set to catch the fish; and oil and other chemical pollution pose threats in shallow coastal waters (9).

Eiders have, in any case, been declining in some other parts of their range, notably Russia, although they have extended southwards and increased in northwest Europe. Probably some ecological change has taken place in Iceland. It is unlikely to be caused by the down-collecting industry itself, although there is evidence that eggs hatch less well if down is taken.

In North America, the tradition of harvesting down is hardly known and, although Eider numbers are high, prospects for future production seem slight (9). Cottage industries of this type are dying out, along with other 'traditional' life styles, rather than being developed.

Eiderdown is unrivalled in lightness, insulation properties and elasticity. The outer edges of the plumules interlock to provide a dense mass that can be compressed and spring out again without damage. Trade figures state that 1.5 kg of goose down, which lacks much of the cohesion and elasticity of Eider down, can provide adequate insulation in a sleeping bag at -35°C; eiderdown can provide the same or better, while a synthetic fill is satisfactory only down to -7°C (9). It will be a pity if the valuable relationship that has existed for centuries between Eider and man is allowed to lapse.

REFERENCES

1. Albin, E. 1731–38. *A Natural History of Birds*. London.
2. Bedford, Duchess of. 1927. Red-breasted Geese (Branta ruficollis) breeding in captivity. *Avic. Mag.* 5: 65–66.
3. Birkhead, M & Perrins, C. 1986. *The Mute Swan*. London: Croom Helm.
4. Chevers, N. 1861. *An enquiry into the Circumstances of the Death of King Charles the Second of England*. Calcutta.
5. Crompton, D. 1985. Recherche Island Geese. *Avic. Mag.* 91:157–159.
6. Darwin, C. 1985. *The Correspondence of Charles Darwin*. Vol.1 1821–1836. CUP.
7. Delacour, J. 1954–59. *The Waterfowl of the World*. Vols 1–3. London: Country Life.
8. Delacour, J. 1966. *The Living Air: The Memoirs of an Ornithologist*. London: Country Life.
9. Doughty, R. W. 1979. Eider husbandry in the North Atlantic: trends and prospects. *Polar record* 19: 447–459.
10. Dumbell, G. 1986. The New Zealand Brown Teal: 1845–1985. *Wildfowl* 37: 71–87.
11. Fair, J. 1985. *The Mute Swan*. Limington: Gavin Press.
12. Fiennes, C. 1949. *Illustrated Journeys 1685–1712*. Edited by C. Morris. London: MacDonald.
13. Frazer, A. 1979. *King Charles II*. London: Weidenfeld & Nicholson.
14. Gray, G. R. 1846. *Gleanings from the Menagerie and Aviary at Knowsley Hall*.
15. Hayes, F. N. & Williams, M. 1982. The status, aviculture and re-establishment of Brown Teal in New Zealand. *Wildfowl* 33:73–80.
16. Ilchester, the Earl of. 1934. The Abbotsbury Swannery. *Dorset Nat. Hist. & Arch. Soc.*
17. Johnsgard, P. 1965. *Handbook of Waterfowl Behavior*. Cornell University Press.

18. Johnstone, S. T. 1968. The Slimbridge collection – the first 21 years. *Wildfowl* 19: 125–129.

19. Jones, P. E. 1965. *The Worshipful Company of Poulters. A Short History.* OUP.

20. Jones, R. D. 1963. Buldir Island, site of a remnant breeding population of Aleutian Canada Geese. *Wildfowl* 14: 80–84.

21. Jones, T. R. 1860. *Cassell's Book of Birds.* London: Cassell.

22. Kear, J. 1977. The problems of breeding endangered species in captivity. *Int.Zoo Yb.* 17:5–14.

23. Kear, J. & Berger, A. 1980. *The Hawaiian Goose.* Calton: Poyser.

24. Kear, J. & Williams, G. 1978. Waterfowl at risk. *Wildfowl* 29:5–21.

25. Lorenz, K. 1951–3. Comparative studies on the behaviour of the Anatidae. *Avic. Mag.* 57: 157–182; 58: 8–17, 61–72, 86–94, 172–184; 59: 24–34, 80–91.

26. Lorenz, K. 1952. The scientific value of a group collection of live animals. *Wildfowl* 4: 47–50.

27. Lorenz, K. 1973. Why waterfowl? *Int.Zoo Yb* 13: 1–6.

28. MacKenzie, M. J. S. & Kear, J. 1976. The White-winged Wood Duck. *Wildfowl* 27:5–17.

29. Matthews, G. V. T. 1973. Some problems facing captive breeding and restoration programmes for waterfowl. *Int.Zoo Yb* 13: 8–11.

30. Matthews, G. V. T. & Evans, M. E. 1974. On the behaviour of the White-headed Duck with special reference to breeding. *Wildfowl* 25: 56–66.

31. Meltofte, H. 1978. A breeding association between Eiders and tethered huskies in North-east Greenland. *Wildfowl* 29:45–54.

32. Ounsted, M. L. 1988. Attempts by The Wildfowl Trust to re-establish the White-winged wood duck and the White-headed duck *Cairina scutulata* and *Oxyura leucocephala.* *Int.Zoo Yb* 27: 216–222.

33. Pollard, W. 1871. *The Stanleys of Knowsley.* London: Warne.

34. Ripley, S. D.1973. Saving the Wood Duck *Aix sponsa* through captive breeding. *Int.Zoo Yb* 13: 55–58.

35. Savage, C. 1952. *The Mandarin Duck.* London: Black.

36. Sclater, P. L. 1880. List of the certainly known species of Anatidae, with notes on such as have been introduced into the zoological gardens of Europe. *Proc. zool. Soc.Lond.* 1880: 496–536.

37. Scott, P. 1961. *The Eye of the Wind.* London: Hodder.

38. Scott, P. 1973. Reconciling the irreconcilable. *Int.Zoo Yb.* 13: 6–8

39. Scott, P & The Wildfowl Trust. 1971. *The Swans.* London: Michael Joseph.

40. Stanley, E. S. (13th Earl of Derby). 1834. A note on a specimen of a young Sandwich Island goose. *Lond.& Edin.Phil.Mag. & J. of Sci.* 5: 233–235; and *Proc.zool.Soc.Lond.* Part II: 41–43.

41. Ticehurst, N. F. 1957. *The Mute Swan in England.* London: Cleaver-Hume Press.

42. Trevor-Battye, A. 1909. *Lord Lilford on Birds.* London: Hutchinson.

43. Whitaker, J. 1918. *British Duck Decoys of To-Day.* London: Burlington.

7: Aliens

Movement of plants and animals by man's accidental intervention must have happened since earliest times. Deliberate relocation is probably no older than the advent of agriculture when our ancestors settled down into stable communities and began to domesticate plants and animals. The eras of increasingly easy transport, by beasts of burden, by ship and, lastly, by plane, gave speed to the process.

There is now very little of the earth's surface that has a pristine fauna and flora – certainly the natural world of the English-speaking peoples is an amalgam of the exotic and the native, and that mixture is both regretted and admired (17,18,26). The rabbit, the grey squirrel, the Little Owl, rhododendrons and grey alders are in England to stay, and are not totally unloved. In New Zealand, Chaffinches *Fringilla coelebs*, trout and red deer are enjoyed for their song or for sport. North America's introduced urban House Sparrow *Passer domesticus* may be a nuisance much of the time but undoubtedly has a talent to amuse.

More than 1,670 releases of birds have been made in several parts of the world and about 25% have successfully established breeding populations (17). Hawaii has the distinction of having had more bird introductions than any other country; 162 have been tried and 45 of those introductions have 'taken' (18), indeed, a visitor to Honolulu sees plenty of birds but not a single one of any native kind. New Zealand comes a close second both in the 144 foreigners that have been added to the avifauna since 1840, and in the 33 that have established themselves (34). It is still a fact, for which we must be thankful, that most introductions do not 'take' – the animals either fail to survive at an early stage or are gradually eliminated by 'catastrophes' such as droughts, cold or irregular food shortages that the natives can cope with.

Wildfowl have been re-located along with the rest. At the beginning of this Century, the Vintners' Company of the City of London 'upped' three pairs of Mute Swans on the Thames and sent them halfway around the world as a present to Perth in Western Australia; their descendants are on the Australian river Avon today (17). In Britain, the introduced Canada Goose, Mandarin, Egyptian Goose and Ruddy Duck thrive to a greater or lesser extent (22), and four newcomers that have arrived under their own steam – the Tufted Duck which first bred in the wild in Britain about 1849, Gadwall (in 1850), Goosander (1871) and Goldeneye (1970) – are extending their ranges assisted by escapes from captivity (30). In New Zealand, the foreign Black Swan, Canada Goose and Mallard are now common enough for there to be an open season during which they may be shot (17). In the United States, the Mute Swan breeds so well on Rhode Island that control measures are considered necessary (29). Domesticated Mallard have escaped and are found inter-breeding with native wild Mallard races almost universally; sometimes they cross with other dabbling ducks, such as the African Yellow-bill *Anas undulata* or the New Zealand Grey Duck *A.superciliosa* (17,31), producing fertile hybrids that threaten to swamp the parent stock. Many more wildfowl have been released but have failed to take up permanent residence; the Hawaiian Goose in New Zealand, for instance, where Acclimatisation Societies introduced and bred it in the 1870s (14), and Black Swans, received in exchange for the Vintners' Mutes, which were released onto the river Thames 90 years ago (17).

Why was it done? Usually for sport so that the guns of gentlemen had something to kill, sometimes for a food supply, often for beauty and nostalgia, occasionally for biological control of a pest, and sometimes merely as part of an avicultural exercise – the semi-accidental release of young birds from a collection of exotic wildfowl in which the original breeders were pinioned. Captain Cook recorded having released geese (African Geese?) in Dusky Sound, New Zealand, in his Journal for 1773, thus: 'Having 5 geese out of those we brought from the Cape of Good Hope, I went with them next morning to Goose Cove (named so on this account), where I left them. I chose this place for two reasons; first, because, here are no inhabitants to disturb them; and secondly, here being the most food. I made no doubt that they will breed, and may in time spread over the whole country, and fully answer my intention in leaving them.' Fortunately, this early 'liberation' was among those that failed.

INTRODUCTION OF WILDFOWL INTO THE UNITED KINGDOM

There are three non-native ducks and two geese named in the Wildlife and Countryside Act of 1981, and illustrated here, which are not to be

The five species of exotic wildfowl that, since 1981, may not be released into the wild in the UK. Clockwise from the top: Canada Goose, Carolina, Mandarin, Egyptian Goose and Ruddy Duck. Drawn by Joe Blossom.

allowed to escape into the wild in Britain. They are listed because they, alone among the many that have become feral from time to time, have had some success in establishing themselves in an alien environment (30) – a clear case of the law locking the stable door after the horse has bolted. These five species will be examined in some detail in this Chapter and used as examples of the many wildfowl that have been introduced throughout the world. The same UK legislation has a general prohibition against the release into the wild of any animal 'not ordinarily resident in and not a regular visitor to Great Britain in a wild state'. So it *is* permitted to establish, from captive sources, feral populations of ducks and geese that normally only winter in Britain such as Long-tailed Ducks and Barnacle Geese, both of which are now breeding 'at large' although one might have thought that those releases should be equally discouraged.

The **Mandarin Duck** was imported from China into the United Kingdom before 1745 and bred at the London Zoo in 1834, but it was not until the 20th Century that feral populations became evident (5,27). The first was at Woburn and others soon followed; by far the most important was one centred on Alfred Ezra's collection at Foxwarren Park near Cobham in Surrey. This stock had a traumatic and significant start to its short life in captivity. Jean Delacour had, some time during 1929, found a large consignment of Mandarin in the Paris market still in their bamboo crates from China and containing many dying birds. He rescued nearly 50 survivors and took them, wing-clipped not pinioned, to England. Six pairs remained at Foxwarren (1) and bred freely; soon they and their offspring spread into the areas around Virginia Water and Windsor Great Park where, today, there are estimated to be nearly 5,000 birds (4). They nest in tree holes in parkland associated with water meadows, using mature oak, sweet chestnut (also introduced) and beech woods up to a mile from water where naturalized rhododendron produces favourite cover (27,30). The provision of elevated nest-boxes has increased substantially the number of breeding pairs during the last decade.

Most of the other scattered groups of feral Mandarin in Britain are fed artificially in winter (as well as needing nest-boxes) and without this supplementary food they would not survive. For instance, the large group of captive-bred birds established around Fallodon in Northumberland by Lord Grey (8) did not last long after 1933 when he died and the food supply was curtailed.

There is still occasional reluctance by naturalists and birdwatchers to accept the Mandarin as a British bird. It gained official admission to the British and Irish list only in 1971 when it had been breeding in the wild for 40 years (30). Paradoxically, there is probably more chance of seeing a Mandarin flying in the Berkshire and Surrey countryside than in its original home in the Far East (3). There, the wholesale cutting of the northern Chinese Imperial hunting forests after 1911 when the Manchu emperors were deposed, and the spread of agriculture, mining and other industry in Manchuria, have reduced its native woodland habitat (27). Japan is now believed to be its main eastern stronghold with around 5,000 pairs, Britain has about 7,000 individuals (4), South Korea about 300, while China is suggested to have rather less than 1,000 pairs – although information is hard to obtain and to evaluate. In *The Birds of Changbai Mountains* (7) published in Chinese in 1987, the Mandarin is described as a common summer visitor. The significance of the British population of this rare and beautiful duck in world terms seems unmistakable (3). Further

Lord Grey of Fallodon kept a large collection of full-winged wildfowl, including Mandarins, one of which is sitting on his hat. They never became established in the wild, numbers dwindling to nothing soon after his death. Photograph by Seton Gordon.

releases, under licence from the Department of the Environment, of birds hatched from eggs collected in the region of Virginia Water occurred in Somerton, Somerset, in 1985 and 1986 as part of a plan to extend the English range. A flourishing, but fed, population of some 550 introduced Mandarin is also resident in oak, alder and willow woodland in California at about 38°N (17), sharing this habitat with wild Carolinas.

The Mandarin's cousin, the **Carolina** or North American Wood Duck, was also released by British aviculturalists, especially near Exeter in Devon, and again at Foxwarren Park and Fallodon. This perching duck appears to have similar requirements to the Mandarin, but has not managed to establish a self-sustaining population and is not fully accepted on the British and Irish bird list (30). Why not? What are the essential differences between these two closely-related woodland ducks that allows one introduction to 'take' and the other to do so only tenuously? The principles apply to all introductions and are worth investigating at this point.

Both are hardy when adult and fairly omnivorous, feeding on large and medium-sized seeds that they obtain from land or from the shore line rather than on or under water (5,11). The Mandarin in England exploits, particularly, beech mast, chestnuts and acorns; the food preferences of the feral British Carolina are not so well known but appear to be similar. Both have adjusted to a sedentary life and lost any migratory habits; both nest in tree-cavities up to 10 m (33 ft) from the ground and, although it is true that there is a general lack of such holes in our tidy modern forests, this shortage might be thought to affect each duck to the same extent.

Christopher Savage in his book *The Mandarin Duck* (27) suggested that the Carolina's longer fledging period in England (8), of ten weeks as opposed to the Mandarin's eight, might extend the time of vulnerability to predators and thus lead to the Carolina's comparative lack of rearing success. Savage has highlighted one important discrepancy here, and there are others that can be linked to the basic fact that the two ducks originate from different temperate latitudes. The mid latitude of the Mandarin's Asian breeding range (5) is about 47°N (between 36° and 55°N), while that of the Carolina in the New World (5) is 41°N (about 31° to 51°N). Such a contrast in distribution, although small, is likely to affect many features such as laying-date, clutch size, egg and duckling weight, incubation and fledging periods, and dates of eclipse plumages and feather moult (20). We would guess that two related species, breeding in different parts of the temperate zone, would vary in all these characteristics for the reason that spring arrives earlier nearer the equator but comes when days are shorter, so that they nest under different daylength cycles.

If we examine records kept at Slimbridge and Peakirk, at latitudes of 52° and 53°N, of birds breeding in captivity, we find that the Carolina is 'programmed' to lay earlier than the Mandarin (20). The first Carolina egg ever, appeared on 1 March while, on average over 36 years, earliest eggs have been laid on 20 March. The first Mandarin egg was laid on 22 March on a daylength that is more than one hour longer and, on average over 33 years, clutches of eggs have been started on 15 April. Records kept of hatching dates at the London Zoo during the last Century (28) show the same difference, with the Carolina ducklings (or Summer Duck as it was then called) usually appearing three weeks earlier than Mandarins. This fits the climate of their native ranges but means that the Carolina in England is sitting on eggs and hatching ducklings when temperatures are still cold. As 'bad' as that or worse, its eggs are smaller on average (38.5 g from a Slimbridge sample of 100 instead of the Mandarin's 43.5 g) so that its ducklings hatch about 16% lighter in weight than young Mandarins; they thus lose heat faster and need more brooding by the female. All this adds up to a species whose genes adapt it excellently to the circumstances of Illinois and the Mississippi Valley (5), much closer to the equator than Britain, but one whose ducklings are poorly suited to the wet and cold of the English early spring. The Carolina in England has three points potentially in its favour: because it nests earlier it can win the competition for tree-hole nest sites; however, as Lord Grey noticed (10), the UK Mandarin may add eggs to Carolina clutches that the Carolina rears along with its own. Secondly, as both ducks stop laying at about the end of May, the Carolina has the longer breeding season: 95 days at Slimbridge compared to the Mandarin's 66. Finally, as it tends to lay a slightly larger clutch, it can hatch more eggs but, as the ducklings are not so heavy, this also seems insufficient reason for comprehensive success.

Even the British Mandarin is unlikely to increase its numbers at a vast rate; its duckling is small and not particularly well insulated, and the winter food of the adults is insecure during years when the beech mast and acorn crops fail. Mandarins might not have succeeded in Surrey (and, remember, most introductions do not) had the birds been many generations from the pressures of the wild, and had they not been selected for viability by the severe conditions of their importation from China into France; this experience must have weeded out all but the 'best' of the stock. A quirk of fate is responsible for the feral British Mandarins; they come from a vigorous founder stock (1) that filled a vacant niche among the parkland trees and rhododendrons, sharing it with the much more successful introduced grey squirrel. The Carolina releases into Britain, on the other hand, have been of small numbers of birds that had spent many generations in captivity (although this history of captive breeding did not seem to matter to the Belgium/Litchfield birds (see Chapter 6) which were reintroduced into their natural habitat rather than introduced into an alien one).

Somewhat similar difficulties are faced by the **Egyptian Goose** in England. This sheldgoose was first introduced in the 17th Century as an ornamental water bird, and was present in King Charles II's menagerie in St James's Park (32). Today it occurs as a feral species in East Anglia, where its population is centred on the large estate of Holkham in Norfolk, and numbers four or five hundred individuals. There is also a naturalised flock of about half that size in the Netherlands (17). A modest increase occurs after mild winters and springs but, like the Carolina, the goose lays early, as suits its African origin around 32°N, and a cold March affects its hatching and rearing success badly. It nests significantly earlier (in captivity at Slimbridge first eggs are on average laid on 1 March) than the similarly introduced but much more successful Canada Goose (whose first eggs appear on 28 March). This early reproduction probably limits population growth. If, as sometimes happens, it loses the first clutch or brood to harsh weather and then re-lays, it finds itself competing with the larger, more numerous Canada for nest sites, and seems unable to hold its ground. We do not know the origin of the Holkham Egyptian Geese, but it is perhaps not unreasonable to suppose that Thomas Coke himself brought them back from the Grand Tour that he undertook in the early 18th Century after which his estate was redesigned by Capability Brown and the long lake added (Chapter 6).

'An Episode of the Happier Days of Charles I' by Frederick Goodall (1822–1904). The young Charles II, in the right background, was to have one of the first wildfowl collections, and is said to have found feeding his ducks more congenial than affairs of state. He kept Egyptian and Canada Geese for the first time in England. Photograph courtesy of the Metropolitan Borough of Bury.

A large North American **Canada Goose**, probably of a semi-sedentary race, was also introduced into England around 1665 by agents of King Charles to his London collection of waterfowl (32), and by 1785 was breeding freely on the estates of wealthy landowners (17). The first national Canada Goose census organised in 1953 counted 2,600 to 3,600 birds, many again around Holkham Hall. At those numbers it had already become unpopular with local farmers, since it caused summer damage to growing crops. One of the control measures employed was to round up the moulting geese in July and move them to other parts of the country where new breeding sites, such as flooded sand or gravel pits and reservoirs, were continually being constructed, and where it was hoped they would be less troublesome – 'small manageable flocks' in areas where there were no other geese was the hopeful aim (22).

The result was, instead, huge increases in numbers, particularly in the

Thames valley, the West Midlands and Yorkshire, which wildfowlers were expected to control by shooting in the autumn and winter. This they would not do because the birds were found to be so tame that any 'sport' was negligible. By 1976, therefore, there was a British population of nearly 20,000 which was rising at the rate of 8% per annum. A continuation of the trend resulted in 39,000 birds by 1985 and will mean more than 50,000 by 1990. To maintain the Canada Goose at the 1980 level, an extra 2,000 birds must be killed every season, and there is no indication that this is being done; so further complaints from farmers and landowners near the thousand sites they occupy can be expected (22). The fact that the goose is hand-tame in many town parks and the grounds of stately homes is thought to limit the possibilities for control. Geese could be rounded up during the wing-moult and destroyed, which would reduce the populations drastically within a few years, but the public outcry if this were done would probably be loud and long (22). Curiously, as if anticipating trouble, part of the large Yorkshire population has developed migratory behaviour, and many geese spend the late summer moulting in safety near Inverness on the Beauly Firth about 500 km (300 miles) north of the area where the rest of the population breeds. ADAS, the government's Agricultural Development Advisory Service, is considering methods of control with landowners and farmers.

To a limited extent, the Canada fills a niche that was left vacant by the English Greylag Goose which, through over-exploitation and drainage schemes, became extinct as a breeder 300 years ago until reintroduced from Scotland. However, the Canada was more at home as a parkland goose, and the recent creation of permanent inland fresh-water areas (which were a rare phenomenon in England after the drainage of the fens

A Canada Goose, probably recently introduced, and drawn for Francis Willughby's *Ornithologia* published in London in 1676–8.

and meres) has provided additional habitat. In the 1930s, Greylags were reintroduced to southwest Scotland and East Anglia for shooting purposes, and wildfowlers released a further 1,300 birds in the 1960s. For this goose also, the new gravel pits and reservoirs have provided a haven, and the population had risen to an estimated 13,000–14,000 by 1985, when competition with the Canada Goose for island nesting sites seemed a real possibility, and summer agricultural damage was again evident. In a few places, Greylags have increased despite the presence of the Canada, and one consequence has been the regular occurrence of hybrids – presumably infertile, as *Anser* and *Branta* geese are thought to be genetically far enough apart that second generation crosses are impossible.

The Canada Goose has also been naturalised in continental Europe, especially in Sweden since 1929, where numbers are increasing even faster than in Britain and had reached 50,000 by the early 1980s, with 5,000 breeding pairs (17). In Finland, there are up to 3,000 birds which migrate south in winter. In New Zealand, considerable numbers of Canada Geese were imported from eastern USA as potential game birds (34); they did particularly well in South Island and a shooting season was declared in 1925 in Otago and Canterbury. They soon started to cause damage to pastoralists and 3,000 were shot during 1950 by the Wildlife Service; nevertheless, there are about 20,000 in total today. The environment that they have adopted is not significantly different from their native one in another hemisphere (latitudes are similar) and is full of the same grasses – introduced from northern lands where the pasture plants, unlike the vegetation of New Zealand, have evolved to withstand much pressure from grazing birds and mammals.

Another success story is that of the little North American stifftail, the **Ruddy Duck**. The Wildfowl and Wetlands Trust at Slimbridge is responsible for this newcomer to the British scene but, unlike the other four introductions, its arrival in the wild was accidental (12). Three hand-reared pairs and one drake were successfully imported in 1948 from Salt Lake City and Pennsylvania (where they had started to breed in captivity a decade earlier) and began nesting the following season. The highly aquatic ducklings had to be left with their mothers and, since they dive extremely well, every year a number managed to evade the Curator's attempts to catch and pinion them. About 70 juveniles flew away between 1956 and 1963 (most in the 1962/3 hard winter) and it is from those that the present British feral population descends. So again, this introduction comes from a tiny founder stock that was not more than a couple of generations from the wild. One pair bred in Somerset in 1960, by 1972 at least 25 pairs were nesting in the West Midlands and the increase continued to around 1,800 ducks by 1984 and to a count of 2,700 by January 1989. These were mainly in Cheshire, Shropshire, Staffordshire and the County of Avon where one record flock of 1,064 appeared on Chew Valley Reservoir in March 1987 (22). In 1973 a female nested on Lough Neagh in Northern Ireland, producing four young; in 1979 the

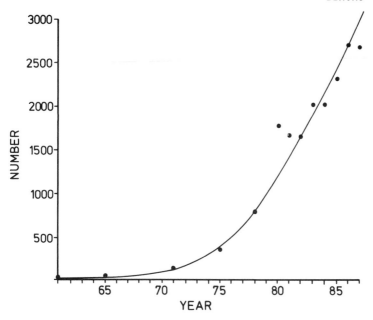

NUMBER

YEAR

The number of Ruddy Ducks estimated to be in Britain between 1960 and 1987; the graph is based on the assumption that 90% of the population was counted accurately. Drawn by John Turner.

Ruddy Duck was in Scotland and it is now frequently seen on the Continent, breeding first in France in 1988.

The Ruddy seems destined to become a most successful western palearctic colonist, with a population increasing at 30–50% a year (22). Competition with the Tufted Duck for chironomid larvae, which they both eat, and with grebes for nesting sites, are possibilities; and fears have been expressed that if it does as well on the Continent as it does in Britain, it may oust or hybridise with its relative, the White-headed Duck of the Mediterranean which, as we have seen in Chapter 6, is the subject of reintroduction programmes being coordinated by The Wildfowl and Wetlands Trust in Hungary and Italy. This bird is rare in Europe and its situation is critical even without the British Ruddy Duck's unplanned invasion of its range. We do not know whether the two will compete for food or nest sites, but the White-headed Duck is so uncommon that its biology has been little studied, and the reasons why it has failed to adapt to man-made changes to its environment are unclear (see Chapter 10). There may be further dangers ahead.

The Ruddy Duck's success in Britain seems to be due to a number of features that suited its native North American life-style and stood it in good stead when it was transposed to Britain. The latitude of its true range (5) is such that it might have been expected to show the same need for

The 'Ruddy Duck' is an inn in Peakirk. It was once called the 'Black Bull', but Peter Scott persuaded the brewery to rename it after The Wildfowl Trust Centre opened in the village.

warm weather as the Carolina. Instead, like all near-tropical stifftails, the duckling dives at a day old and must be well insulated from the cold water and independent of its mother. She therefore lays a large egg from which emerges a fat, vigorous duckling and, unlike all British wildfowl (including the other naturalized ones), she is able to lay for an extended period beyond midsummer (20) – another attribute of a near-tropical origin, shared, for instance, with the wild Muscovy (Chapter 2) – so that her ducklings hatch when there is plenty of underwater insect food available and little competition. (The occasional park Mallard that breeds in the English autumn probably has domestic blood and her young would not survive if they were not fed by man – see again Chapter 2). Ruddy Ducks have found a winter home in the new static waters with, except for the Tufted Duck, no obvious competitors for a diet of bottom-living invertebrates. And they disperse readily during hard weather to any open water that is available; starting in the winter of 1988–89, researchers from The Wildfowl and Wetlands Trust have been putting white plastic wing-tags on birds in order to study these movements. Peter Scott initially felt rather shamefaced about the Ruddy's escape from Slimbridge but, since the West Midland Bird Club adopted it as their emblem, and because he seriously doubted that it would become a pest or a competitor with native species, he became rather less concerned (17).

INTRODUCED PREDATORS OF WILDFOWL

Wildfowl themselves have suffered greatly from the introduction of other alien animals into their native lands (16,33). The one that has had the greatest effect, of course, is man himself. The natural environment of many originally uninhabited islands, particularly those of the southern hemisphere, has been catastrophically altered by fire and by grazing, and man has frequently eliminated entire animal populations, like that of the Dodo *Raphus cucullatus*, merely by hunting the tame individuals that had no reason to be suspicious of his approach. The Hawaiian Goose is delightfully confiding and proved exceedingly easy to shoot; the winter shooting season was not even closed until 1907 after someone had at last noticed that it bred in winter (14). The drake Blue Duck *Hymenolaimus malacorhynchos* of New Zealand is similarly inclined to stand his ground and merely whistle at a dangerous human intruder on his territory (13). During the 1869–71 war against the Maori chief Te Kooti, soldiers sometimes killed 30 or 40 Blue Ducks a day in Urewera country. The last Auckland Islands Mergansers *Mergus australis* were shot in 1902 by a member of the Governor of New Zealand's party who found that they did not even dive to escape (15). It all makes rather frightful reading today.

Interestingly enough, a New Zealand Shelduck with unfledged young, after thousands of years of evolution in a land without mammals except for seals and bats, gives a 'broken-wing' display to man (see Chapter 1) and the performance matches that of any European parent duck. I have induced this behaviour more than once when I have surprised a family on a New Zealand shore, and puzzled about its origin. What two-legged predator do I resemble, other than the man that has, in evolutionary time, only just arrived? Did they try to lure away the browsing moas, and if so, why?

Examples of man's introductions that have been devastating include the arctic foxes (for their pelt) to the Aleutian Islands where they nearly eliminated the Aleutian Canada Goose (see Chapter 6); cats, pigs, dogs, rats and mongooses to the Hawaiian Islands where there has been a drastic decline in the numbers of the native ducks and geese; dogs, cats, and pigs to the Auckland Islands, thus bringing the Flightless Teal *Anas aucklandica* close to extinction and reducing the Merganser to the point where a shot could wipe it out; and mongooses to the Caribbean Islands, where they were supposed to eat rats and snakes but found the eggs of the ground-nesting Cuban Whistling Duck an easy supplement (16). Pigs and goats were routinely released onto remote southern ocean islands to provision any shipwrecked sailors of the whaling fleets that might turn up later, and they did undreamt-of damage to fragile ecosystems.

The black rat, with its egg-eating tendencies, spread into Western Europe in the 12th Century but, in Britain, has been largely replaced by the brown rat which arrived some 600 years later and is more robust. Both they and their parasites carry bird diseases.

Avian pathogens have been spread accidentally to many parts of the world, especially distant islands, where the birds had no resistance to them. The New Zealand Brown Teal may have been affected this way – it is, as we have seen, very uncommon – and the Hawaiian Goose or Nene, like many native Hawaiian birds, seems to be susceptible to avian pox spread from the blood of introduced song-birds via the mouthparts of mosquitoes, which arrived in 1826 via a ship that cleaned out its fresh water tanks in the harbour of Maui (14).

INTRODUCED FOOD COMPETITORS

Ducks that live in torrents are not only highly specialised for swimming in white water but exploit an insect food supply that in calmer waters elsewhere is taken by fish. Mostly the ducks consume bottom-living caddis and stone fly larvae that also enjoy the highly oxygenated mountain streams. The New Zealand Blue Duck, Salvadori's Duck *Anas waigiuensis* of New Guinea and the Torrent Ducks of South America do well until the sport fishermen and sociologists, planning a 'better life' for the native humans, introduce trout and other insectivorous fish into the rivers. Waterfalls are a natural barrier to many fish, so in New Zealand at least the trout are often helped higher and higher upstream, and more and more Blue Duck, finding it hard to compete successfully for a limited food supply, fail to breed (13,16).

The activities of a fish *Tilapia*, introduced into the island's single lake, exterminated the Rennell Island Grey Teal *Anas gibberifrons remissa* within living memory. It was described as recently as 1942 by Dillon Ripley, and was not seen again after 1959 (16). Rabbits, put onto Laysan Island by fur-traders in the early part of this century, ate down the vegetation

on which the insect food of the endemic Laysan Teal depended. It was reported that in 1930 the bird had declined to the ultimate population low of a single female with sufficient semen in her oviduct to replace a destroyed clutch. What is more certain is that on several occasions during the 1910s, single figure counts were obtained. The last rabbit was removed in the 1930s, since when the population of the Laysan Teal has fluctuated but risen at times as high as 700 birds (16).

EXOTICS THAT BENEFIT WILDFOWL

Not all of man's introductions have been to the detriment of ducks, geese and swans. We need look no further than the import of the rabbit from its native Iberia and North Africa to Norman England as a source of meat and fur. Its burrows, once it had escaped the warrens to which it was confined originally, provided nesting sites for the Common Shelduck *Tadorna tadorna* and undoubtedly proved safer than a home shared with the native red fox. Much of the Shelduck population expansion during this century can be related to protection from shooting, but an explosive increase in rabbits helped to accommodate the extra numbers. The ducks are fairly catholic in their choice of nesting sites: of 100 nests on Sheppey in Kent, 29 were in hollow trees, 28 in haystacks, 27 in rabbit burrows, 23 under buildings, and the rest in the open. In Aberdeenshire on the Ythan estuary, on the other hand, all were in rabbit holes, as were most of those found at Aberlady Bay in the Firth of Forth; the same is probably true of most dune and shoreland situations around the British Isles (23).

A few other plant and animal introductions to Britain have provided wildfowl with an original food supply. Two small freshwater shellfish have been especially important in helping the spread of the Tufted Duck (9,21). Neither is native to the British Isles and they are both peculiar in other ways. The zebra-mussel is the only fresh-water bivalve that has a free-living larval stage as do the marine mussels; indeed, the animal seems to have invaded from the sea relatively recently. It was first noticed in England in 1824 in London's Commercial Docks and is thought to have been introduced via timber ships from the river Volga or the Baltic (19). An increase in man-made static waters – docks, canals, reservoirs and flooded gravel pits (2) – which has been referred to more than once in this Chapter, provided it with a habitat in which its fragile larva was not swept away by the current. The adult had solved the problem of life in moving water by developing an anchorage; it is the only fresh-water bivalve that can attach itself to the bottom by sticky threads – another sign of its salt-water origin. It lives at 6–12 m (20–40 ft) deep – further down in winter than in summer – and grows up to 50 mm (2 in) long, although most specimens are smaller than this. It is now widely distributed in England and southern Scotland. It has been pointed out that new arrivals, if they succeed at all, sometimes flourish exceedingly well at first but then sink back to a less outstanding position in the biological scheme; maybe this will happen to the zebra-mussel. Meanwhile its high reproductive rate and unique ability to tie itself down make it a great nuisance to water engineers. In 1912, 90 tonnes of zebra-mussel were removed from a 400 m ($\frac{1}{4}$ mile) stretch of water-main at Hampton, Middlesex, where they had reduced the diameter of the pipe from 90 cm (3 ft) to 22 cm (9 in) (6).

The Tufted Duck first bred in the wild in Britain in the late 1840s and has multiplied particularly in the last three decades. The numerous town-reservoirs gave both duck and mollusc a home, and mussels up to 25 mm (1 in) long are easily pulled off and swallowed whole by the birds

ZEBRA MUSSEL
Dreissena polymorpha

The zebra-mussel is another introduction that has provided food for the Tufted Duck and perhaps been dispersed by it. Since 1824, when it was found living in Surrey Commercial Docks, it has spread widely through gravel pits and reservoirs. Its shell is handsomely marked with zigzag brown bands. Drawing by Sue Hazeldine.

The tiny Jenkins' spire-shell has become naturalized in Britain since being introduced to the Thames estuary, presumably by ship, sometime prior to 1883. Tufted Ducks and, to a lesser extent Teal, are fond of it. Drawing by Sue Hazeldine.

JENKINS' SPIRE SHELL
Hydrobia jenkinsi
actual size

(21). The same association and spread has been noted in other European countries such as Switzerland, where an invasion of Lake Neuchatel by zebra-mussels in 1967 led to a great increase in the winter population of Tufted Ducks (24).

Jenkin's spire-shell is the other important invader from the sea and another alien – perhaps originally from Australasia although no-one seems certain – that the Tufted Duck favours and whose spread probably contributed to the birds' successful colonisation of Britain's running-water areas. Until about the end of the 19th Century, this 5 mm long winkle was found only in brackish conditions, having been first recorded in 1883 in the Thames estuary. Ten years later it was in fresh water and has since spread abundantly all over the British Isles. How do molluscs of this sort cross land barriers? Perhaps on the boots of the fisherman or on the plants that he brings in to benefit his fish, or on the naturalists' unwashed sampling net, or the feet and plumage of birds (19). Spread they have, since their initial arrival in Britain by boat, and in their wake have come the ducks. Maybe the ducks are manipulating their own environment by assisting the dispersal of their preferred items of diet. That birds are capable of bringing about their own introductions is not in doubt: the rare yellow-cress grows in Britain only on the winter feeding grounds of geese, and its seeds were probably brought from its native Iceland by them (25).

Many introduced plants have become the food of herbivorous birds, and geese and swans, in particular, have profited. Even the Hawaiian Goose, in its precarious wild state, takes the seed-heads of the alien grass Yorkshire fog and the seeds, leaves, stems and flowers of the dandelion-like gosmore in preference to some of its native fodder (14). Canadian pondweed and its relative Esthwaite waterweed are submerged perennials that were brought to Britain from America as aquarium plants; they soon escaped to still or slow-moving fresh-water and are now eaten and spread by wildfowl including Whooper Swans and Wigeon (19). The introduced Black Swan in parts of the North Island of New Zealand feeds on the same naturalised Canadian pondweed and also eats the leaves of equally foreign willow trees among the roots of which it nests (28).

The key to the success of many of these British introductions has been man's development of numerous inland water areas during this century (2). Our needs for fresh-water for domestic and industrial consumption on the one hand, and of sand and gravel for concrete and roads on the other, have meant changes to the landscape that have benefited certain adaptable waterfowl greatly. The same novel wetlands are a feature of modern man's developments throughout the world and they sometimes result in a duck, goose or swan thriving in the 'wrong' place. Also, as a principle, those introductions that have been successful have been founded by individuals that have never been in captivity (like the zebra-mussel) or whose great-grandparents were wild (like the Ruddy Duck); the rabbit may be an exception.

Introduced agricultural crops, such as beans, potatoes, maize, swede turnips and carrots, have all been adopted as new foods by the grazing geese of the northern hemisphere. The history of these encounters is dealt with in the next Chapter because, in consuming such foods, the birds often come into conflict with man.

REFERENCES

1. Anon. 1930. (Comments concerning the import and distribution of Mandarin Ducks). *Avic. Mag.* 4th Series 8: 55;79.
2. Atkinson-Willes, G. L. 1961. The importance to wildfowl of reservoirs in England and Wales. *Wildfowl* 12: 29–33.
3. Davies, A. 1985. A place for Mandarins. *Birds* 10: 12–14.
4. Davies, A. 1988. The distribution and status of the Mandarin Duck *Aix galericulata* in Britain. *Bird Study* 35: 203–208.
5. Delacour, J. 1954–9. *The Waterfowl of the World*. Vols 1–3. London: Country Life.
6. Fitter, R. S. R. 1945. *London's Natural History*. London: Collins.
7. Fu, T. Gao, W. & Song, Y. 1984. *Birds of Changbai Mountains*. Northeast Normal University Press.
8. Fallodon, Lord Grey of. 1927. *The Charm of Birds*. London: Hodder.
9. Gillham, E. 1987. *Tufted Ducks in a Royal Park*. Romney Marsh: E.Gillham.
10. Gordon, S. 1937. *Edward Grey and his Birds*. London: Country Life.
11. Grice, D. & Rogers, J. P. 1965. *The Wood Duck in Massachusetts*. Mass. Div. of Fish & Game.
12. Hudson, R. 1976. Ruddy Ducks in Britain. *Brit.Birds* 69: 132–143.
13. Kear, J. 1972. The Blue Duck of New Zealand. *Living Bird* 11: 175–192.
14. Kear, J. & Berger, A. 1980. *The Hawaiian Goose*. Calton: Poyser.
15. Kear, J. & Scarlett, R. J. 1970. The Auckland Islands Merganser. *Wildfowl* 21: 78–86.
16. Kear, J. & Williams, G. 1978. Waterfowl at risk. *Wildfowl* 29: 5–21.
17. Lever, C. 1987. *Naturalized Birds of the World*. Harlow: Longman.
18. Long, J. L. 1981. *Introduced Birds of the World*. Sydney: Reed.

19. Macan, T. T. 1974. *Freshwater Ecology*. 2nd Ed. London: Longman.

20. Murton, R. K. & Kear, J. 1978. Photoperiodism in waterfowl: phasing of breeding cycles and zoogeography. *J.Zool.,Lond*. 186: 243–283.

21. Olney, P. J. S. 1963. The food and feeding habits of the Tufted Duck. *Ibis* 105: 55–62.

22. Owen, M.& Salmon, D. G. 1990. Introductions of wildfowl in Europe – problems and prospects. *Proc.IUCN Sym.Introductions in Europe*. September 1988.

23. Patterson, I. J. 1982. *The Shelduck*. CUP.

24. Pedroli, J. 1982. Activity and time budget of Tufted Ducks of Swiss lakes during winter. *Wildfowl* 33: 105–112.

25. Perring, F. 1974. *The Flora of a Changing Britain*. BSBI Publications.

26. Roots, C. 1976. *Animal Invaders*. London: David & Charles.

27. Savage, C. 1952. *The Mandarin Duck*. London: Black.

28. Sclater, P. L. 1880. List of the certainly known species of Anatidae, with notes on such as have been introduced into the zoological gardens of Europe. *Proc.zool.Soc.Lond*. 1880: 496–536.

29. Scott, P. & The Wildfowl Trust. 1971. *The Swans*. London: Michael Joseph.

30. Sharrock, J. T. R.(ed) 1976. *The Atlas of Breeding Birds in Britain and Ireland*. Berkhamsted: Poyser.

31. Williams, M & Roderick, C. 1973. The breeding performance of Grey Duck, Mallard and their hybrids in captivity. *Int.Zoo Yb* 13: 62–69.

32. Willughby, F. 1676–8. *Ornithologia*. London: John Ray.

33. Weller, M. W. 1969. Potential dangers in exotic waterfowl introductions. *Wildfowl* 20: 55–58.

34. Wodzicki, K. & Wright, S. 1984. Introduced birds and mammals in New Zealand and their effect on the environment. *Tuatara* 27: 121–126.

8: Conflict

A few examples of the problems that can occur when the interests of man and wildfowl conflict will be examined in this Chapter. Because of the birds' dependence on water, drainage effects can be catastrophic, but pollution is also serious. Trouble with the farmer mainly involves the grazing geese, but complaints against swans and ducks are made as well. The history of agricultural damage to pasture, and later to arable crops such as wheat, beans, potatoes, swede turnips and carrots, is a long one. I investigated early instances of swede damage in Scotland (13), and have seen farmland-feeding Greylag and Pinkfeet change their habits over recent decades. There are a few benefits in having the birds on cultivated ground – they can keep the soil relatively pest- and weed-free and, very rarely, their droppings are useful (16). Often the worst damage can be prevented by the establishment of refuges nearby where food is grown or can be provided (23,25), and this has been done both in Europe and North America. In interactions with fisheries, wildfowl droppings are usually beneficial (16). Most difficulties here involve swans or goosanders ('land cormorants' to give them their Dublin name), although Eiders have taken to helping themselves to shellfish from farmed mussel-beds (and sometimes one feels, of course, why not? They were there first).

Disturbance to wildfowl by man's water-based pursuits is increasing, as is mortality that is indirectly due to man's activities – Long-tailed Ducks *Clangula hyemalis* still get caught in deep-fishing nets, our throw-away society still leaves anglers' hooks where birds can swallow them, and the invention of nylon fishing line has been especially harmful because it is so indestructible. Ready access to electricity has meant that power cables are placed in the way of flying birds. Pollution can be immensely harmful, and oil and seed-dressings consistently take an annual toll, although the cleaning up of sewage outflows has not always been to the benefit of the birds.

The story behind the loss of English swans from some of our best known rivers over the last 20 years became a 'who-dun-it' that made the letter pages of *The Times*. Lead shot from cartridges is a continuing hazard that lasts years beyond the moment that the gun is fired. Not a few ducks and geese have reached a state of extinction, or come perilously close to it, through man's direct and indirect activities such as the introduction of the food competitors and predators dealt with in Chapter 7. Strife is common, and most often the birds come off worst (19).

CONFLICTS WITH AGRICULTURE

The conflict between the farmer and grazing geese is of long standing, probably as old as agriculture itself. There is an Egyptian text (12), directed at an idle student, that produces a smile 3,000 years after it was written: 'You are worse than the Egyptian Goose of the river bank, that abounds in mischief. It spends the summer in destroying the dates, and the winter in destroying the emmer [primitive wheat]. It spends its free time of the year pursuing the cultivators, and allows not the seed to be thrown to the ground before it has got wind of it. It cannot be caught by snaring, nor is it offered up in the temple, that evil bird of piercing sight that does no work'. The same goose exasperates the farmers of the southern Nile today.

It is likely that the magic birds that were described in the Celtic story *Compert Con Cuilaind* as grazing, down to the very roots, the grasses and herbs of Emain Macha (Navan Fort, County Armagh, traditionally the seat of the Kings of Ulster) were geese (27). The first English complaints of damage come from the 7th Century, and relate to a princess of Mercia called Werburgh who trained as a nun at Ely and later became an abbess and a saint (1,5,6). She was a contemporary of St Cuthbert and is chiefly remembered for having reproved a flock of wild geese for eating field crops at Weedon in Northamptonshire. The winged thieves were subdued by her scolding, and stretched their necks asking for forgiveness before leaving, never to return. These geese may have been Greylags that bred in the fens to the east of Weedon or, more likely, were a large flock of wintering Bean Geese from the Continent. The story, or at least the 11th Century version that we have of it (5), suggests confusion between 'wylde gees comunely called Gauntes' and tame birds. The descent upon the 'landes, pastures, waters and feldes' of Weedon was by truly wild geese not usually seen there, but the creatures that were rounded up, penned and brought with wings trailing and necks outstretched before the saint's judgement must surely have been domesticated ones. Another Anglo-Saxon saint, Milburgh, who lived on the Welsh borders a quarter of a century after her cousin Werburgh (1), also protected local corn from the ravages of wild geese, perhaps Whitefronts this time. A poem commemorates her talents as a scarecrow:

> *If old dame Mil will our fields look over*
> *Safe will be corn and grass and clover;*
> *But if the old dame is gone fast to sleep*
> *Woe to our corn, grass, clover and sheep.*

St Werburgh with her geese depicted in a stained-glass window of the Parish Church at Weedon, Northamptonshire. Photograph by Anne Cook.

The Bean Goose acquired both its English name and its scientific one, *Anser fabalis*, in the 18th Century by association with the field bean *Vicia faba* which was more extensively grown then than now (24). The French name is *Oie de moissons* or Harvest Goose; in Germany and Scandinavia it is *Saatgans* and *Sädgås* which mean Seed Goose; while in parts of Russia it is *Gumennik*, the thresher bird. It was the first British species to capitalise on farm crops in a big way, mainly in the north of the British islands and, during the 18th and 19th Centuries, was much commoner than the Greylag or Pinkfoot.

The Greylag once bred in the fens, but drainage and an increasing human population banished it. Its name is a puzzle; the bird does not have grey legs, so is the grey 'leading edge' of the wing the feature being described? Some authorities have suggested that 'lag' means slow, as in laggard, because the goose remains when the rest have migrated. Others suppose that 'lag' has an acoustic origin – in Lincolnshire tame geese were driven on with cries of 'Lag 'em, Lag 'em' (Chapter 2). A further theory suggests that, like the Bean Goose, it was originally named for its food and was the 'lea-goose' that fed on fields or 'leas'. At any rate, the correct name is probably Grey Lag-goose.

The Pink-footed Goose which, like the Greylag, is today numbered in many thousands and which feeds only on agricultural land in winter, was not known to be different from the larger Bean Goose until 1839, and seems to have been a newcomer and scarce at that time. The Bean Goose was said to resort to the upland fields and open land in winter, feeding on the tender shoots of wheat, clover and other herbage; in the early spring

'Pinkfeet Stubbling', an oil painting from *Morning Flight* by Peter Scott.

it visited fields newly-sown with beans and peas, devouring what it found scattered or could dislodge – this was in the days before drilling placed the seed out of immediate reach, and when the growing of legumes, such as beans, was the easiest way of increasing the nitrogen content of the soil. Undoubtedly, the geese also gleaned the bean and grain stubbles in the autumn upon their return from breeding.

Before man cleared the woods from Britain's lowland areas and drained the marshes, wintering goose species would not have overlapped in range (23). Even now, their preference for traditional habitats, and for foods to which their bills are adapted, separates the major wintering grounds. The Greylag used to keep to the southern inland marshes and feed on wild roots and tubers; the scarcer and more mobile Pinkfoot was an estuarine bird, grazing western salt-marshes; the Greenland Whitefront was restricted to the raised bogs of Wales, western Scotland and of Ireland, where it grubbed out cotton-grass roots; Barnacle Geese occurred around west coast islands where salt spray and high tides kept the grass short, whereas Brents fed below high water on intertidal plants such as eelgrass (23).

Geese, migratory and resident, turned to man's fields in increasing numbers as vegetation more nutritious than 'wild' grasses was developed and grown intensively. Spilled grain and then beans from the harvested fields provided an attractive autumn diet in comparison with the smaller seeds of indigenous plants. The young green shoots of winter wheat, and of clover and rye-grass which were introduced as sown crops during the 1700s, provided excellent alternatives to rough pasture. The details of this early association between wildfowl and agriculture were not written down; however, the more recent additions of potatoes, turnips and carrots to the diet of these birds is reasonably well documented.

Potatoes were introduced into Britain about 1590 but, to begin with, were little grown except in Ireland where food and land were notoriously in short supply. They were taken to Scotland towards the end of the 17th Century but, like turnips, became widely grown only after 1750 when many of the old open fields were enclosed. Before that, it was the practice to allow common grazing (by geese as well as cattle and sheep) of all arable fields after the grain was harvested. Throughout the 19th Century, potato-growing increased and the production of new varieties with good yields expanded the seed and maincrop industries in the Scottish lowlands in the 1890s (14). There was a substantial spread of potato-growing into Lincolnshire, the Isle of Ely and adjacent counties during the first world war – changes in distribution that were important for wildfowl. Modifications in the way roots were harvested affected their availability. So long as potato-growing was only for consumption at home, farmers were content to lift the tubers by hand and then turn the pigs on to grub out anything that remained. With the development of a demand from the towns and the requirement for marketing, small fields were joined to make larger ones that needed mechanical harvesting. Larger fields were much more likely to attract wary birds, and geese were now to be found

'"Old Pink," the albino Pinkfoot, feeding with a thousand others on potatoes and young wheat', an oil painting from *Morning Flight* by Peter Scott.

where there were only ducks before. Mechanical lifters (the 'spinner' was introduced in 1870 and the 'elevator' in 1920) produce more wastage because some tubers are damaged and the smaller ones not always extracted. Pigs were increasingly fattened under cover and the build-up of waste on the fields after harvest encouraged many forms of wildlife, often to the farmer's benefit since potatoes left in the ground harbour disease (14).

Climatic extremes may force birds to change their feeding regimes in order to survive; deep floods or snow, a prolonged frost or fog mean that they are hungry and will explore. The more adventurous young ones, in particular, come upon new sources of food that will be returned to, even after the weather improves, if they are nutritious and easily obtained. Very cold or snow winters have occurred in Britain recently in 1940, 1947, 1956, 1963, 1973–4, 1978–9 and 1981–2 and, occasionally, it has been possible to pinpoint the connection between a particular bad winter and the appearance of some new feeding habit.

The first wildfowl to take potato as a staple item of diet in Britain was the Mallard (14). The habit started and spread during the last century and two factors may have led to its development. The first was a succession of winters with a number of severe months between 1837 and 1855, and again between 1878 and 1897, and the second was potato-blight ('The Famine' in potato-dependent Ireland), a disease unknown in Europe until 1845, but which continued to cause irregular failures of the crop for decades. Many early reports indicate that rotting potatoes were taken by ducks, and that there were considerable acreages available. The blighted tubers were seldom harvested but left exposed on the fields, often in greatest quantity in wet, low-lying areas with a wildfowl population already to hand. The first published record comes from Moray in Scotland

'Pinkfeet flighting to a field of young wheat in the brown land', an oil painting from *Morning Flight* by Peter Scott.

where, by 1863, Mallard were said to be preferring the diseased tubers to corn. English authors wrote of ducks consuming decaying potatoes with relish, thus rendering their flesh unpalatable! And another writer suggests that this 'luxury for ducks' could be taken advantage of, presumably by using blighted potatoes as bait (14).

Regular flights to harvested fields to eat the remaining sound potatoes followed in Scotland, Ireland and eventually England. An increase in the popularity of wildfowling after the last war led to a realization that ducks could be shot on old potato 'plough' or encouraged into flight ponds by scattering tubers. The severe winter of 1947 provided at least one instance of another duck species taking frosted potatoes: Pintail were found to be feeding on a field in Kent with Mallard (14). Wigeon will nowadays sometimes join them.

The inclusion of potato in the diet of the Pinkfoot probably occurred as a result of their long-standing habit of grazing young winter wheat because, from the middle of the 19th Century, wheat followed potatoes in rotation. The potatoes taken by the birds would have been frosted and therefore soft, having been on the surface of the field from harvest until the wheat sprouted. Presumably the geese flew to the fields earlier and earlier in the winter until they arrived before the wheat was up, to eat nothing but tubers. The first reports of geese eating waste potatoes in the autumn appear about 1890 and relate to Pinkfeet in Lancashire (14). When potatoes were cultivated extensively on the Lincolnshire wolds at the end of the first world war, Pinkfeet turned to them at once. Elsewhere, the intensive growing of the crop was quickly followed by geese on the harvested fields. In Scotland, the Pink-footed Goose was eating potatoes due to a change in roosting habits that brought the night-time flocks inland. Reservoirs and curling ponds had made this influx possible, because the geese settled on these new waters rather than flying to the coast every evening. Today, potatoes are an important food of Pinkfeet throughout their winter range in Britain. At Martin Mere, large quantities of rejected tubers are donated by local farmers as they prepare stored potatoes for the market; these are placed near the winter roost, where Pinkfeet, Bewick's and Whooper Swans, Mallard, Pintail, Coot and the occasional Teal enjoy them greatly. Most importantly, the birds stay longer on the reserve rather than venturing out onto the surrounding agricultural land, where they might damage a valuable crop.

The Greylag Goose turned to potato-eating more recently than the Pinkfoot – not really until the second world war – and, even today, fewer Greylags in proportion to the total population take potatoes than do Pinkfeet (14). However, this is due more to the Greylag being less numerous in good potato-growing areas than to any dislike of the root if it is available. There are now records of potato-eating during the summer by Greylags in Iceland, and there the effects are much worse as it is the growing crop that is being taken.

Potato-eating by swans has become regular only recently. The Mute Swan is nowhere habituated to them. On the other hand, in Scotland the Whooper is found regularly on sprouting wheat in winter and on potato fields in the autumn, while the Bewick's Swan in England and Ireland has taken to the tubers in the last two decades with enthusiasm – again

John Busby's Whooper Swans from C. D. Hutchinson's *Birds in Ireland.*

probably as a result of an earlier partiality for the shoots of winter wheat (17).

Swede turnip-eating is a fairly modern goose initiative and is almost always harmful to agricultural interests. Damage is still rare and only occurs where the roots are left uncovered on the fields all winter. On the whole, turnips are not a preferred food, being rather full of water and low in carbohydrate and protein. However, the hard winter of 1947 produced a number of complaints from farmers, mostly concerning the activities of Greylags, which are less mobile than Pinkfeet, choosing to remain in bad weather and to resort temporarily to untypical foods. In 1947, green tops, frosted roots and sound turnips were eaten in the island of Bute, and in Aberdeenshire and Wigtonshire; and in a few other places Greylags were seen feeding on roots put out for cattle (13). Most of the birds did not continue to take swedes once their normal feeding grounds were free of snow; however, the Bute geese went on eating roots in increasing numbers. In 1963, the habit was reinforced by another hard winter, and measures had to be taken to disperse the roosts.

One of the most serious allegations of crop damage was made in southwest Lancashire around Martin Mere during the winter of 1973–74, when large numbers of Pinkfeet visited unharvested carrot fields and nibbled the root-tops to a depth of a few centimetres making the whole of the crop susceptible to frost and therefore unmarketable. Carrots had only recently been planted in this area on a large scale and had become a high value crop on the fertile peaty ground. In addition, varieties had been developed that could be left in the ground until needed for sale, instead of being lifted and stored in autumn. They were therefore available to the birds all winter. Generally geese do not turn to these roots unless the weather is foggy, and they cannot see to travel far, or snow blankets their normal pastures. Some damage has been prevented by siting the carrot fields close to disturbance from humans, such as roads, or by covering the crop with a thick layer of straw and by regular scaring; but, in fog, trouble can be caused before the farmer realises it.

Goose scaring is quite effective if the farmer is determined enough to vary the devices and their position (15). The gas banger, scarecrow and the suspended body of a dead bird are the most effective, especially if supplemented by the occasional shot from a gun. The birds do become tolerant of objects that do them no harm – even explosive ones – and protected species are particularly hard to remove from a favoured field for any length of time; presumably they can remember from year to year that a plastic bag, balloon or scarecrow does nothing dangerous. As goose populations increase, demands for official control or compensation for the farmers on whose land they feed are bound to grow (25). The introduced Canada Goose in Britain can cause damage throughout the year, and wildlife biologists at ADAS said in November 1988 that they would be pleased to discuss farmers' problems 'with a view to agreeing appropriate measures'.

CONFLICTS WITH FISHERIES

Some ducks, such as the mergansers, are specialist fish-eaters. Although Goosander ducklings at first take insect larvae under water, fish is predominant in their diets by the time they are 12 days old. At first, the prey are very small but, at four weeks of age, they can take salmon up to 10 cm (4 in) long. In salmon rivers, the food of both juvenile and adult Goosanders is largely young salmon, and experiments in captivity suggest that it takes 33 kg (72 lb) of fish to rear one Goosander (35). The smaller Red-breasted Mergansers hatching on Lake Windermere each ate over 20 kg (44 lb) of fish in 100 days, so the estimate was that the average of 131 ducklings produced there eat 2.6 tonnes every summer (2). Calculations on Canadian Goosanders have suggested that the ducks can account for two-thirds of the potential smolt, although such estimations take no account of the high natural mortality of the fish (35) and assume that all losses are due to predation.

In general, there is an abundance of fish where there are fish-eating birds but, if the prey is being farmed, mergansers can do damage (25). The Goosander is considered a pest in various parts of its range; for instance, in Scotland (33) the 1954 Protection of Birds Act permitted the widespread persecution of it and the Red-breasted Merganser. Nevertheless, both have spread south into England and, in places where they have not been so much in conflict with commercial fisheries, increases in their populations have been dramatic. The 1981 Wildlife and Countryside Act protected the Goosander and Merganser throughout the British Isles but allowed licensed shooting to enable fish hatcheries and farms to protect their stock. In the 14-month period up to December 1983, 347 Goosanders and 523 Red-breasted Mergansers were reported to have been killed in Scotland under licence.

The Eider does not dive in order to catch fish, but uses its strong bill to prise molluscs from the rocks, then swallows them whole. Since mussels have been farmed in the coastal waters of western Scotland, Eiders have been causing complaints. By capitalising on an easily obtained food, as have mergansers at fish farms, they have become unpopular and again licences have been issued to kill them. Unlike oysters and salmon, mussels do not need to be seeded, penned or fed; they are free food for both wildlife and man. The mussel farmer looks for a clean sea-loch and for the presence of mussel predators – where there are plenty of Eiders there is a liberal supply of shellfish. The young mussel 'spat' need only ropes hanging from rafts to cling to and, within two years, can be hauled in and sold. Rope-grown shells are thin and free of barnacles, and Eiders like them as much as the clients of London restaurants.

Fishing is the commonest British sporting activity, an estimated 3.7 million individuals participating, and its operations can reduce drastically the usage that wildfowl make of inland waters (25). As well as disturbance, there is the chance of birds being caught themselves and, if they have a long enough reach, they may eat the lead split-shot sinkers that keep the lines and hooks beneath the surface.

In general, fisheries gain from the fertilizing effect of wildfowl droppings added to the water. This is especially true on inland lakes and meres where grazing geese roost at night after spending the daylight hours on fields nearby; the birds are shifting nutrient from the land to the water where it can be utilised by the plant-life and indirectly by invertebrates and fish (16). In Poland, at least, it is a widely held view that large numbers of Mute Swans and their droppings improve the spawning grounds of bream and other commercial fish (4).

LEAD POISONING

Lead is a hazard to wildfowl in two different ways: the birds may be shot, or they may eat some of the spent lead that missed them and die later of poison. Until quite recently, it was thought that lead poisoning of wildfowl came after the ingestion of spent shotgun pellets; then, in the late 1970s, public concern was expressed about the deaths of almost all the Mute Swans on the Avon at Stratford (9). The total absence of birds feeding on the water below the Memorial Theatre's balcony prompted the Minister of State for the Environment to ask the Nature Conservancy Council to investigate. The NCC set up a working group which included anglers and, among the academics and conservationists, Professor Matthews of The Wildfowl Trust, as it then was, and Dr Perrins of the Edward Grey Institute. In 1981, the group concluded that anglers' lead weights were the single biggest killer of Mute Swans on most of England's rivers and recommended that they should be withdrawn within five years (21).

Anglers were outraged; they pointed out that they had been using lead weights for well over 100 years on waters traditionally inhabited by Mute Swans, and that their relationship was a happy one. They felt that the problem was more likely linked with a recent deterioration of swan habitat through loss of waterweed, river improvement schemes, and the huge increase in boating. (The atmosphere of debate had been soured by early statements from the conservationist side that 250 tonnes of lead shot were being deposited on the land by anglers every year, which seems to have been quoted in error for 25 tonnes – still a vast quantity). The anglers pointed out that deaths were commoner in the weedless, heavily boated urban or semi-urban areas, so bread and other unnatural foods were suggested as a cause. Leaded petrol used in powercraft whose exhausts discharged under water might also be implicated. The anglers were tempted to blame the boaters with such words as 'these vessels look extremely cumbersome and very heavy, in fact the type of craft which would use a considerable amount of fuel'. The boaters retorted that, although they did use plenty of fuel, it was diesel and contained no lead!

The heavy metals in the river Thames which was, like the Avon, losing

A Mute Swan showing signs of suffering from lead poisoning; it finds it difficult to lift the base of its neck from its body. The bird above is normal. Drawings by John Turner.

its swans, were monitored and the soluble lead content found to be extremely small, not even requiring treatment to reduce its level before it was allowed for human consumption. Yet the amount in the blood of the Thames Mutes – tested by scientists from the Edward Grey Institute, sometimes during the four-day odyssey of swan-upping – was found to vary from 26 to 260 micro grammes of lead per 100 ml of blood, and to be highest downstream near London (4). This was worrying as studies in the USA had already indicated that values above 40 might be harmful. Detailed *post-mortem* examinations of 288 swans from all over Britain undertaken in 1980–81 showed that 39% had died of lead poisoning and that each of these had an average of nine pellets of lead in their gizzards.

The pellets were angler's split shot or leger weights. The calculation was made that every year between 3,370 and 4,190 Mute Swans were dying unnecessarily.

Originally, voluntary methods to restrict the use of lead weights were tried; the trade was asked to improve dispensers to avoid spillage, public notices were placed on heavily fished waters warning of the dangers of discarded tackle, and much extra grit was added to certain waters in an effort to prevent the birds from picking up the pellets. Tackle manufacturers responded well to the need for alternatives and products were put on the market made of steel and tungsten. However, these were slow to gain acceptance despite being proclaimed satisfactory by anglers' leaders after extensive tests by club members. Eventually the government introduced legislation which made it illegal to import or supply any lead weights between 0.6 g and 56.7 g (2 oz) after 1 January 1987. This is the range of weights that had been shown to be the major cause of death (4). The use or possession of lead weights already bought and stock-piled by the anglers was never made illegal.

Like most birds, swans must eat grit in order to break down their food before digestion, and lead weights seem to be taken, in mistake for tiny pebbles, often, apparently, directly from a discarded line. Lead is ground against the stones in the gizzard, and digestive juices produce a poisonous solution that can be absorbed into the bloodstream. Slow paralysis is the result; the bird finds it difficult to raise its head, to walk, to fly and, ultimately, the gut muscles stop functioning and the creature may die with a full crop of food. The characteristic kinked-neck of a swan suffering from lead poisoning enables a sad prediction that it is soon to succumb to starvation. The chief symptoms in man are colic (but without paralysis of the gut muscles), limb paralysis, especially of the wrists, fits and anaemia.

Why had the swans suddenly started taking lead sinkers that had been available for many decades? The synthesis of nylon in 1938 seems partly to blame. Strong nylon line or monofilament became so cheap that many more anglers appeared at the water's edge with tackle that could be discarded without much loss. In the old days, the fisherman would have taken home his cotton or linen line (our word 'line' comes from linen which is made from flax or *linum*, while 'nylon' is derived from **N**ew **Y**ork and **Lon**don) and dried it for re-use, carefully removing the attached split shot; now the whole indestructible collection, including the hooks, can be left where it snagged. And a lot was being left: on the River Trent before the ban, two men collected more than 1,100 pieces of lead in an hour. Other river banks in England and Wales were cleared of lead and line at the start of the 1985–86 fishing season and, on one stretch, 3,974 pieces of metal and 7.7 km ($4\frac{3}{4}$ miles) of line removed; at the end of the season, the same stretch yielded an accumulation of a further 3,564 bits of lead and 7.0 km of nylon. The situation with regard to lead, if not to line, is bound to improve as lead weights become impossible to buy (4); indeed, during the 1988 swan-upping on the Thames, more cygnets were present

A Bewick's Swan with a tangle of indestructible nylon line held by a fish-hook in its bill. The obstruction was removed when the bird was caught for ringing, and it recovered to spend six more winters visiting Slimbridge. Photograph by Philippa Scott.

than for a decade, and the incidence of poisoning was down to 16%, having been over 50% in the early 1980s. In the Birthday Honours List for 1987, Her Majesty was pleased to appoint Chris Perrins, Director of the EGI, a Lieutenant of the Victorian Order for his services to her swans.

Areas of land and water that have been shot over in the past will contain lead from a different source, shotgun pellets. British shooters fire an estimated 2,000 tonnes of lead shot per year, and a typical cartridge contains about 200 pieces of shot. Most of these, having fallen to the ground, will be lost; but lead corrodes only very slowly, and will be present and lethal 30, 40 or 50 years after it left the barrel. In the USA, eight out of ten sites examined had soils that contained in excess of 300,000 pellets per ha; in Denmark, concentrations of up to 4,000,000 pellets per ha were found where clay pigeon-shooting occurred, while in Britain a researcher sponsored jointly by The Wildfowl Trust, the Royal Society for the Protection of Birds, and the British Association for Shooting and

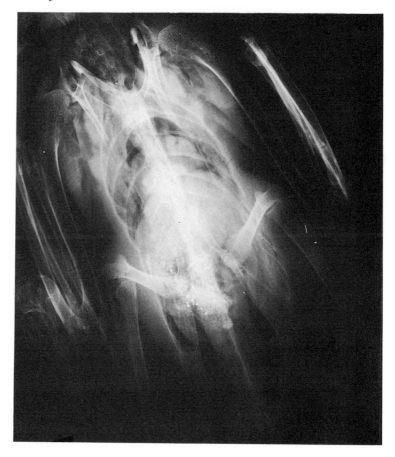

An X-ray of a Canada Goose that has died of lead-poisoning after eating shotgun pellets. The lead is visible as a collection of bright spots in the gizzard at the bottom centre of the picture. The bird's neck is upper left. Photograph by Martin Brown.

Conservation found up to 300,000 per ha, although three of 22 sites examined had no lead at all (20). Pellets usually sink out of reach in the mud at a centre of a pond but there is often a store near the edge due to the erosion of the bank and the relative lack of soft soil there to cover the metal. The edge is where many wildfowl search for food and they take in the pellets along with grit and seeds.

Wildlife biologists in North America and on the Continent of Europe have been aware of the problem of lead from shotguns for many years (22). Experimentally, one No.6 shot was found to be fatal for six out of ten Mallard fed on a diet of mixed grain; two or three would probably end the life of a swan. Birds often take in quite a few more than that; a female Pochard found dead in a duck trap in Essex in 1960 had eaten 84 pellets! An incidence of poisoning of 4–5% is reported in wild Pintail and Mallard, a lower one in Shoveler and Teal, while grazing Wigeon are largely unaffected (22). On the Ouse Washes (also known as the Hundred Foot Washes), it is estimated that the average annual mortality due to lead poisoning is 400 to 700 birds (34). How can their predicament be overcome? Can substitute non-toxic substances be found similar to the angler's steel and tungsten sinkers? The answer must be 'yes', but some of the difficulties of getting those substitutes accepted by traditionalist hunters are discussed in Chapter 10; meanwhile wildfowlers can take care to avoid needlessly scattering lead by not shooting out of range, or pointing their gun directly towards waters that are used by wildfowl. Many tonnes of lead are deposited over the countryside every winter, and it is especially dangerous on wetlands.

The occasional crunch as the teeth contact a lead pellet in a mouthful of cooked game is unlikely to harm a human being, even if the shot is swallowed; we do not have grit in our stomachs and our digestive acids are not so powerful that they will render the lead soluble without grinding. Lead pipes that carried soft water are thought to have been associated with reduced fecundity in Roman times; a sub-lethal dose might have a similar long-term affect on our birds in making them less successful breeders, but there is no evidence of this. In theory, it could also affect their eye-sight, because of optic nerve atrophy and, for instance, make it more difficult for flying swans to avoid obstacles.

There is yet another source of lead in some places in England that is not often considered. Until the coming of the motor car, most city streets were cleaned daily of horse droppings and straw, and the resulting 'night soil' went out to local fields. Martin Mere was fertilised this way throughout the Victorian era; the street sweepings arrived in canal barges and contained much other refuse such as broken clay tobacco pipes. Lead used in 'tinkering', or the mending of metal objects with lead solder, was also lost in the streets. Our birds still occasionally find lumps of it and the vet retrieves them from their gizzards at *post-mortem* examination.

There does seem to be a greater chance of lead poisoning if the birds are eating grain (22,34). Does grain slow the passage of food in the gut because it needs more grinding, so affecting the time available for lead absorption, or interfere with calcium metabolism, since lead is stored in the bones? Whatever the reason, there are implications for avoiding feeding large amounts of wheat to wintering swans in places that have been or are being heavily shot over.

POWERLINES

Now that the purchase of large lead fishing-weights is effectively

A member of the staff at Slimbridge with a Russian White-fronted Goose killed by collision with a power-line. Photograph by J. L. Leach.

banned, it may be that electricity-carrying cables strung across their flight path will be the swan's greatest threat. This is not new; 21 Mute Swan bodies were found beneath a 400 m ($\frac{1}{4}$ mile) stretch of overhead cable on Romney Marsh in a single month of 1962 (11). In the Hebrides, where lead poisoning is unusual, over 80% of Mute Swan deaths are due to birds hitting wires and either being electrocuted or mortally injured by the impact (4); and in 1987, UK swan deaths due to collisions with powerlines ranked second only to death from poisoning caused by fishermen's weights. The haunting moan of the wind in the wires may be, as one researcher suggested, their swan-song. Ironically, fishermen are also at hazard from the pylons across our canals and rivers. Their modern carbon-fibre rods are excellent conductors of electricity and a few anglers have been killed because their tackle touched the lines.

It is not only swans that are at risk from powerlines, although their large size seems to make them particularly vulnerable; geese and ducks hit them and are usually killed or badly injured.

OIL AND PESTICIDE POLLUTION

Oiled waterbirds, especially on the coast, have become a familiar problem. A bird with oiled feathers no longer has any protection against the water or a cold wind, and will eventually die of exposure or from poisoning (due to one of the great variety of toxic substances in petroleum products) as it attempts to clean itself and swallows what it nibbles from its plumage. Catching and treating them in captivity is seldom worthwhile on conservation grounds, although the desire to help for humanitarian reasons is often irresistible.

Seed-dressings containing organophosphorus were responsible for the deaths of 1,500 Scottish and English Greylag and Pinkfeet in eight incidents in the early 1970s (3,10). In the severe weather of January and February 1979, starving Brent Geese came inland in a number of places and, in the Colne Estuary, naturalists and wildfowlers put out wheat, peas and various other seeds obtained from farmers (32). Some of the wheat had been treated with the same organophosphorus insecticide against wheat-bulb fly, and dead geese were soon found lying in the snow of the salt marsh. Twenty-five Bewick's Swans similarly died after feeding on treated grain left exposed on the surface of fields adjacent to a refuge (10). Wheat-bulb fly is an important economic pest in eastern Britain; in the 1950s, aldrin and dieldrin were used against it but these persistent organochlorines caused the deaths of many seed-eaters and birds, such as Peregrines, that preyed upon them. The seed-dressings were withdrawn and replaced by more effective but less persistent organophosphorus insecticides such as carbophenothion. It was this that killed the geese and swans; ironically, it *had* been laboratory tested on geese before being released for market use, but on Canada Geese which were later shown to be relatively immune. Carbophenothion was voluntarily withdrawn from Scotland and areas of England where geese and wheat-bulb fly are common, and an alternative chlorfenvinphos provided instead (10,33).

Spraying water surfaces against mosquitoes with chemical insecticides is likely to destroy insects that are essential duckling foods. Likewise, the food supply of seaducks has been at risk from the use of anti-fouling paints containing tributyltin on the bottoms of boats and fishing nets. The paint prevents barnacles and other shellfish from settling down but also passes in solution into the water of coves and sea-lochs where it has affected whelk and mussel populations. Its use on boats less than 25 m in length and on salmon-farm nets was banned in the UK in 1987, probably before any great harm was done to birds.

Sometimes a very polluted river or estuary may still be rich in wildfowl. The Mersey has been said to be 'dead', but for some unknown reason it is home for internationally important flocks of duck and waders every winter; in particular, it is famous for its Pintail, over 10,000 of which are counted regularly, with 18,450 occurring in November 1980, three-quarters of the British population at that time (25). Likewise, the sewage outfalls of large towns have provided good feeding grounds for wintering salt-water ducks such as Scaup, Pochard and Goldeneye. For instance, the Firth of Forth held, in the 1960s and early 1970s, 80–90% of the British Scaup population with a peak of 25,000 in the late 60s; the sewage treatment works of Edinburgh were modernised in 1978, and Scaup dwindled in numbers to a mere 50 (29). The Pochard roosting on Duddinston Loch, a small water close to Edinburgh, and the Goldeneyes at Seafield in the southern Forth were also affected by that 'improvement' which reduced drastically the food supply of the invertebrates on which the ducks depended (7,25,33).

VANDALISM

It is swans again that bear most of the burden of human vandalism. Because they nest in such public places they are subject to disturbance and attack, mostly caused by boys. One incident that reached the newspapers involved the fastening around a swan's beak of a tight rubber band that prevented it from feeding and drinking; it was only when the bird had worn the band for eight days and was sufficiently weakened, that an RSPCA officer was able to recapture it and remove the constriction. It has been calculated that out of every 2,400 swan eggs laid, only 1,000 will hatch; 78% of this loss is due to human interference and more especially to the removal or destruction of eggs by small boys (4). When staff at the RSPB reserve at Fairburn Ings in West Yorkshire realised that only six young swans had fledged in 1984 from their very large numbers of Mutes, it was decided to show local children how the swans were suffering because of their activities. A project called 'Swan Time' visited schools in the summers of 1985 and 1986 and attempted to develop an awareness of the swans and their feelings. The process of education is further examined in Chapters 5 and 10.

THE ROAD TO EXTINCTION

There are four reasons why animals become endangered: loss of habitat,

A pencil and watercolour painting by Thomas Heaphy (1775–1835) entitled 'Two servant boys taunting swans' suggests that there is nothing new in the recent finding that the majority of British Mute Swans' eggs fail to hatch because of molestation by young men. Photograph courtesy of the Drawings Department of Christie's.

over-exploitation, introduction of predators, and pollution (19). We have seen them all at work. A particularly well-publicised example of potential habitat loss occurred on the inner Hebridean island of Islay where, in 1985, the distilling industry came into conflict with the rare Greenland White-fronted Goose. This bird had a special place in Peter Scott's affections since he had been the first to realise that it differed from the Russian Whitefront, and in 1948, with Christopher Dalgety, gave it its full scientific name of *Anser albifrons flavirostris*. The distillers needed a new supply of peat to flavour their famous malt whiskeys, and decided on a bog called Duich Moss which, as well as being a Site of Special Scientific Interest because of its plants, happened to be the winter feeding ground and roost of a significant number of Whitefronts. Television cameras at a public meeting showed local people treating conservationists, including Dr David Bellamy, with uncharacteristic rudeness, and the affair was polarized by the media into a 'jobs or geese' confrontation, with strangers apparently dictating terms to the islanders. In the end, an alternative source of peat was found, with EEC help the site was designated a Special Protection Area, and honour satisfied on both sides.

Considering how many wildfowl there are, that they taste excellent, are often shot, and live in wetlands that are so subject to drainage, it is perhaps surprising that none is declining in numbers in Britain today (25) and that only four ducks world-wide have become extinct in historic times (8,26). Three otherwise plentiful species appear to have lost races in the last hundred years, including the Rennell Island Grey Teal (Chapter 7). In this, wildfowl differ from some other bird groups such as the pheasants (many of which are seriously threatened because they are eaten) and birds of prey (which attract the activities of uneducated shooters and are also at special risk from a range of pesticides). The Redbreast has

John Busby's flying Greenland White-fronted Goose from C. D. Hutchinson's *Birds in Ireland*.

recently become Europe's rarest goose, maybe through its peculiar relationship with the Peregrine which has been affected adversely (19,24). This goose can be used as an example of how complicated effective conservation often is.

Many birds nest in association with other species; the Eider, for instance, nests in gull colonies (see Chapter 6) perhaps so that predators will eat the gulls' eggs rather than the ducks'. Any small goose breeding in the far north must protect its nest from arctic foxes; some choose inaccessible sites on cliffs and islands, but the Redbreasts of Western Taimyr (USSR) select the proximity of a bird-of-prey, usually a Peregrine Falcon or sometimes a Rough-legged Buzzard *Buteo lagopus*. Up to ten pairs of geese lay around the eyrie, and the falcon drives away foxes and other undesirables. The bird-of-prey seldom hunts near its own nest (it might kill its offspring if it did) and this immunity extends to the geese, at least until hatching; there is then a dash for goslings and parents to reach the nearest water before the falcon starts hunting. The symbiotic benefit for the Peregrine is that the Redbreasts warn of the approach of danger. Pesticides have brought unexpected declines in the world's birds-of-prey and, in many cases, have been found to cause egg-shell thinning and breeding failure. The Peregrines of Western Taimyr which winter in parts of the Indian sub-continent, where DDT is still an important weapon against insect-borne diseases such as malaria, have been affected in this way, so perhaps it is a shortage of their protective guardians that has caused the decline of the geese.

In winter, the Red-breasted Goose is directly dependent on man, since it feeds on cultivated land (24). Many of the 20,000 or so that remain migrate to the edge of the Black Sea in Romania, and feed with White-fronted Geese on maize stubbles and winter wheat; here Peter Scott counted, studied, painted and photographed them and, by taking an interest, encouraged the Romanians to do the same (30,31). In 1973, I was lucky enough to accompany him to Tulcea on the frozen Danube to census these attractive rarities. A distinguished film-maker was recording our party goose-watching for Romanian television so that the message could be better spread. Peter Scott's interest in the wildlife, including Great Bustards *Otis tarda*, White-tailed Eagles *Haliaeetus albicilla* and roe deer, extended even to the cockroaches that lurked beneath the rim of the hotel baths, and he recorded them all in his diaries (31).

Of the four recently extinct ducks – the Korean Crested Shelduck *Tadorna cristata*, the Pink-headed Duck, the Labrador Duck *Camtorhynchus labradorius* and the Auckland Islands Merganser – man was probably involved in the demise of the last three (8). The **Crested Shelduck** is known from the skins of one male and two females, plus some drawings, and nothing is understood of its habitat requirements. It was last certainly recorded in 1916 and, although there are occasional reports of re-sightings (in 1943 and 1964, for instance), it is now presumed to have gone. It was spectacular in appearance but, when the first specimen was found, it was thought to be a cross between a Ruddy Shelduck and a Falcated Teal; it is likely that, without the illustrations in Japanese 19th Century avicultural works and on tapestries found in China, the bird really would have been dismissed as a hybrid. The avicultural references imply that the bird was imported alive into Japan from Korea until about 200 years ago, and was once a reasonably common bird that may have been in decline for a considerable time (8).

The disappearance of the **Labrador Duck** may be another example of 'natural' extinction. Again surprisingly little is known about it. It was certainly shot and its eggs collected, but probably no more than any other kind of North American wildfowl during the first part of the 19th Century. Its curious bill suggests that it was a specialised feeder, vulnerable to even the slightest alteration in its habitat. It was said to have been available on the meat markets of New York and Baltimore during the early 1800s but its flesh tasted fishy and was so unpopular that carcasses often rotted unsold. The last specimen was taken in 1875, when numbers had been dwindling over a long period (8).

The **Pink-headed Duck** disappeared for two reasons, a contraction of its habitat due to drainage, and exploitation by sportsmen in India (in the region that is now Bangladesh) who often failed to observe a close season (28). It was shy, wary and difficult to shoot, as are many diving ducks,

A pair of the presumed extinct Crested Shelducks, the male on the left, painted from skins by N. Kobayashi; from volume 1 of J. C. Phillips' *Natural History of the Ducks.*

A trio of extinct Labrador Ducks painted from skins by the American artist Louis Agassiz Fuertes; from volume 1 of J.C. Phillips' *Natural History of the Ducks*.

and apparently, like the Labrador Duck, did not even make attractive eating. In the 19th Century, the species was fairly frequently offered for sale; however, by the early 1900s, specimens were no longer easily obtainable and a decline was obvious. A number of individuals reached captivity in Britain and France; as late as 1925, a consignment of three pairs was received by Alfred Ezra at Foxwarren Park, and another ten individuals, which were seen by Peter Scott, were obtained four years later. These birds thrived but unfortunately never bred. The year 1936 seems to have seen the end of the Pink-headed Duck, when the last one of those in England died, far away from its native haunts (see Chapter 6).

At the time of its discovery by a French Lieutenant Jacquinot, the number of **Auckland Islands Mergansers** was already very limited (18). It is clear that the species occurred in New Zealand itself since bones have been collected from middens of Polynesian settlers, so it is likely that it was hunted out on the mainland by Maoris, and that the Auckland Islands, 320 km (200 miles) away, were at the edge of its range. Here, many predators – pigs, cats, dogs and mice – followed the arrival of the explorers, the pigs being placed there so that any subsequently shipwrecked mariners did not starve. These mammals had the usual disastrous effect on the islands' birds, most of which had little fear of man or beast; indeed, the

Two extinct Auckland Islands Mergansers painted from skins by Henrik Grönvold (1858–1940) of Denmark; from J. C. Phillips' *Natural History of the Ducks.*

Merganser appears to have taken no evasive action when Europeans 'collected' it. It is a sad fact that, as soon as a species declined to rarity, the demand by museums for its skins increased; the ultimate reason for the Merganser's extinction may well have been the relatively large number that was shot by museum collectors during 1901. Captain R. F. Scott (Sir Peter's father who, by writing that famous instruction 'Make the boy interested in natural history', set the course of a most successful life) arrived in the Auckland Islands in his ship *Discovery* in March 1904, and the company searched during a fortnight's stay but, when the ship sailed, Edward Wilson had to record that none of the company had seen Mergansers. Today, 26 skins exist in ten museums; the first bird ever seen, a drake, was shot in March 1840 and its remains are in the Museum National d'Histoire Naturelle in Paris. The last pair, shot on 9 January 1902, are skeletons in the Natural History Museum at Tring in England (18).

REFERENCES

1. Arnold-Forster, F. 1899. *Studies in Church Dedication*, vol 2. London: Skeffington.
2. Atkinson, K. M. & Hewitt, D. P. 1978. A note on the food consumption of the Red-breasted Merganser. *Wildfowl* 29: 87–91.
3. Bailey, S. *et al.* 1972. Accidental poisoning of wild geese in Perthshire, November 1971. *Wildfowl* 23: 88–91.

4. Birkhead, M. & Perrins, C. 1986. *The Mute Swan*. London: Croom Helm.

5. Bradshaw, H. 1513. *The Life of St Werburgh of Chester*. Re-issued 1887 Early English Tract Society.

6. Bridgett, R. W. 1985. *The Life of St Werburgh*. Burslem: The Parish Priest & Churchwardens of the Parish of St Werburgh.

7. Fox, A. D. & Salmon, D. G. 1988. Changes in non-breeding distribution and habitat of Pochard *Aythya ferina* in Britain. *Biol. Conserv.* 46: 303–316.

8. Fuller, E. 1987. *Extinct Birds*. Viking Rainbird.

9. Hardman, J. A. & Cooper, D. R. 1980. Mute Swans on the Warwickshire Avon – a study of a decline. *Wildfowl* 31: 29–36.

10. Hardy, A. R. , Stanley, P. I. & Grieg-Smith, P. W. 1987. Birds as indicators of the intensity of use of agricultural pesticides in the UK, in *The Value of Birds*, ICBP Technical Public. No.6.

11. Harrison, J. 1963. Heavy mortality of Mute Swans from electrocution. *Wildfowl* 14: 164–165.

12. Houlihan, P. F. 1986. *The Birds of Ancient Egypt*. Warminster: Aris & Phillips.

13. Kear, J. 1962. Feeding habits of the Greylag Goose on the Island of Bute. *Scot. Birds* 2: 233–239.

14. Kear, J. 1963. The history of potato-eating by wildfowl in Britain. *Wildfowl* 14: 54–65.

15. Kear, J. 1963. The protection of crops from damage by wildfowl. *Wildfowl* 14: 66–71.

16. Kear, J. 1963. The agricultural importance of wild goose droppings. *Wildfowl* 14: 72–77.

17. Kear, J. & Pilcher, R. E. M. 1966. The spread of potato-eating in Whooper Swans. *Brit. Birds* 59: 160–161.

18. Kear, J. & Scarlett, R. J. 1970. The Auckland Islands Merganser. *Wildfowl* 21: 78–86.

19. Kear, J. & Williams, G. 1978. Wildfowl at risk. *Wildfowl* 29: 5–21.

20. Mudge, G. P. 1984. Densities and settlement rates of spent shotgun pellets in British wetland soils. *Environmental Pollution (Series B)*. 9: 299–318.

21. NCC. 1981. Lead Poisoning in Swans. *Report of the working group*.

22. Olney, P. J. S. 1960. Lead poisoning in wildfowl. *Wildfowl* 11: 123–134.

23. Owen, M. 1976. Factors affecting the distribution of geese in the British Isles. *Wildfowl* 27: 143–151.

24. Owen, M. 1980. *Wild Geese of the World*. London: Batsford.

25. Owen, M., Atkinson-Willes, G. L. & Salmon, D. 1986. (2nd Ed) *Wildfowl in Great Britain*. CUP.

26. Phillips, J. C. 1923. *Natural History of the Ducks*. vol 1. Boston: Houghton Mifflin.

27. Ross, A. 1967. *Pagan Celtic Britain*. London: Routledge.

28. Salim, A. 1959. The Pink-headed Duck *Rhodonessa caryophyllacea* (Latham). *Wildfowl* 11: 55–60.

29. Salmon, D. G. 1988. The numbers and distribution of Scaup *Aythya marila* in Britain and Ireland. *Biol. Conserv.* 43: 267–278.

30. Scott, P. 1970. Redbreasts in Rumania. *Wildfowl* 21: 37–41.

31. Scott, P. 1983,1985,1987. *Travel Diaries of a Naturalist* Parts I,II,III. London: Collins.

32. Stanley, P. I. & St Joseph, A. K. M. 1979. Poisoning of Dark-bellied Brent in Essex, February 1979. *Wildfowl* 30: 154.

33. Thom, V. 1986. *Birds in Scotland*. Calton: Poyser.

34. Thomas, G. J. 1975. Ingested lead pellets in waterfowl at the Ouse Washes, England, 1968–73. *Wildfowl* 26: 43–48.

35. White, H. C. 1957. Food and natural history of Mergansers on Salmon waters in the maritime provinces of Canada. *Fish.Res.Board Canada Bull.* 116.

9: Language, legend and art

The names that we give to objects around us are often very ancient. English is part of the great Indo-European family of 130 languages spoken from the Faroes to Bengal, from Catalonia to the Ukraine (32). Our modern words for duck, goose and swan derive from *duce*, *gos* and *swan* in Anglo-Saxon, the vernacular of the people of Denmark and North Germany who settled in England in the 6th Century. Our agricultural words are typically Anglo-Saxon; all are short and many are four-letter. The invaders of 1066 and after, who spoke French, influenced very few of these farming terms but did change urban court-life a great deal. The Norman aristocracy had *beof*, *moton* and *porc* on their tables, although the live animals continued to be known to the labouring classes as ox, sheep and pig. Roast cygnet was also served in high places and that word came to mean, in English, the young of the swan – the only stage that the conquerors considered edible. We are still inclined to use French as a gastronomic language but, to etymologists, French is a 'Romance' as opposed to a 'Germanic' tongue. The word *cygne* seems to have nothing in common with our word *swan* but French is, like English, part of the same Indo-European heritage. Let us look at the names that Europeans and some Asians have attached to wildfowl and try to find the threads that link them. In the following chart referring to *goose*, four major language groupings are shown: Germanic, Romance and Celtic, Balto-Slavic and Indo-Iranian. These include most western tongues with notable exceptions (Hungarian, Finnish, Basque, Turkish and Hebrew, for instance), some of which are also interestingly similar: Basque for goose is *antzer*, Estonian is *hani*, Finnish *hansi* and Xhosa *uranisi*, the latter said to be a corruption of the Afrikaans *gans*.

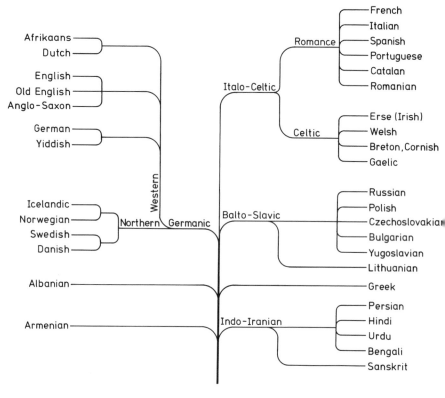

A family tree of the Indo-European languages. Drawn by John Turner.

It has been suggested by Professor Colin Renfrew (32) that the spread of European tongues occurred much earlier than is usually supposed and coincided, perhaps ten thousand years ago, with the development of farming and its extension from Anatolia through Greece to western Europe in one direction, and to India in the other. In the domestic life of members of the ancient Indo-European community there were terms for cow, sheep, pig, dog, goose, duck, bee, oak, beech, willow and grain, and today these words are often alike in widely separate geographical areas. The similarity of the Sanskrit *hansa* and the English *goose* is not initially obvious, but the diagram and list indicate an evolutionary relationship. Even the domestication of the goose, 5,000 years ago, did not produce an animal so different that the single name needed alteration. *Hansa* is representative of the name-type for goose (and gander) in almost all Indo-European languages, and the honking voice of the bird must be its basis.

Table 1. The evolution of the word 'goose', possibly the most ancient bird name in our vocabulary (24), through the Indo-European languages.

In the Germanic languages:
English: Goose
Anglo-Saxon: Gos
Dutch and Flemish: Gans (Goele in region near Ghent)
Afrikaans: Gans
Old High German: Kans
German: Gans
Yiddish: Gands
Icelandic: Gas
Norwegian: Gas
Swedish: Gås
Danish: Gas

In Romance and Celtic languages:
Latin: Ánser
French: Oie
Italian: Oca
Spanish: Ánser
Portuguese: Ganso
Romanian: Gpscă or gîscă
Irish (Erse): Goss
Welsh: Gwydd or Cwydd
Gaelic: Gèadh

In the Slavonic languages:
Lithuanian: Žasis
Russian: Gus
Polish: Gęś
Czech: Husa
Bulgarian: 'G'ska

In Greek and Indo-Iranian:
Ancient Greek: Chēn or Khen
Ancient Egyptian: Chen, Ka or Pta
Modern Greek: Chēnari or Sonar
Sanskrit: Hansa, Hamsa or Hasa
Bengali: Hoñgsh (male), Hoñgshi (female)
Hindi: Hans

Table 2. The evolution of 'swan' in Indo-European tongues looks like this:

In the Germanic languages:
English: Swan
Anglo-Saxon: Swan or Swon
Dutch: Zwaan
German: Schwan
Yiddish: Swan
Icelandic: Svanr
Swedish: Svan
Norwegian: Swane

In Romance and Celtic languages:
Latin: Cycnus or Cygnus
French: Cygne
Italian: Cigno
Spanish: Cisne
Portuguese: Cisne
Romanian: Lebădă
Old Norse: Elpt
Old English: Elfetu or Ielfetu
Poetic latin of Horace: Olor
Irish: Eala

Welsh: Alarch
Gaelic: Eala
Breton: Alarc'h
Cornish: Elerch
Old Northumberland and Yorkshire: Elk or Ilke

In the Slavonic languages:
Lithuanian: Gulbé
Russian: Lebeđ
Polish: Labęoź
Czech: Labuť
Yugoslav: Labud
Bulgarian: Lebed

In Greek and Indian languages:
Albanian: Mjelleme
Armenian: Garab
Greek: Kyknos
Sanskrit: Hamsa or Hansa

Table 3. And for 'duck' we can assemble the following:

English: Duck
Anglo-Saxon: Duce
Old English: Ened or Aened
Dutch: Eend
Afrikaans: Eend
German: Ente
Yiddish: Katshke
Icelandic: Ond
Norwegian: And
Danish: And
Swedish: And

In Romance and Celtic:
Latin: Anas
French: Canard
Italian: Ánatra
Spanish: Ánade or Pato
Portuguese: Pato (male), Pata (female)
Romanian: Raţă
Catalan: Ànec
Irish: Lacha or Lachar
Welsh: Hwyaden
Gaelic: Lach

In the Slavonic Languages:
Lithuanian: Antis
Russian: Utka or Ýtka
Polish: Kaczka
Czech: Kachna or Kačka
Bulgarian: Patka

In the Greek and Indian languages:
Albanian: Patz
Ancient Greek: Netta or Nessa
Modern Greek: Papia
Persian: Baṭ or Baṭak
Sanskrit: Ātí or Āḍi
Bengali: Pati
Hindi: Baṭ or Baṭak
Romany: Papi

The word geese is an example of a 'mutated plural' of which only seven remain of the many used up to the time of the Norman Conquest – the others are men, women, feet, teeth, mice and lice.

The word for duck does not follow quite the same satisfactory common route because the domestic duck and a variety of dabbling and diving cousins needed to be named and identified. Swans likewise were not familiar birds in Asia (there is no word for swan in Hindi) and were, in any case, likely to be confused with geese, so that in Sanskrit *hansa* was used for both.

Our word swan means 'the sounder' and is a reference to the loud voices of the Whooper and Bewick's or the pulsating wings of the Mute (the combination of Mute and Swan is therefore something of a paradox). From the same root comes the verb *svanati* in Sanskrit and *sonare* in Latin which mean 'to sound', and such words as sonnet and resonance in English. Once again, it is its calls, or possibly the noise of its wings, that gives us the bird's name (24,31).

However, the duck is described by its behaviour: in Dutch, *duicken* is to dive, and the word is *tauchen* in German (31). It is odd that *duce* became restricted to the waddling domestic duck while *ened* (from the quacking voice of the female) was used for the more actively diving wild bird. Mallard originally meant only the male of the common species; the first element derives from a French adjective for the male sex, while the ending -ard implied the masculine as well – 'hardy' or 'bold' – also found in Buzzard and haggard (a falcon). Wigeon was likewise once the Old English name for a male bird whose female was a 'whewer' (19,24,41). Drake, the word now used for any male duck, is related to the Gaelic *dràc*, but is otherwise puzzling, not being found in Old English.

PLACE-NAMES FROM WILDFOWL

The Oxford Dictionary of English Place-Names (14) records nearly 30 towns and villages whose names derive from wildfowl associations. Of obvious relationship are Swanbourne in Buckinghamhsire and Swanmore in Hampshire. However, most other places with the same first element are said to derive from a very different meaning – swineherd or swain, as in Swanley and Swindon. The older *elfetu* and *elpt*, which originated in the Norse word for swan and probably refer to the Whooper, are commoner in the north and east of England where there is Aldmire in Yorkshire, Elvet Hall in Durham, Elterwater in the Lake District, Altham ('water meadow where swans are found') in Lancashire, and Iltney in Essex.

The goose is found in the place-name of Gaisgill, Westmorland ('wild goose valley'), and many other Gosdens, Gosfords, Gosports, Gusbornes and Goswicks which must refer to the tame bird (14). In an earlier Chapter,

The 'Gospelgate' at Louth in Lincolnshire was once the site of a goose pool where geese were watered. Drawn by Joe Blossom.

I mentioned Goswell Road that leads into London and the Gospel Gates at the edge of towns with an old goose market; both indicate the position of an ancient 'duck pond' where the birds were watered on their way to be sold. Goose Green is a name left over from the days when geese walked to market in large herds and needed grazing on the journey; there used to be one on the Camberwell Road, at the fourth milestone from London (34).

Ducks are immortalised in Doughton ('duck farm'), Dukinfield, and in Duckworth ('enclosure for ducks'). As with swans, the older word for duck *ened* is more common and presumably identified wild birds. Andwell, Anmer, Enborne, Enford, Enmore and Entwistle ('river fork frequented by ducks') are some of these (14). The habit of naming places after wildfowl was not confined to England. In Wales, The Wildfowl and Wetlands Trust has established a new centre at Penclacwydd – the hill of the gander – near Llanelli. Goose Bay, Labrador, Gander in Newfoundland and Goose Green in the Falklands also come to mind, as does Cygnet in Tasmania and Swan River in Western Australia (27). This last was originally named Black Swan River by an amazed Dutchman, W. de Vlamingh, who had never before seen swans that were not white (39). Alftafjordur in Iceland is still famous for its Whoopers. In France, rotisseurs sold roast geese as a main item and were known as 'oyers'; the Paris street in which they concentrated was thus called *rue aux Oues*. It was not far from the old market of *Les Halles*, and ran into the *rue St Martin*, the great Roman road that entered the city from the north. Later, the etymology went astray and the name became *rue aux Ours* ('Bear Street') which it is today.

PEOPLE NAMED AFTER WILDFOWL

Most Englishmen acquired surnames in the 13th and 14th Centuries, the Welsh not until the 18th (1). 'Swan' and 'Drake' seem clear in origin but surprisingly come from swain and dragon instead (11). 'Fletcher' derives from the trade of arrow-maker – the fletching of the arrow's shaft with the flight feathers of the goose. 'Gosseman', 'Gozzard', and 'Gazard', and perhaps 'Goslin' and 'Negus', are also from the occupation of an ancestor who herded or sold geese, as is 'Duck' – short for duck-seller or breeder. 'Fowler' was a hunter of birds and sometimes a poulterer; 'Wildgans' is a fairly common German surname, and 'Osler' is a Fenland name for 'wildfowler' from the Old French *oiseleur*. Many people took surnames from localities, and might originally have been 'de' Entwistle, Dukinfield, Duckworth, Gosden, etc (11). Anyone styled thus would have been unlikely to live in the town concerned but would probably have arrived from there, a 'stranger' in some other place. St Werburgh has been referred to already in relation to crop damage by geese; she gave her name to Warburton ('Werburgh's town') in Cheshire which was built on the banks of the Mersey, the northern edge of her father's kingdom of Mercia. Warburton is now a common surname in surrounding areas. Warbstow in Cornwall is also named after her, quite why is uncertain, but the area is full of goose-greens and was once famous for its tame geese, so that may be the connection.

First names that record a wildfowl association seem rare: Gossamer (from Dylan Thomas's *Under Milk Wood*), Dafila (an old name for the Pintail and one that Peter Scott (38) chose for his younger daughter), Penelope (the Wigeon, according to Pliny) and Brent are among the few that I can find. The noun 'hild' meant 'battle' in Old English, and 'hilde' is the feminine ending, so Swanhilde presumably was 'swan battle'.

WILDFOWL NAMED FOR PEOPLE

Some 29 species and sub-species of wildfowl have English or scientific names that are associated with the person who first described them or with someone in whose honour they were named. The American Eider *S.m.dresseri* is called after H. E. Dresser (1838–1915) an English ornithologist and author of books on birds, and the Hawaiian Goose *B.sandvicensis* after the Earl of Sandwich (1718–1792) who was First Lord of the Admiralty at the time of Captain Cook's arrival in Hawaii; he achieved greater fame by having his servant place a piece of meat between two slices of bread so that he could remain longer at the gaming table. Sometimes the connection is distant: the Canvasback *A.vallisneria* is named after the waterweed *Vallisneria spiralis* on which it feeds, while the plant took its title from an Italian naturalist Antonio Vallisnieri de Vallisnera (1661–1730).

Two particularly well-known wildfowl named for people are Bewick's Swan and Barrow's Goldeneye. Thomas Bewick was born in 1753 and became a naturalist and artist of genius (7). He and his son produced woodblock engravings of the Whooper and Mute Swans, but he may never have realised that a third, smaller species existed. William Yarrell, a London businessman who was also a Fellow of the Linnean Society, described and named this bird in Bewick's memory two years after the artist's death in 1828. Bewick's telescope is now kept in Sir Peter Scott's studio at The Wildfowl and Wetlands Trust's headquarters at Slimbridge where large numbers of swans spend the winter. The 'original' Bewick's Swan (the one Yarrell described) was stuffed, and the mounted skin could be seen in the Hancock Museum in Newcastle not far from The Trust's reserve at Washington. Sir John Barrow (1764–1848), like Lord Sandwich, rose to high office in the Admiralty and was one of the founders of the Royal Geographical Society. He was a promoter of Arctic exploration and, in particular, of attempts to find the North-West Passage, and was responsible for the selection of naturalists for most naval expeditions. The name Barrow's Goldeneye was first used in 1831 in *Fauna Borealis*

Americana, a book on the animals of North America; his name is also preserved in Barrow Straits, Cape Barrow and Point Barrow, all in Alaska or the Canadian Arctic.

BIRDS AS RELIGIOUS SYMBOLS

In the middle ages, it was considered that saints differed from ordinary mortals by having, among other things, power over animals (8,15,16). Friendships between saints and wild creatures were of a supernatural nature, and the beasts lost their shyness and fear because of holy power. A number of saints are associated with wildfowl. The Eider Ducks of the Northumberland coast are still called St Cuthbert's or Cuddy Ducks, after the saint who protected them in the vicinity of his hermitage. The goose that St Werburgh is said to have restored to life after it had been boiled and served for dinner, appears beside her in many pictures. Her bones were, like those of St Cuthbert, carried to the west when the Danes invaded in the 9th Century. She found an eventual resting place at Chester, where she became the patron saint of the Cathedral and is carved on a

St Werburgh with two geese. Drawn by Sue Hazeldine.

Saint Pega with Whooper Swans in the village church at Peakirk ('Pega's Kirk'). Photograph by Anne Cook.

misericord with her goose flying above her. (This miracle is probably borrowed from a Flemish saint called Amelburgh by the monk who wrote Werburgh's life in Norman times; the story of the raid on fields at Weedon by wild geese seems likely, on the other hand, to have resulted from a real and unusual incident). St Werburgh is commemorated on 3 February, said to have been the day of her death.

A goose or geese are also the emblems of St Brigid and of St Martin (16). Brigid (Bridget, Brigit or Bride) of Ireland, who died about AD 525, was abbess of Kildare. Her usual attribute is a cow, but the geese link her to Brig, the goddess of a pagan fire-cult also celebrated on 1 February. St Martin of Tours (about AD 316–397) was a monk and a bishop. His emblems are a globe of fire over his head and (from the 15th Century) geese, whose migrations coincided with his feast on 11 November. The goose was, in Celtic times, thought to have powers over fertility, and the custom of roasting and eating a goose at the feast of St Martin or St Michael (29 September) probably had its roots in a pre-Christian ritual when a sacred bird was sacrificed to increase next season's crops (Chapter 2). A flock of wild geese appears on portraits of St Milburgh (23 February) and a dead goose in a wolf's mouth with St Vedast (6 February) who is said to have brought the bird to life again (8).

St Hugh with the Whooper Swan that befriended him and is reported to have searched the saint's sleeves for bread. Drawn by Sue Hazeldine.

A swan or swans are the attribute of St Leger (2 October), of St Hugh of Lincoln, St Hugh of Grenoble (1 April), St Kentigern (1 January), St Cuthbert (20 March) and St Pega of Peakirk (8 January). Hugh of Lincoln, whose feast is also in the winter season on 17 November, was born in 1140 and, on the day of his enthronement as bishop in 1186, an unknown bird arrived who 'within the space of a few days, overwhelmed with his great bulk and slew all the swans, that he found there in great numbers; one however, of the female sex, he saved alive, not for the increases of her fertility, but for the comfort of her society. He was in truth by quite as much larger than a swan as a swan is larger than a goose; he was nevertheless in all things very like a swan, especially in colour and whiteness; in addition to his size he was also unlike them in this, that he did not exhibit the knob and the black colour on the bill after the manner of swans, but had in truth the same part of the bill flat' (42). Here was a Whooper Swan described by a writer who was familiar only with the Mute. The ferocious bird attached himself to the saint, fed from his hand and allowed no-one near him; it lived in the moat of the bishop's residence for some years, probably unsettling the lives of everyone else.

It is clear, and not surprising, that the saints symbolically associated with wildfowl have their feast days during the winter half of the year when wild swans and geese are present or migrating. The tradition was to celebrate the memory of a saint on the day of his or her death which was their 'birthday' in heaven. Often therefore, the bird associations may have been arranged posthumously.

Pre-Christian gods and goddesses were also accompanied by animals, and geese and swans were among these. Statues of the Celtic god of war have a goose standing beside the deity (4,33). A goose was one of Aphrodite's birds; it appears at her feet or flies with her on its back. Juno,

Aphrodite riding on a goose; 4th Century BC. Drawn by Sue Hazeldine.

the Roman fertility goddess who was the consort of Jupiter, had white geese placed in her honour on the Capitoline Hill, and it was these birds that saved the city in 390 BC (Chapter 2). The title of Juno Moneta ('she who warns') was subsequently bestowed upon her, she became the protectress of the people and the coinage of Rome was minted in her temple; indeed, it is from the Latin *moneta* that we get our English words 'money' and 'mint' (15). St Augustine was later to observe that the credit for the warning belonged entirely to the geese since they had stayed awake while the gods slept.

In Hindu culture Brahma the Creator may be represented seated with, or even on, a *hansa*, and the goose was likewise associated with his wife Sarasvati, the goddess of learning (43). The swan has now ousted the goose as Sarasvati's *vahana* (Sanskrit for 'vehicle', and from the same root as our word) in Nepal and some parts of India; she is shown with a rather gaudy Mute instead. In Egyptian mythology, Geb was the Old Kingdom earth

Sarasvati, the Goddess of Learning in the polytheistic religion of Hinduism, with the swan that was originally a Bar-headed Goose beside her. Drawn by Sue Hazeldine.

god whose head is surmounted by a goose – usually identified as an Egyptian Goose. Some legends describe him as a gander called the Great Cackler whose female laid the egg of the sun and whose calling first broke the silence of the world. During the Middle Kingdom, the Egyptian Goose was held sacred to Amun who came to prominence at Thebes and was, like Geb, the Great Cackler associated with the cosmic egg. Because of their sacredness to Amun, noblemen kept geese as pets and, in tomb paintings and reliefs, they often appear under their owner's chairs or standing in the prow of his boat (Chapter 4).

THE ORNITHOLOGY OF INNSIGNS AND HERALDRY

Boards and signs that proclaim the trade of innkeepers date from 1353, when alehouses were first regulated under Edward III, and were practical necessities when most of the population was illiterate. Many animal signs have their origins in heraldry, and here the importance of the swan is reflected in the number of inns that bear its name; indeed, of all bird names for inns, the 'Swan' is the most popular (2). Many dating from Tudor times were named for Anne of Cleves, whose family claimed descent from the Swan Knight (see later); tavern keepers may have associated her with the graceful swan, but her husband Henry VIII, who married her in January 1540 as his fourth wife, described her as 'The Flanders Mare'! It is also said that the popularity of the alehouse sign was related to the bird's fondness for liquid. Many towns had more than one 'Swan Inn' which meant that distinguishing adjectives were needed: the 'Black Swan' was common before the discovery of Australia, at a time when the bird was still a mythical creature – the original *Rara avis* of Juvenal. York, for instance, had a 'Swan', a 'White Swan', an 'Old White Swan', a 'Black Swan' and a 'Cygnet' (39). The 'Black Swan' seems especially common as an innsign in Yorkshire for some reason – where pubs of that name are often known as the 'Mucky Duck'. The 'Swan with Two Necks' is a corruption of the 'two nicks' cut in the bill of the young bird to denote its ownership by the Vintners' Company. The Vintners' supplied wine to many hostelries, and the sign is quite usual.

There are few inns named for birds in Scotland and Wales, Devon or Cornwall, where the tame Mute may not have been a familiar creature. There is a shortage of pub-signs in Calvinist Scotland anyway, since

The Decoy Inn at Peakirk. Originally called The Red Cow, it was renamed after The Wildfowl Trust started to operate Borough Fen Decoy for duck-ringing. Photograph by Joe Blossom.

alcohol tends to be consumed behind anonymous doors without advertisement. The 'Swan and Harp' is the coat-of-arms of the Company of Musicians, and it became a popular sign for the early music-halls most of which originated as public houses; many were later translated, in ridicule, to the 'Goose and Gridiron' (15,34). The 'Swan and Antelope' comes from the supporters of the arms of Henry IV, who married into the family of the Swan Knight.

The 'Fox and Goose' is said to indicate that a board-game of this title was played at the inn. The 'Goose Inn' at Burslem is near St Werburgh's Parish Church in Haywood Road, and takes its name from the bird that she miraculously restored to life. There is a 'Gaping Goose' at Garforth, West Yorkshire, and any number of ducks around the country – notably the 'Duck Inn' at Aylesbury (2). The 'Whistling Duck' at Banwell, Avon, got its name from an eight-year old girl who won a competition organised by the brewers to find the most original title for a new inn. The 'Wild Duck' at Ewen has a sign based on a painting by Sir Peter Scott. The 'Ruddy Duck' and the 'Decoy' at Peakirk were renamed at his instigation in the 1960s to mark The Wildfowl Trust's association with the village. The story of the 'Drunken Duck' at Hawkshead in the Lake District is of a broken beer barrel in the pub yard. The ducks drank the beer and were found in a coma by the inn-keeper's wife; thinking them dead, she plucked them for eating. But then they came round and, in remorse, the good lady made each of them a woolly jumper – the innsign is a duck in a knitted coat. The 'Mucky Duck', when not a rude reference to a 'Black Swan', apparently derived from the practice of putting a tame bird down the chimney to sweep out the soot!

A coat of arms was originally (at the time of the crusades) used to cover a knight's armour and was colourfully embroidered with a personal badge and crest to which retainers would show allegiance. Many depicted birds, especially swans. A white swan was the badge of the de Bouillons from Normandy (or Bohuns as they became) who, like the de Cleves, claimed descent from the Knight of the Swan. Because Mary Bohun married Henry IV, Henry V carried a swan on his pennon at Agincourt (39). The Dukes of Buckingham descend from Mary Bohun's sister, so they also bear a swan and today the swan appears on the Buckinghamshire County Council's coat of arms. The bird is often shown 'gorged', that is, with a collar encircling its throat to which is attached a chain; this it acquired from the Swan Knight legend in which, as we shall see later, the hero travels in a boat drawn by swans.

A cob and pen stand as supporters on the arms of the Company of Vintners 'both nicked in the beak'. The Poulters Company was granted arms in 1634 and it shows swans and cranes instead of the hens and Turkeys that became their more recent stock-in-trade. A swan crest, presumably a reference to William Shakespeare as the Swan of Avon, has been chosen by the Performing Right Society.

Dursley Rural District Council in Gloucestershire has a White-fronted

Goose 'close proper'; these arms were granted in 1952, six years after the establishment of The Severn Wildfowl Trust headquarters among the wintering geese of the estuary. Aylesbury, of course, has a duck on its crest, and the coat of arms of Duckworth and Billiat is a fine example of a pun – the duck is holding the billet in its bill.

METAPHOR AND SIMILE

In the symbolism of animals (for instance, the lamb carrying a flag is a symbol of Christ, and the serpent of Satan), the duck stands for deceit (thus, in French, *Canard* also means a hoax), the goose signifies conceit and folly, while the swan is a symbol of grace (4,15).

When Clement Attlee who, it is said, perfected the art of making dullness the stuff of sure government, called Stafford Cripps a 'political goose' it was at once recognised that Cripps was learned, but hopelessly impractical and naive to the point of folly. To describe someone as a goose suggests a trusting, self-important nature that never sees the stupidity of following the butcher to the point of slaughter. At the time of the crusades, a goose was portrayed on the banner being carried at the head of one group proceeding to Palestine in order to deliver the holy places from the infidel – one German party even had a goose marching before them. It has been wickedly insinuated that the emblem matched the performance of many of the crusaders.

There are probably more English proverbs, sayings and similes relating to the goose than to any other bird (4,15,34). 'To kill the goose that lays the golden egg' is a common expression, meaning that someone has taken more than his due and so destroyed any chance of future gain. The fable of Aesop tells of a man that had a goose that laid golden eggs; thinking to make himself immediately wealthy, he kills the bird to get the whole stock, thus ending the supply. 'A wild goose chase', equivalent to an unsuccessful search, derives from the wariness of the birds, and was used by Shakespeare as long ago as 1595. A man who cannot 'say boo to a goose' has no spirit and is despised for his timidity. Another who has 'cooked his goose' has fatally ruined his chances of success and, if 'all his geese are swans', he has biased vision and deceives himself into thinking things better than they are. 'What is sauce for the goose is sauce for the gander' is a familiar saying in these days of equality. Reference has already been made (Chapter 2) to 'go shoe the goose' as meaning to play about or trifle.

There are many others. I particularly like 'children to bed and the goose to the fire' (34) for its implication of relief from care and anxiety, and of peace and plenty to come. A Winchester Goose was a name for a prostitute, and comes from Winchester Square, Southwark, once the site of the Bishop of Winchester's Inn (p.36), which was a haunt of such ladies in the 18th Century, while a Greenwich Goose was an old and poor sailor – a

Greenwich pensioner from the seamen's hospital. In the English climate, we suffer from goose pimples or goose flesh on a daily basis, and soldiers (of other countries) still goose-step.

Ducks are apparently seen to be more sensible than geese, not usually deceitful (at least, not in English), and someone called a 'duck' is a darling or a sweetheart, but not of great importance. 'Duckie' is a familiar Cockney mode of address – equivalent to 'luv' in the north. We can be 'as miserable as a dying duck in a thunderstorm'; 'play ducks and drakes' with money, usually someone else's, as the saying means to spend recklessly; 'be as quick as two shakes of a duck's tail'; take to something as well 'as a duck to water'; shake off what we don't want 'like water from a duck's back' and, unless in conservative government, we help 'lame ducks' (who were originally defaulters on the stock exchange).

A 'duck' in any ball game means a zero score, presumably from the shape of an egg, while the game of 'ducks and drakes', played with small flat stones, is irresistible to children, who can shift a pile of pebbles into water for the satisfying plops and ripples faster than it takes a duck to wag his tail. A DA hairstyle was fashionable not so long ago: it stood for 'duck's arse', and meant that the hair was brushed up and together at the back like a drake's curly tail. One of President Reagan's memorable lines, and certainly his most heart-warming, was to his wife soon after being shot: 'Honey, I forgot to duck!'

The swan has been preserved from this ribaldry; we have shown little

Cartoon by Robert Gillmor.

respect for the duck and goose (after all, we often ate them) but much for their royal relative. A 'swansong' is the last production of an artist, and is a reference to the call of the dying swan. There is no basis for the story in reality, because swans do not sing before they die; but perhaps before migration and the annual disappearance, swans were seen and heard to fly around calling to one another (if they were Whoopers) or making loud wing-music if they were Mutes, and this behaviour gave rise to a lovely myth. Great poets are called swans as a compliment to their graceful power of verbal melody; Shakespeare is thus the Swan of Avon, Virgil the Mantuan Swan and Homer the Swan of Meander (15,39). However, 'to swan around' does not suggest all that is praiseworthy; it implies lazy aimless movement, and was a popular expression among troops in the last war to describe tanks moving apparently pointlessly across a battlefield.

MYTH AND LEGEND

The purpose of myths and legends is to explain the natural world to unsophisticated man; 'spells' may increase the abundance of useful creatures and make them more vulnerable to his approach. Birds have exercised a hold over man's story-telling for thousands of years (4,5,6), both because they could fly and because many departed in the spring and returned with young in the autumn, apparently by magic. The Gabriel Hounds, named for a supernatural hunt during which the archangel and his dogs chased the souls of the damned across the wild sky were, in reality, geese migrating at night and calling so that family members kept in touch. Presumably they were in territory where they were unfamiliar, otherwise local people would have recognised the sounds. Ownership of the yelling pack was sometimes ascribed to Herne, Arthur, or even Anubis the dog-headed Egyptian god who conducted souls to the underworld.

The night sky also contains Cygnus the Swan, a constellation that is particularly visible in summer in Britain. With a bit of imagination, the shape of a long-necked bird can be picked out flying down the milky way, with the brightest star Deneb (meaning 'tail') bringing up the rear. Deneb is, in fact, a monster star, 140 times bigger than the sun and 200,000 times brighter. Cygnus in Greek legend was a son of Neptune and a friend of Pheaton. Pheaton was killed by a thunderbolt from Zeus for various misdeeds, and Cygnus lamented his fate so grievously that Apollo changed him into a swan and placed him in the heavens (39).

Apollo, the Greek sun-god, had a chariot of swans in which he travelled to the land of the north-wind in spring as birds were leaving on migration. The innsign the 'Swan and Harp' has been referred to earlier; there is a more ancient association between the swan and the lyre that is united in Apollo, the god of music, to whom the swan was sacred. The lyre signified tension – a striving towards love – while the swan denoted chastity. The constellation of Lyra is beside that of Cygnus; together they are symbols

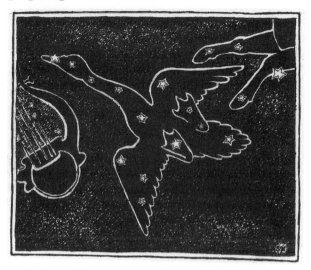

The constellation of Cygnus is found in the autumn sky beside that of the Lyre which is the other attribute of the god Apollo. Drawn by Sue Hazeldine.

of the mystical journey to the other world, whether this was an unknown land that Apollo and the birds visited every summer, or death.

Swans were sacred also to Apollo's mother Leto, 'because of their white plumage, and because the V-formation of their flight was a female symbol' (39). Zeus, the father of the Greek pantheon, became involved in the best-known conjunction of human being and animal which occurs in the tale of Leda and the swan. On a warm summer day in Sparta, Leda bathed in the Eurotas river; Zeus saw her and, on touching the water, changed himself into a swan. Thus disguised he achieved his purpose and, nine months later, she laid two huge eggs out of which came Love and War – Clytemnestra and Helen (of Troy) – or Castor and Pollux (the story varies).

For the Indians, the *hansa* (usually identified as the Bar-headed Goose) is a noble creature because it is mostly white and a high-flying bird of passage (43). Like human beings, geese 'marry' and have families and show grief if one of the pair is lost. At a certain time of the year, they flock together and, in a northward flight across the snowy Himalayas, disappear from sight. After some months, again at a fixed time, they return to familiar lakes accompanied by their young ones. The virtuous character attributed to the goose by the Buddhists is clearly expressed in the *Hamsajātaka*, a story that concerns a large tribe of geese that dwelt with their king at Lake Manasa. The chief minister, Sumukha by name, was endowed with great intelligence and deftness in matters of policy. Now, when autumn had come, a couple of geese flew from Lake Manasa and passing over Benares, saw the wonderful lake of King Brahmadatta.

Returning home, they told of the beauty of their discovery and urged the lord of the geese to betake himself to that marvellous place. The goose-king consulted his wise minister who advised against the journey, remarking that men are deceitful and false – 'birds are dictated by their hearts, but men are the only beings skilled in the reverse'. Despite the warning, the king of the geese, accompanied by Sumukha and a large flock, set out. Their arrival was reported to King Brahmadatta who ordered his fowlers to snare the two leading birds 'whose beautiful wings shone like gold'. The first to be caught was the unfortunate goose-king; he uttered a cry of warning and the entire flock rose save for Sumukha who would not leave the side of his master. The hunter was amazed to see two geese but only one of them ensnared, and even more so when the bird at liberty addressed him in human tongue offering his own body for the life of his lord. The fowler, greatly touched, released the captive and, at Sumukha's request, carried them both to the royal palace. Brahmadatta welcomed his guests courteously and assigned them each a seat according to rank – a golden throne for the goose-king and a bamboo stool for his minister. There then ensued a discourse in which the king of the geese set forth the virtues of a righteous ruler. After taking leave, he rose in the sky and, followed by Sumukha, joined his flock. In the customary epilogue in which the personages of the story are identified, Buddha explains that he is the goose-king and that the minister (in western eyes, surely the hero of the piece) is his principle disciple (43).

The reverence paid to the goose in ancient India can be explained partly by its close association with water, so essential to growth and prosperity. The lotus flower appears in poetry for the same reason and, in the water of life, the goose and the lotus are closely associated. Because of its fundamental importance, water has significance in many creation myths so that water birds, such as swans and geese, figure in stories of diverse origin. A creation myth of the Iroquois says that the first people lived beyond the sky because there was no earth beneath (9). When the chief's daughter became ill, a wise man told them to dig up a tree and lay the girl beside the hole. However, as they dug, the tree fell through, dragging the girl into an endless sheet of water where two swans floated. The swans supported her while consulting the Great Turtle, master of all the animals, who at once called a council. The animals were told that the woman from the sky foretold good fortune and, since the tree had earth on its roots, the Turtle commanded them to bring some of it and put it on his back to make an island for the woman to live on. The swans led the animals to the place where the tree had fallen, although only the Old Toad (or the Duck in the version told by the Crow Indians of Montana) was able to dive deep enough to bring up a mouthful. But this was magical soil and had the power of growth; the woman was set upon it, the two white swans encircled it, and it became at last the world island, supported on the back of the Turtle.

An old Norse legend contains similar elements and tells of a great ash-tree that is the sanctuary of the gods and is supported by three outspreading roots, one of which is the sky. Beneath the tree is a sacred spring called the Spring of Urd. Here dwell the Fates, whose names are Past, Present and Future, and on the water live two swans from whom the whole race of swans has descended (39).

A legend of the Australian Aboriginals tells how the first Black Swans appeared (39). Two members of a raiding party, out to steal boomerangs, changed themselves into white swans in order to divert the camp of a neighbouring tribe that was composed entirely of women. The scheme was that the swans, being strange, would entice the women to rush out in order to look more closely. The plan worked and, as soon as the camp was empty, the men seized the boomerangs and were gone. In order to escape from the enraged women, the swans flew into the territory of a pair of eagles who attacked them, tearing out most of their plumage and eventually leaving them to die of cold. However, a flock of passing crows plucked feathers from their own bodies: 'the eagles are our enemies also' they said, 'our feathers will keep you warm and help you grow strong again'. From that day, swans in Australia have been black except for the tips of their wings and the blood on their beaks. Perhaps this legend is of recent origin and invented in response to the European settler's question: 'why are all your swans black?'

A very widespread Indo-European folk tale is that of the swan maiden who assumes human shape and marries (4,6,39). It has many variations, but usually involves the birds divesting themselves of their plumage, and bathing. If a man can steal a feathery robe, he assumes power over the girl who wore it. She becomes his wife and remains with him until, one day, she finds her clothes, and flies away never to return. The basis of this myth also must lie in uncomprehending observations of migration, perhaps even of the annual wing-moult after which birds are on the move again and gone.

To this day the swan is esteemed in Scotland and Ireland. There are many stories of men and women that assume swan-shape, and a strong feeling that it is wrong to kill one of these birds since it may have a human soul. In Richard Johnson's romance, *The Famous Historie of the Seaven Champions of Christendom*, published in 1596, St Andrew of Scotland restored six ladies who had lived as swans for seven years (15). In another well-known legend, *The Fate of the Children of Lir*, a wicked stepmother transformed Finola and her three brothers into swans who were condemned to wander over the lakes and rivers of Ireland until released by baptism into Christianity. As we shall see later, this theme has inspired many writers and composers. In the Grimms' story (20) of 'The Six Swans' another wicked stepmother changed six brothers into swans; they can be released only if their sister remains silent while sewing them shirts of starflowers. At the eleventh hour, the shirts are ready 'all but the last which yet wanted the left sleeve' and so, when the brothers lose their feathers, the youngest retains a swan's wing.

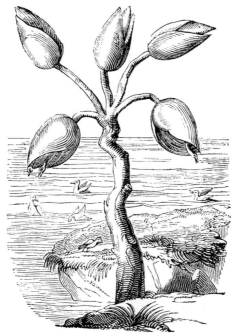

1998.—Bernicles transforming into Geese.   (From Gerard.)

Barnacles changing into geese. From Gerard.

The Knight of the Swan is a romance that goes back to the time of the crusades, although elements of the story are much older (6,39). Again, there is a hero (Helyas, Gerard Swan, Salvius or Lohengrin) some of whose family, usually a brother, have been changed into swans. He appears mysteriously and, after a battle, wins the hand of a noble lady. He marries her but warns that she must never ask about his origins. Of course she forgets, breaks the taboo, and he is removed in a boat drawn by a chained swan. Several prominent European families, including the de Bouillons, asserted that he was an ancestor.

The myth that accounts for the birth of the Barnacle Goose is yet another attempt to come to terms with the fact that birds went away and then returned having multiplied (24). It declares that the geese are produced from trees in the North of Scotland or, in Lancashire, from a species of shellfish which adheres in clusters to sea-washed timbers and the bottoms of ships. These invertebrates are called goose barnacles and, in 1597, Gerard the herbalist was describing (18) from personal experience the production of the little goose that dropped off, 'gathereth feathers and groweth to a fowle'. The same barnacle reference occurs in the Spanish and French names for the goose while, in German, the shellfish itself is called the 'duck mussel' (19). The eventual recognition that a hoax was involved is suggested by the word 'canard' that, in *L'histoire d'un Canard*, came to mean a tall story. Earliest records date from the 8th Century (although suggestions have been made that even earlier Minoan pottery shows geese and barnacles) and it may be that the crustacean is called after the bird rather than the other way around, and that the goose's name is a shortened and corrupt form of *Hiberniae*, the old world for Ireland where the fable was strongest. Its fishy nature meant that the goose could be eaten on Fridays and during Lent with impunity; Giraldus Cambrensis wrote in 1185 'Bishops and religious men in some parts of Ireland do not scruple to dine off these birds at the time of fasting because they are not flesh nor born of flesh'.

A large bird's egg was almost everywhere a symbol of the sun, the largest body in the sky and the most powerful force in nature. The goose egg was particularly a sign of fertility, as was the bird itself on account of its connection with water. The mystery of the emergence of a gosling from the hard shell was equally symbolic of rebirth and immortality. Marriage gifts of eggs, and of the ducks and geese that laid them, were therefore common especially in China and Korea (4).

From 200 BC, Chinese and Japanese Buddhists were setting the Mandarin Duck as a model of fidelity and affection (35). The form of the beautiful male bird was sometimes assumed by the Buddha in order to teach lessons of kindness and consideration. It was claimed that if one of a pair should be lost, the other pined away and died. Their mutual affection was suggested by their habit of nibbling one another's facial plumes and by the fact that, for that part of the year that they are in China (November to March), they are seldom far apart especially when at rest. Thus a pair was often presented as a wedding present and, presumably, marriages did not occur during the summer when drake Mandarins were in eclipse far away in the north and the pair-bonds had broken. A similar legend of fidelity is told of the Ruddy Shelduck or Brahminy Duck in Sanskrit literature (43). Again the birds are usually encountered in couples, although often some distance apart and keeping in touch by calls. The Hindu story goes that two lovers were turned into birds of this species and condemned to pass every night on opposite banks of the river ceaselessly crying: 'Charkwa, shall I come?' 'No, Charkwi'. 'Charkwi, shall I come'? 'No, Charkwa'. The ducks acquired the name 'Brahminy' because of the saffron colour of their plumage which resembles the robes of holy men and, in certain places such as Mongolia, they were regarded as sacred.

An old legend of the University of Oxford tells that when All Souls' College was being built in about 1438, the masons found a huge dead Mallard in one of the drains. This provided the opportunity on Founders' Day (14 January) for dining on duck and hunting the bird with lanterns, staves and much merriment. Fellows and members (remember, this is a college without the excuse of undergraduates, and founded to honour the 'Souls of all Faithful People departed') under the leadership of a Lord

Mallard, rambled through the college precincts singing a lusty 'Merry Old Song of the All Souls' Mallard'. This odd ceremony has similarities to the twelfth-night 'hunting of the wren' in Ireland, Wales and the Isle of Man which commemorates the defeat of winter and hoped-for triumph of light over dark; it became so rowdy that its observance is now confined to once a century and the next is not due until 2001.

CHILDREN'S RHYMES AND STORIES

The difference between stories intended for children and tribal myths that are handed down by word of mouth is often slight. The traditional emphasis of a child's tale is of the consoling triumph of good over evil, with sometimes a powerful moral message. Again, ducks, geese and swans have significant parts to play.

Mother Goose features in the title of numerous books of fairy-stories and nursery rhymes. The character seems to have originated in France, where 'Conte de la Mère Oye' was the expression used for a folk-tale from the mid 17th Century (29). Perhaps the chief tellers of tales were the peasant women who looked after the geese; at any rate, when Perrault's (1628–1703) *Histoires ou Contes du Temps Passé* (containing Cinderella, for instance) was published in 1697, the frontispiece showed an old woman sitting by the fire with three listening children at her feet. A plaque on the wall reads 'Contes de Ma Mère L'Oye'. The earliest publication of these fairy-stories in English appeared in 1729 with the plaque translated to read 'Mother Goose's Tales'. She gradually became a figure to credit with other nursery authorship and, in 1806, appeared in pantomine at Covent Garden in 'Harlequin and Mother Goose, or the Golden Egg'. This seems to have led to her association with the fable of 'The Goose that laid the Golden Egg' and to the ditty:

> *Old Mother Goose when she wanted to wander,*
> *Would ride through the air on a very fine gander.*

The affection in which she is held in the United States has given rise to the legend that 'Mother Goose's Melody' was first printed in Boston in 1719, that many of the tales contained in it were American in origin, and that Mother Goose herself was an American lady. There seems, sadly, to be no truth in the story: the Massachusetts text of 'Mother Goose's Melody' came from the 1729 publication in London (29).

One of the best known rhymes for children is:

> *Goosey, goosey gander,*   *There I met an old man*
> *Wither shall I wander?*   *Who would not say his prayers*
> *Upstairs and downstairs*   *So I took him by the left leg*
> *And in my lady's chamber.*   *And threw him down the stairs.*

The authors of *The Oxford Dictionary of Nursery Rhymes* (29) tell us that the earliest record of this rhyme does not have the last four lines, and that they probably had a separate origin. The version of 1784 finishes:

> *There you'll find a cup of sack*
> *And a race of ginger.*

both ingredients in which to cook the wandering goose once it was caught. Today the further verse is added:

> *The stairs went crack, he broke his back,*
> *And all the little ducks went 'quack, quack, quack'*

Poems for children that figure ducks are not uncommon; as with the goose, it is the domestic bird that appears, and their fate is inevitable:

> *Dame, what makes your ducks to die,*
> *On Christmas Day in the morning?*
> *Their wings are cut and they cannot fly,*
> *Cannot fly, cannot fly;*
> *Their wings are cut and they cannot fly*
> *On Christmas Day in the morning.*

The Tale of Jemima Puddle-duck (30) introduces one of Beatrix Potter's much loved characters (Jemima is Hebrew for 'dove' not duck), who was determined to incubate her own eggs and not let the farmyard hens do the job for her. She got in such a dither that she even appointed a fox as a guardian of her nest, and when eventually she was allowed to sit on a second clutch, she had only four offspring. She is a victim of her domesticated genes which have made her a bad incubator and upset her maternal faculty. Hans Andersen's 'The Ugly Duckling' has an equally sympathetic starring part for the hero, but perhaps a happier outcome (3). An orphaned cygnet is adopted by a family of ducks; while young, the swan is uglier than the ducklings and is ostracised by them. With maturity, however, the cygnet turns into a beauty – a comforting homily for many a plain child. Wilhelm and Jacob Grimm (20) set down the fairy-story of 'The Golden Goose' that belonged to a simpleton; every time thieves tried to steal the gold feathers, they could not let go and were dragged behind the goose and its owner. Eventually the lad takes the whole procession to the King, makes the princess laugh and wins her hand in marriage. The brothers Grimm (20) wrote of another princess, this one in disguise and robbed of her birthright in 'The Goosegirl'. The imagery is unusual in taking a positive view of female power over nature: this girl can command the wind and has a horse that talks although its head is severed. Eventually, as in many stories that begin 'Once upon a time', she leaves her lowly position tending a flock of geese and is restored to a royal destiny.

The Tortoise and the Ducks is an old Indian fable (in which the original was probably a terrapin and the wildfowl were geese) now translated for children into many languages (43). In a certain pool there lived a tortoise

Arthur Rackman's 'Goosegirl', painted in 1909 to illustrate Grimms' fairy-tale. The sad, disguised princess is listening to the head of her talking horse.

who had two web-footed friends to whom he was greatly attached. When drought threatened the water supply, the tortoise begged the ducks not to leave him – they could fetch a light stick that he would seize in the middle in his teeth and which they could carry, holding on to both ends, to a new lake with abundant water. The birds agreed but pointed out that the tortoise must keep a vow of silence or he would fall. All went well

A tortoise being carried by two ducks while villagers marvel at the spectacle; this is a Persian version of the Indian tale. Drawn by Sue Hazeldine.

until the party flew over a town and the clamour made by the people watching the unlikely spectacle caused the tortoise to open his mouth; his exclamation was half-spoken when he hit the ground and was done to pieces by the crowd. The moral is that we must act on the advice of well-meaning friends or take the consequences.

And one of the best-known children's characters of all is Donald, Walt Disney's terrible-tempered duck, who was 55 years old in June 1989. He joined the navy, like Sir Peter Scott, and was the cartoon character used to instruct US naval recruits.

MODERN LITERATURE AND POETRY

Allusions to wildfowl in literature mix reality and imagery. The theme of migration is popular, as is the realism of the birds' vulnerability. D. H. Lawrence's short story *Goose Fair* (23), of which the opening lines appear in Chapter 2, takes as its background the burning of a factory in Nottingham at a time when trade was poor – ruined, apparently, by the French who 'had gone to war with the Prussians and got beaten'; the limping geese are driven in to town to sale and certain death. Ibsen's *The Wild Duck* (22) is a play about the shock of growing up in which the duck symbolises many attributes of the human family. It is the heroine's most precious thing, and she sacrifices it so that she will be loved again, but finally turns the gun on herself. As already said in Chapter 4, Lawrence Durrell (13) wrote movingly of a duck shoot at dawn in the marshes of the Nile delta. The punt fills with sodden victims, 'red blood running from the shattered beaks on the floor-boards, marvellous feathers dulled by death'. Again, the mortality of human being and wild birds is juxtaposed. When one of the party is killed, the bodies of the ducks seem untimely, and any loss of life a matter of importance.

Paul Gallico's *The Snow Goose* (17) gained some of its undoubted popularity because its English edition was illustrated by Peter Scott. Sir Peter (38) related in his autobiography how this came about. The actor James Robertson Justice had sent a copy of the 1941 American publication to him with a note saying 'this should be actionable'. The story involved a hunchbacked painter of birds, who lived in an East Coast lighthouse and had brought to him one day a wounded Snow Goose. The painter tamed it so that it followed him about – indeed, flew with him to Dunkirk and returned home when he was killed to give the news to the heroine Fritha. Scott's first boat, a duck-punt was called *Grey Goose*, as was his wartime Steam Gun Boat. He had earlier told Gallico of his boat and lighthouse and felt that, at the beginning of the story, he was only thinly disguised; however, he did not think that a claim that he had been injured by the tale would be recognised by any court. A more agreeable proposition was the invitation to illustrate the next edition and Gallico's request that Fritha should be painted to resemble Mrs Scott. 'So that is what I did. The frontispiece of the illustrated editions of The Snow Goose, which have been selling well down the years, show a blond version of my beautiful and much-loved Jane' (the novelist Elizabeth Jane Howard, Sir Peter's first wife). When the television film of 'The Snow Goose' was in preparation, staff at The Wildfowl Trust were asked to hand-rear a goose to take the title role. The gander became imprinted and so lost much of his natural fear (Chapter 5). Although used in the flight shots, he had to be understudied by a Hollywood-trained bird after he bit the human star, Jenny Agutter. 'Snoose', hatched in 1970, still remains at Slimbridge, nipping a few ankles, but now fully part of the Snow Goose flock and father of some of its goslings.

Another short story by Daphne du Maurier (26) called 'The Old Man', is an apparently mysterious tale of a fisherman, broad and strong, who lives with his wife near a lake far from civilisation. He does not care for strangers, and even his own children are driven away. One son returns, and seems to come between the couple, staying close to his mother while his father broods 'with murder in his eyes'. And one day, a body is found with a great gash in its back. The Old Man is seen bending to his wife and embracing her while she lifts her head to him. Only in the last paragraph does the author reveal that she is describing an incident in the life of a pair of territorial swans.

In poetry, the intensity of feeling that wild birds invoke is at its greatest, and poems about wildfowl are often lyrical – referring to their power of flight and freedom – but also sometimes humorous. In 1691, the Irish Jacobites capitulated to William of Orange, signed the Treaty of Limerick and left for France; this incident became known as 'The Flight of the Wild Geese' and has inspired much romantic art. Dora Sigerson's is a poetic example:

> *Flinging the salt from their wings, and despair from their hearts*
> *They arise on the breast of the storm with a cry and are gone.*
> *When will you come home, wild geese, in your thousand strong?*
> *Not the fierce wind can stay your return or tumultuous sea,*
> *Only death in his reaping could make you return no more.*

The lines are about Irishmen fighting as mercenaries in other men's wars (all mercenaries from then on became known as 'wild geese'), but the seasonal migration of the birds is beautifully described, as is the melancholy passage of time measured by their annual cycle. Irish poets have had an even greater fascination with swans. Thomas Moore wrote the words of a song about the sad swan-children of Lir in his *Irish Melodies* published in 1808. One of W. B. Yeats' books of verse, published in 1917, was entitled *The Wild Swans at Coole*, while his fine sonnet 'Leda and the Swan' is from a collection of 1927; here he is describing an annunciation 2,000 years before Christ, and inviting comparisons that were unwelcome at the time.

The poem that begins 'From troubles of the world I turn to ducks', by the Gloucestershire poet F. W. Harvey, introduces a little humour, as does S. T. Coleridge's epigram on a singer who had volunteered to amuse the company:

> *Swans sing before they die –*
> *'twere no bad thing*
> *did certain persons*
> *die before they sing.*

MUSIC AND DANCE

Music with a wildfowl theme has the same mixed purpose, most pieces conveying beauty and a few others childish pleasure. In the first category, slow graceful melody often mirrors a dignified swan on placid water. The universal image of ballet is of girls turned into swans, yet only two classical dances have this theme; both are Russian and were staged around the turn

A ballerina as a swan. Drawn by Sue Hazeldine.

of this Century. There is Saint-Saens' 'La Cygne' (the 13th movement from *Le Carnaval des Animaux*) which Pavlova, the most famous ballerina of the age, danced as a dying swan to great effect. Tchaikovsky's first ballet, *Lac des Cygnes*, has the concept of a black and a white swan – Odile and Odette – signifying evil and good, and has become the most popular in the world. 'The Swan of Tuonela' by Sibelius is from a suite of four legends for orchestra based on the Finnish epic *Kalevala*, and was originally written as a prelude to a projected opera. Here, the swan is a Whooper and black because it floats in the river that divides the living and the dead; the music has an altogether darker, more sombre quality than Saint-Saens'. 'Schwanengesang' by Schubert was given that title by the publisher, as they were the composer's last songs and appeared posthumously in 1828 (10,36).

As for geese: we have an unfinished comedy-opera by Mozart called *L'Oca del Cairo* ('The Goose of Cairo' K.422) started in 1783 but soon abandoned, perhaps because it was not a commissioned work; a version was performed in London during the war in 1940, and included a man-sized mechanical goose. Ravel's *Ma mère l'oye* consisted originally of piano duets for children; it was later orchestrated and turned into a ballet; five of Charles Perrault's *Histoires* were included: Sleeping Beauty, Tom Thumb, Empress of the Padodas, Beauty and the Beast, and the Fairy Garden (15). Hamilton-Harty's (1879–1941) tone-poem for orchestra 'With the Wild Geese' was written with that stirring episode of Irish history in mind, and is in the same series as 'The Daughter of Lir' which depicts four changeling swans wandering the wild waters of Ireland until the coming of Christianity.

The modern composer Edward Cowie (born in 1943) has found inspiration in the wetlands of northwest Lancashire and produced, as part of a quartet, a piece entitled 'Martin Mere' in which the calls of wildfowl are turned into delicate images.

Some of man's earliest wind instruments were fashioned from the hollow bones of birds, and the leg bones of geese and swans, being larger than most, were especially sought-after for the construction of musical whistles. Examples have been found in many northern regions, especially among the American Indians.

Ducks do not seem to have excited much musical composition, although Prokofiev in *Peter and the Wolf* had an oboe imitate a duck's quack – even, after it has been swallowed whole, from the belly of the wolf (10), and the words fitted to Souza's march 'The Stars and Stripes for Ever' are relevant:

> Be kind to your web-footed friend
> For a duck may be somebody's brother,
> Remember he lives in a swamp
> Where the weather is always damp.
> You may think that this is the end,
> Well it is.

PAINTING AND ARTEFACTS

Nowhere in the ancient world have birds been portrayed so frequently and so accurately as by the Egyptians (21). Much space in their tombs was devoted to scenes that mirrored the perfect life on earth, thus magically ensuring that that life continued into eternity. Clearly recognisable geese, ducks and a few swans abound. Geese are shown in aviaries and poultry yards, feeding or being crammed with food by hand, herded into flocks, carried in procession in baskets and being trapped in marshes with clapnets. The masterpiece 'The Geese of Meidum' from the mastaba of Atet just south of Cairo, painted during Dynasty IV about 2600 BC, shows White-fronts, Redbreasts and a pair of Bean Geese feeding. A beautiful rendering of an Eastern Greylag from the North Palace of Akhenaten at El-Amarna, some 3360 years old, has been referred to in Chapter 2. A 1400 BC wall painting from a Theban tomb (Chapter 4) shows a tame Egyptian Goose standing in the prow of his master's punt, perhaps acting as a decoy on the fowling expedition. Among the ducks, Pintails are figured abundantly in art and hieroglyphs. Several scenes show the bird as a decorative motif in flight across the ceiling of a tomb or on the floor.

Ducks and swans are persistent themes in the art style that developed in Europe from the 12th Century BC (28). They were associated with solar cults, and sun discs and waterbirds appear together on many early bronze objects. A perfectly recognisable duck or swan motif is found until the 3rd Century BC, but the head of a crested duck is evident again and again as an almost intangible, flowing image on many beautiful pieces of late insular Celtic workmanship.

A Celtic duck of the late 5th or early 4th Century BC, swimming up the spout of a bronze flagon from Basse-Yutz, Moselle, France. Photograph by J. V. S. Megaw.

There are other cultures in which wildfowl became part of a powerful artistic style (Chinese depictions of Mandarin Ducks come to mind (35), as well as the many paintings with the erotic metaphor of Leda and the swan). The theme of domestic geese with a goosegirl was much favoured by Jean François Millet, who died in 1875, and other members of the Barbizon school of French painters. The simple peasant child and her flock were seen, by an urban audience at least, as portraying all the beguiling calm of country living (10) – a false notion, of course, since country men and women were generally impoverished. The same rose-tinted concept appealed to many Victorian artists in Britain. A non-sentimental example dated 1895 and illustrated overleaf is entitled 'To Pastures New'. It is a painting of great charm; the marching birds are splendidly solid and bright-eyed. The sleeping ducks and 'White Drake' in Chapter 2, and J. B. Oudry's many 'canards' are other lovely pictures of frankly domestic wildfowl which in the 1990s would be hardly accepted as proper subjects for wildlife art. On the other hand, Charles Tunnicliffe, who Sir Peter Scott rated the greatest wildlife artist of the 20th Century and who died as recently as 1979, was reared in the country and drew many farmyard

'To Pastures New' by Sir James Guthrie (1859–1930) who was a largely
self-taught artist but became President of the Royal Scottish Academy.

animals. He found inspiration in the handsome Chinese Goose for some
very decorative compositions (12).

For many years, it was usual to paint easel pictures *in tempera* in which
the powdered colour was worked with goose egg-yolk and thinned with
water; oil-based glazing was used for the finishing touches only. Some

A Schiffli lace duck appliquéd on net, about 1920. Photographed by Mrs
Pat Earnshaw and from her book *Lace Machinists and Machine Lace*.

artists mixed the whole egg, and illustrators of fine manuscripts used merely the white. Other domestic birds' eggs must eventually have been employed, and the evolution of the non-seasonal laying domestic hen will have allowed painting to continue during the winter months. Rubens apparently still used egg tempera and oil, while Rembrandt, whose lifetime overlapped with Rubens, painted in oils alone.

Artefacts in the form of ducks, geese and swans are numerous; we can find examples in sculpture (I should love to have a David Wynne swan

'Pintail Drakes', a watercolour by Robert Gillmor, President of the UK Society of Wildlife Artists.

at Martin Mere), porcelain, jewellery, lace, tapestry, felt, mosaic, stained-glass, armorial bearings and cartoon (the three flying china ducks on the lounge wall became popular symbols of 'lower middle-class suburban culture'). The elegant Pintail Duck has remained an artistic favourite since the days of the Egyptians (21); Charles Tunnicliffe was fascinated by its decorative potential (12), Robert Gillmor has continued that tradition and Peter Scott used them on the cover of his best-selling *Coloured Key to the Wildfowl of the World*. Among the great 'modern' wildfowl illustrators are John James Audubon, Thomas Bewick, Edward Lear, Bruno Liljefors (regarded by Sir Peter Scott as the best wildlife painter of the generation

'Bewick's Swans preening' photographed at Slimbridge by Philippa Scott.

before Tunnicliffe), Louis Agassiz Fuertes (page 152), Robert Bateman, Rodger McPhail, Coleen Nelson who specialises in downy young, John Busby who draws mergansers better than anyone (page 126) and Keith Shackleton. Peter Scott, although a naturalist, author, broadcaster, naval officer, glider pilot and yachtsman of great distinction, always earned his living as an artist and tried to do some drawing every day (38,40). He said that he could not remember a time when he did not draw; as a wildfowler, while still at university studying the History of Art and Architecture, he painted his quarry, and when he started to keep wildfowl it was in order to paint them (Chapter 6). He is perhaps best known for his atmospheric skies with ducks and geese in flight, and had a remarkable and almost unique ability to get them looking exactly 'right' as they land into the wind or bank to avoid the hunter (37). In recent years, the delightful water-colour sketches from his diaries have given especial pleasure.

There are some outstanding wildfowl photographers, including Eric Hosking, Pamela Harrison and Sir Peter Scott's wife, Philippa, whose study of three Bewick's Swans is shown here. Konrad Lorenz's book *The Year of the Greylag Goose* (25) contains a superb collection of photographs by Sybille and Klaus Kalas, while Teiji Saga has taken lovely shots of Whooper Swans, one of which was chosen by the RSPB as the cover of their hundredth anniversary publication *For Love of Birds*.

REFERENCES

1. Addison, W. 1978. *Understanding English Surnames*. London: Batsford.

2. Alexander, W. B. 1953. The ornithology of inn-signs. *Bird Notes* 36: 26 (winter 1953–54).

3. Andersen, H. C. 1914. *Fairy Tales and Other Stories*.

4. Armstrong, E. A. 1944. The symbolism of the swan and goose. *Folk-lore* 55: 54–58.

5. Armstrong, E. A. 1970. *The Folklore of Birds*. London: Dover.

6. Baring-Gould, S. 1869. *Curious Myths of the Middle Ages*. London:

7. Bewick, T. 1797. *A History of British Birds*. Reprinted in 1976 London: Paddington Press.

8. Bond, F. 1914. *Dedications and Patron Saints of English Churches*. OUP.

9. Burland, C. 1965. *North American Indian Mythology*. London: Hamlyn.

10. Campbell, B. & Lack, E. (eds). 1987. *A Dictionary of Birds*. Calton: Poyser.

11. Cottle, B. 1978. *The Penguin Dictionary of Surnames*. 2nd Ed. London: Allen Lane.

12. Cusa, N. 1985. *Tunnicliffe's Birdlife*. London: Orbis.

13. Durrell, L. 1957. *Justine*. London: Faber.

14. Ekwall, E. 1960. *The Concise Oxford Dictionary of English Place-names*. 4th Ed. OUP.

15. Evans, I. H. 1981. *Brewer's Dictionary of Phrase and Fable*. 2nd Rev.Ed. London: Cassell.

16. Farmer, D. H. 1978. *The Oxford Dictionary of Saints*. OUP.

17. Gallico, P. 1946. *The Snow Goose*. London: Michael Joseph.

18. Gerard, J. 1597. *The Herball*. Reprinted in 1975 New York: Dover.

19. Greenoak, F. 1979. *All the Birds of the Air*. London: Book Club Associates.

20. Grimm, The Brothers. 1853. *Household Stories*. Reprinted in 1984 London: Chancellor Press.

21. Houlihan, P. F. 1986. *The Birds of Ancient Egypt*. Warminster: Aris & Phillips.

22. Ibsen, H. 1884. *The Wild Duck*.

23. Lawrence, D. H. 1934. Goose Fair, in *The Tales of D.H. Lawrence*. London: Martin Secker.

24. Lockwood, W. B. 1984. *The Oxford Book of British Bird Names*. OUP.

25. Lorenz, K. 1979. *The Year of the Greylag Goose*. New York: Jovanovich.

26. du Maurier, D. 1976. The Old Man, in *Echoes from the Macabre: Selected Stories*. London: Gollancz.

27. Matthews, C. M. 1972. *Place Names of the English-speaking World*. London: Weidenfeld.

28. Megaw, J. V. S. 1970. *The Art of the European Iron Age*. Bath: Adams & Dart.

29. Opie, I.& P. 1951. *The Oxford Dictionary of Nursery Rhymes*. OUP.

30. Potter, B. 1908. *The Tale of Jemima Puddle-duck*. Re-issued in 1987 Warne, Harmondsworth: Penguin Books.

31. Potter, S.& Sargent, L. 1973. *Pedigree, Words from Nature*. London: Collins.

32. Renfrew, C. 1987. *Archaeology and Language*. London: Cape.

33. Ross, A. 1967. *Pagan Celtic Britain*. London: Routledge.

34. Rowley, G. D. 1878. *Ornithological Miscellany*. Vol 3. London: Trubner.

35. Savage, C. 1952. *The Mandarin Duck*. London: Black.

36. Scholes, P. 1970. *Oxford Companion to Music*. OUP.

37. Scott, P. 1938. *Wild Chorus*. London: Country Life.

38. Scott, P. 1961. *The Eye of the Wind*. London: Hodder & Stoughton.

39. Scott, P. & The Wildfowl Trust. 1972. *The Swans*. London: Michael Joseph.

40. Scott, P. 1980. *Observations of Wildlife*. London: Phaidon.

41. Swainson, C. 1885. *Provincial Names and Folklore of British Birds*. London: Trubner.

42. Ticehurst, N. F. 1957. *The Mute Swan in England*. London: Cleaver Hume.

43. Vogel, J. P. 1962. *The Goose in Indian Literature and Art*. Leiden: Memoirs of the Kern Institute II.

10: The Future

The final Chapter will review some previous topics and suggest problems and opportunities that may occur in the future. The Wildfowl and Wetlands Trust will, we hope, continue to develop and flourish as its founder, Sir Peter Scott, would have wished. A change of title in 1989 to The Wildfowl and Wetlands Trust gives general recognition to an expansion of interests that has taken place since its creation in 1946 as The Severn Wildfowl Trust (shortened in 1955, with the opening of Peakirk, to The Wildfowl Trust).

THE FUTURE FOR DOMESTIC WILDFOWL

The Trust has not involved itself in domesticated breeds of wildfowl so far, but a display of farmed ducks and geese, with explanations of how evolution and selective breeding 'work', offers interesting educational opportunities. This might be especially enjoyable if it were done in a farmyard setting where children could walk among the birds and feed them, appreciate why their great-grandparents found them useful, and observe differences and similarities at close quarters. A collection of domestics would also allow research into aspects of breeding performance and physiology that is not done readily on wild species.

Further wildfowl domestication will probably be beyond The Trust's remit; nevertheless, there are fascinating possibilities (6). Faced with the task of feeding an over-populated world, agriculturalists are becoming more and more interested in the untapped resources represented by wild animals. Naturalists have argued that one reason for conserving large African mammals, for instance, is their potential as human food in habitats that do not suit traditional farm breeds. In various parts of the world, experiments in domesticating the eland and the red deer are producing encouraging results. The history of domestication has spanned more than ten thousand years, yet it is only in the last century that our ability to modify animals from one generation to another has been properly documented and scientifically investigated (11).

Few animal groups have adapted successfully to such a wide variety of habitats as wildfowl; they have colonised regions from the tropics to the arctic. Their omnivorous feeding habits have been a factor in their success, and this lack of dietary fastidiousness could have further significance in the production of food for humans especially if, like the grass-eating geese, they do not compete with us directly (6).

Some of the behavioural and physical characteristics found in wild ducks and geese (for example, the rapid growth rates of arctic-nesting geese, the short incubation periods of small northern duck and the tameness of many island forms) could be used to improve the utilitarian qualities of farm breeds. In choosing fast growth and long breeding seasons, man has also selected inadvertently for obesity (as he seems to have done with most of his domestic animals); the amount of fat below the 'swim-line' of the supermarket duck reduces its popularity. Why not mate the Pekin Duck to a close relative that does not swim a great deal, and therefore does not need the insulating fat – like the Laysan Teal? The offspring would almost certainly be fertile, and could pass on the Laysan Teal's leaner tendencies. 'Hybrids' between 'wild' game-farm Mallards and a domestic strain are being produced by the British poultry trade at the moment. Developing the new strain (called the Gressingham Duck) has taken two decades; the birds are docile, the females lay some 240 eggs in a ten-month breeding season, and the youngsters are large enough to produce a lean gamey-tasting dinner for two at eight weeks of age. However, these are not crosses of two different species. Some true hybrids might have value in developing new or improved breeds suited to the climate of parts of the world where there is a relative lack of protein food. It seems far-fetched to imagine a Snow Goose crossed with an Embden Goose, let alone a broiler-reared Nene, on our tables but, with the rising cost and scarcity of traditional livestock foodstuffs, we may need to introduce into our farming some of the natural features of wildfowl that have, so far, been ignored (6,11).

Such schemes would have to allow for dietary taboos. It is a fact that far more animals than plants are associated with food taboos, and the avoidance of meat may apply to particular ages, sexes or persons of status – or to days of the week, such as Fridays, or illness and mourning (12). Peoples of Mongolia and Tibet will refuse to eat ducks; and vegetarians, such as religious groups of southern India, will avoid eating the flesh of any birds, although some take their infertile eggs (12). The English find hard-boiled duck eggs containing 18-day-old embryos, prized by the people of the Philippines for instance (Chapter 2), relatively unpalatable. Some Jews do not eat birds with knobs or caruncles on the bill, so that the Chinese Goose is non-kosher for them; a few Jewish communities will not consume birds with webbed feet. The Bible mentions 24 species of forbidden bird, not all of which can be determined today and, in any case, the lists in Leviticus Chapter 11 and Deuteronomy 14 differ slightly. Swans appear in the King James translation of the Old Testament as 'unclean' (and in the illustration of 'unclean animals' on page 111 of the 1976 *Good News Bible*), but recent texts indicate that this is an error and that the Barn Owl *Tyto alba* was the species intended (1)! On the whole, birds are considered kosher if they were eaten in the past, although communities differ in their interpretation of tradition and custom. For most Jews, the goose of the common Greylag type is a truly biblical animal, one that sustained the slaves that built the pyramids and, if killed according to religious observances and not eaten with milk, provides excellent culinary qualities into modern times.

Man has also been selecting 'lines' of geese and ducks that do not protest at being force-fed – whose pain response is not invoked by the process. Need we avoid *pâté de foie gras* in the future, as many would have done in the past? Fat livers will always be diseased livers, but some English culinary writers who go to see *le gavage* seem convinced that any cruelty involved in three weeks of cramming before death is slight enough to be acceptable.

DECOYS AND DECOYING

The era of decoys is passed; only place-names, overgrown ponds and small secluded woodlands continue to record their ghostly presence. Decoy

Storey's Gate into St James's Park records the name of the decoyman employed by King Charles II. Birdcage Walk was the site of the King's aviaries. Photographs by Joe Blossom.

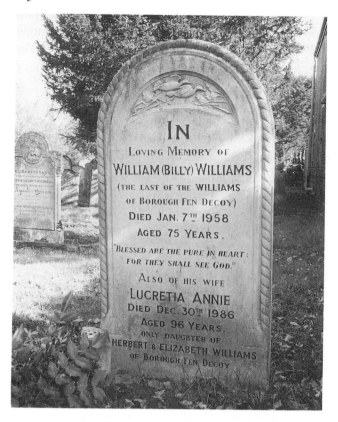

The grave of Billy Williams in Peakirk churchyard; he was the last decoyman to catch ducks commercially at Borough Fen. Photograph by Anne Cook.

Lake is still open water at Newton Abbot in Devon; there is Decoy Broad at Woodbastwick in Norfolk and Decoy Pond at Angmering in West Sussex close to The Trust's Arundel Centre; they are sites at which National Wildfowl Counts have been made, so the ducks are still there. Often it is the diminutive 'coy' that is found in field and street names: Coy Ponds existed until recently on Forest River near Salem, Massachusetts; Storey's Gate, at the southeast corner of St James's Park, passes into Birdcage Walk and records the name and house of the first Royal decoyman who worked for King Charles II. Duck Island, at the eastern end of the lake, is still a refuge for wildfowl. A penultimate chapter in the history of decoys in Britain was written in 1954 when, under the Wild Birds Protection Act, it became illegal to take ducks in them for market – decoys working commercially could continue until the death or retirement of the decoyman but, after that, no successor was allowed. Interestingly, there was similar pressure to close Dutch decoys after the last war; however, it was argued successfully that they formed undisturbed woodland sanctuaries for other birds in a landscape otherwise devoid of such features.

As ringing stations, British decoys have also had their day; they are not cost-effective in comparison with simpler traps. However, a few are surely worth maintaining as monuments to the thousands upon thousands of wildfowl that used them, and to the men and dogs that exploited so thoroughly the birds' instincts. I should like to see the establishment of a National Decoy Museum in the Fens that, as well as showing a decoy, its dog, Call Ducks and workings to the visitor, becomes a depository for all the plans, records of duck numbers down the years and other ephemera that will disappear unless someone shows an interest now. Meanwhile, four active decoys in south and eastern England, listed in Appendix 2, are available for public viewing (dogs are not allowed into any of them!).

FURTHER RESEARCH

The Wildfowl and Wetlands Trust will probably never run out of ideas for what to investigate next – the only difficulty is finding the cash. The need to continue ringing programmes so long as wildfowl continue to be shot was pointed out in Chapter 5; many of the effects of wildfowling are still uninvestigated (see later). Some research that would fascinate me might be done into how wildfowl decoy and onto what objects they can be decoyed. What are young ducks, geese and swans responding to in a model of their own kind sitting on the water, and *exactly* why do they fly in to join it? Its shape is probably of paramount importance, while movement seems not particularly critical. Birds can see colour and pattern, so I wonder whether male breeding plumage is more likely to attract than that of the female or juvenile. The model must obviously look as though it were covered in feathers and not shine or reflect the light. We assume that the presence of an eye is unimportant and we know that it does not matter that it smells. What size should the dummy be? Are there *real* differences between North American and European birds, especially wildfowl, in how they react to an approximate image of themselves?

And what causes ducks and geese to differ in the way they behave towards a land-based predator? What decides whether they all swim towards it, or fly away? It is likely that its shape and outline matter, and whether it has four legs or two. Its size, colour and pattern, and whether it moves or has owl-like forward-facing eyes may influence whether they mob it or rush from it. How do ducks of remote places, that have evolved for millennia without encountering mammalian predators, react? This type of inquisitive study is hard to fund these days when most research is motivated by the need for results that will resolve quickly some compelling problem, or have commercial applications.

It would also be interesting to 'finger-print', by analysing their genetic

Ducks following a land-based predator into a decoy pipe; what are they responding to? Drawn by Peter Scott.

DNA, the wildfowl of isolated islands, as well as those that have been introduced to Britain, and to compare them with their supposed parent populations. How closely is the Canada Goose related to the Nene, and are the English Ruddy Ducks, now significantly different from, and more homogeneous than, their Yankee cousins? Do the genes of the relatively thriving Surrey Mandarins resemble in all particulars those of the winter-fed Mandarins on the River Plym in Devon and the River Tay in Scotland – or the captive ones at Slimbridge? And are their nearest wild relatives found in southern China, Japan or Korea?

THE FUTURE OF WILDFOWLING

Questions about the future of wildfowling in Britain will be put in the following pages, but I cannot pretend to answer them satisfactorily. Again it must be pointed out that no British ducks and geese, many of which are quite legitimately shot, are declining in numbers.

Can wildfowlers recognise their quarry? Is shooting under the moon really such a good idea in view of the disturbance that this may cause to hungry, feeding birds, and of the finding in the early 1970s that 34% of the totally protected Bewick's Swans were carrying lead shot (4)? The situation does not seem to be improving; during the 1988–89 winter, 42% of 40 Bewick's and 15 of 100 Whooper Swans were shown to have pellets in their body tissues. Some of this is surely there by accident, acquired

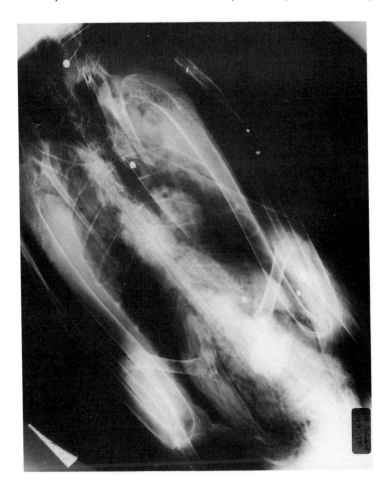

An X-ray of a protected bird: an apparently healthy Bewick's Swan containing lead pellets that will remain for life and are visible as bright spots in her muscles. Her neck is in the upper left-hand corner. Photograph by Martin Brown.

because someone mistook the bird for a goose. We know that over 40% of Pinkfeet and Greylag may have shot in their bodies (3); and, sadly, the proportions of lead in protected geese and ducks are not different from those in quarry species. All will still be flying around, apparently healthy, yet if we X-ray the small sample that collides with power lines, or starves to death in severe weather, the percentage seems higher. Some out-of-range shooting must account for the lead that hits and does not kill immediately. Should British wildfowlers use smaller shot sizes, like their Dutch, Danish, Belgian and Swedish counterparts, in the hope of leaving fewer cripples? We need to know whether the rate of crippling is similar to that of America (20–35 %) and to decide whether these levels are acceptable.

The lead that is spread over almost every marsh in Europe and North American will be there for decades, perhaps for ever and, if picked up by a duck, goose or swan in mistake for grit, will poison it. Coating lead pellets with something less harmful does not help because grit is retained in the gizzard until it is ground down to a small size. Non-toxic steel, or relatively less toxic sintered shot (that contains various proportions of iron and lead) might be better. Their use should be mandatory if that would reduce the number of lingering deaths; but would they be better for the sportsman? The answer here is not clear-cut. Lead and steel are ballistically very different; lead is denser than steel, weighing 30% more the same sized piece, and so travels further. Steel might result in more crippling losses while the shooter learns its characteristics and that, while distant birds can be hit, they may not be killed. So, to begin with at least, the total number of ducks destroyed might not be reduced. Gun barrels may also wear badly and choke mechanisms deform, especially in lighter shotguns. Many old English game guns are both valuable and thin-walled, and particularly likely to be damaged by the higher pressure levels needed for steel shot. However, steel shot is now used extensively in the USA where it was calculated that, for every five birds bagged, one was dying of poisoning; it is employed also on a quarter of Danish wetlands, is being introduced in Holland and assessed for suitability in trials run by BASC.

Many shooters rear and release wildfowl, especially Mallard, in an attempt to put back ducks and geese in exchange for those removed – an estimated 400,000 are added every year in Britain. Is this a worthwhile exercise? Released Mallard do provide additional inland sport in early autumn before food supplies run out and natural mortality takes its toll. On the other hand, attempts to increase the wild population of this already numerous duck have not been successful. The process is an educational exercise, making wildfowlers much more aware of the conservation of wildfowl in general, and there are obvious political reasons why this is a good thing, but the fact must be faced that someone who has reared a duckling is likely to regard birds as more than just quarry in future.

Shooting at geese coming into a roost at dusk is normal but attracts adverse comment if that roost is a sanctuary (as most large ones are).

'A wild goose drive at Berkeley': a party of goose-shooters on the Dumbles (land created by the sea-wall that holds back the river Severn) at Slimbridge. A line of keepers drives the Whitefronts from their feeding grounds over the concealed guns 'as if they were partridges' (from Payne-Gallwey). The geese here were conserved over the centuries by the Berkeley family in order that a proportion of them could be shot.

Hunters wait at the edge, sometimes concealed behind blinds or butts, and fire at the birds as they lose height. This occurred for centuries at Slimbridge, although the birds were usually driven from their feeding grounds over the guns, and now happens at evening flight at Martin Mere, sometimes in full view of the public. Visitors are usually upset and often outraged, and I confess to finding the business distasteful. (Peter Scott, I remember, used to go to the cinema on goose-shoot days at Slimbridge – not to avoid the public but because he could not bring himself to watch and listen).

The National Nature Reserves of Britain are operated by the Nature Conservancy Council, and wildfowling is permitted on a few, such as the Ribble Estuary and Caerlaverock NNRs. Much time and effort, paid for by the taxpayer, goes into the organising of permits and the policing of the hunters. Is this not an obvious target for privatisation, to be done by the wildfowlers themselves and their own organisation, BASC? The ability of BASC to attract a higher proportion of those using shotguns to its ranks, and so to regulate their performance, might be strengthened. The Association is in the best position to tackle a number of the problems outlined here and in Chapter 4, such as the collection of accurate bag statistics, the testing of steel shot and smaller shot sizes, and the ability to identify and shoot within range. The effect of day-time shooting disturbance on birds not actually shot is being investigated at the moment in a project sponsored jointly by The Trust and BASC. We need to know about the situation at night, but an attempt to research into the incidence and effect of night-shooting has met with fierce resistance. Moonflighting is traditional in parts of the UK, and is justified by wildfowlers largely on those grounds; yet it is banned in North America and most of Europe, including Northern Ireland, because of public safety, disturbance to roosts, greater losses through crippling and danger to protected birds.

The public's perception of 'blood sports' is not without influence in moves to protect wild creatures. Wildfowling may once have been work, but is now fun, and there is some disapproval of those who kill because they enjoy the experience. BASC itself says that it does not want to become involved in the shooting of 'pest' species, like Canadas or Brent above the sea-wall, merely because they *are* pests, and adds that any contribution made must be through the 'sporting potential' of the bird. There is no shortage of ducks and geese on the shooting schedules, but members of BASC themselves are apt to object to the killing of large numbers of any duck or goose, perceiving this as 'mass slaughter' and thus 'unsporting'. It has been said that at least another 2,000 British Canada Geese need removing every year if the population is to be stabilized at the 1980 level. The bird is considered to be too tame to be shot with much satisfaction, and wildfowlers need encouragement to go out and fire guns at it – 'Although the Canada Goose currently appears somewhat complacent and little bothered by human presence and activities, a few ounces of No.3. could soon turn it into a truly sporting quarry goose' is a quote from a recent article in *Shooting and Conservation*, the BASC magazine (5). There seems to be a real dilemma here, even among the sporting fraternity.

CONFLICTS WITH AGRICULTURE

Complaints of agricultural damage by geese, and not just the introduced Canada Geese, are bound to increase in Britain if numbers continue to boom – and evidence collected by the research department at Slimbridge suggests that they will. What is to be done? Can we allow major culls of Greylags and Pinkfeet by poisoning them with pesticides, for instance? Currently, the overwhelming cause of death is shooting, but shooting is removing a similar number of birds every season regardless of the increasing number available to be shot. To stabilise the present situation, an average of 20,000 more Greylags and 25,000 more Pinkfeet will have to die annually but, as already said, the wildfowlers are not keen to help with pest control on a massive scale, and have bag limits within their own codes of conduct. If the farmers do the killing themselves, or if shooting were to be permitted on currently safe refuges, there would be great public concern. It is likely that the recent surge in population size was related to the ban on the sale of dead geese imposed in the 1960s. To permit market-shooting again, then, seems one sensible option; however, it would be against international trends and, indeed, the Wild Birds Directive of the EEC prohibits the sale of dead Pinkfeet.

Is there a desirable or minimum level for either species, and who should set this limit? These questions need answering; meanwhile, it seems fair that compensation payments are made to farmers in the few areas where there are large numbers of potentially damaging birds – on the under-standing that they leave the geese alone – and that these payments are related to the current 'set aside' schemes devised to reduce European food surpluses. In Islay, money is already paid by the NCC to owners and managers of Sites of Special Scientific Interest that are visited by Barnacles, and in Holland, the Brent Goose has become known as 'the goose with the golden feet' because of the large sums paid to farmers to compensate for grazed and trampled cereal crops!

CONSERVATION ISSUES

Many other conservation topics will become pressing in the next few years. The need for renewable energy sources is making our estuaries vulnerable to the building of barrages at which tidal power can generate electricity; since the Chernobyl explosion of 1986, this form of energy has many advocates (8). If a few barrages must be allowed, then The Wildfowl and Wetlands Trust must be ready rapidly to create habitats to replace some that are lost, including the construction of brackish and salt water wetlands for wildfowl, something much more difficult to achieve than a seed-producing marsh in the peat soil of Martin Mere.

Electricity needs more powerlines to carry it and, now that the sub-stantial impact of lead poisoning has been removed by the UK ban on sales of large split shot, collisions with overhead cables will again become the most common cause of Mute Swan mortality. To campaign for the burial of all powerlines is unrealistic; however, The Trust believes that where they cross wetlands they should be put underground or fitted with deflectors.

In February 1986, the UK Government published a White Paper announcing its plan to privatise water. This gave great concern to con-servationists, especially in the matter of land and water areas not then used to maximise a financial return (8). Ministers were urged to build into the legislation controls and duties that would ensure that private owners continued to care for the wetland environment.

Threatened wildfowl elsewhere in the world will need our help (added to that of the IWRB), and international cooperation will become increas-ingly important. Estuaries in Africa and Asia may be as important as those in Europe, and often have fewer campaigners to object to their development. How many species will need to be bred in captivity for later reintroduction? Can such programmes be afforded and kept going for long periods while ancient habitats are restored? All should involve captive birds reared close to their natural range, and probably few will be successful in establishing self-sustaining wild populations. But in terms of education and publicity such schemes provide excellent opportunities to raise the profile of a personable zoo animal, along with its essential habitat and less attractive wild neighbours, so that broad-based conservation measures have popular support and can be taken before it is too late.

Should we continue to introduce rare ducks and geese into areas that seem suitable but where the birds did not occur in the recent past? The Mandarin Duck in England is a case in point; should we allow the release of more birds in 'suitable' oak woodlands in southern England because the species is declining in China? (At least, surely, further releases in Britain could be carefully studied and various release techniques tried and assessed with the well-being of other, rarer species in mind). We need to know whether the Nene can sustain itself 'for ever' in a degenerate, predator-rich 'wild' that is all that remains for it on the main island of Hawaii. A programme of research into the nutritional requirements of adults and young, and of the impact of the mongoose, will be implemented soon, and more geese may be released onto mongoose-free islands of the Hawaiian chain, where subfossil evidence suggests their former presence.

The current recovery plan for the White-headed Duck, sponsored jointly by The Trust and the US Fish and Wildlife Service (via IWRB), may be a better model for the future than captive breeding – although for many years yet such schemes will probably be easier to run for European and North American species than for any others. For a rare duck, the annual IWRB census (Chapter 5) has limited value, since isolated flocks are so easily overlooked. The project for the White-headed Duck therefore entails examining all records of past and present distribution and detailing the action needed to protect key sites and improve habitats. Already, protection from shooting and from the disturbance by tourism seems to have resulted in an increase in numbers in Andalucia in Spain, and the population appears not to be dropping below what it was in the 1960s (10,000 – 15,000 birds). The Marbled Teal is now Europe's rarest duck, and numbers there only about 2,000 individuals.

There is also an educational challenge to be met; the 'whole habitat' approach to the interpretation of conservation is essential – as well as a realisation that habitats are used by people. Sir Peter Scott emphasised that wetlands are of greater importance than individual ducks, geese and swans and, although the personal relationship with the animal reinforces the message of concern and must not be lost, the public should be encouraged to see things in the same perspective. Aviculture provides a link here, but those who charge a fee to visitors in order to show them birds in captivity ought to aim, like The Trust, to breed themselves everything that is needed for exhibition in familiar surroundings and not take adult birds from the wild. Pinioning (the operation that renders wildfowl flightless) may become a contentious issue in the future; depriving a bird of its power of flight, even at a day old and even if it would annually spend lengthy periods flightless, can seem unreasonable to some. Wildfowl displays of the future may have to rely more on attractive wetland surroundings than on large numbers of captive animals. The plants and the water itself, the native species that have been reared on the spot and the wonderful winter flocks of wild birds will provide the spectacle. Most of the 800,000 Trust visitors will continue to arrive on a summer day-out 'to treat the children'; for the majority, nothing will replace the friendly bird nuzzling the palm for a piece of bread, and such pleasures need not cease. These visitors support the research, education and conservation activities of The Trust, and many visitors have become members (30,000), so making a longer term commitment.

OUR DEPENDENCE ON WILDLIFE

Culturally, emotionally and physically, we thrive only as part of the natural order (2), and our relationships with wildfowl provide many examples of this dependence. The colour of the northern swans has become symbolic of purity, truth, innocence and hope. Add wildness and vulnerability to that colour, and you have a lot of potent symbols (13). Notwithstanding Peter Scott's studies of Bewick's Swans, mostly we do not see wild, as opposed to captive, birds as individuals, and that lack of personal character means that grief at their death is not so great; they seem to have a sort of timelessness – to fly on forever as tireless travellers – and their springtime departure makes us conscious of our own mortality rather than theirs. W. B. Yeats' poem 'The Wild Swans at Coole', about the 'nine-and-fifty' Whooper Swans that returned year after year to a favourite place of his, has that sense of voyaging into eternity (1). The ambivalence that many of us display towards animals that we occasionally personalise – the mother duck and her babies, or the pet goose – and then kill and eat is, on the whole, better handled by primitive cultures that face the dilemma daily. The Cree of Canada imbue their wild geese quarry with characteristics that are almost holy – they are companions, and part of the life force without which the human race is lost (9). Konrad Lorenz quoted his father as once saying 'after the dog, the greylag goose is the most suitable animal for association with man' (7).

The dog (or rather its wolf ancestor) was apparently tamed as a companion; only later was it used as an agent in hunting. I sometimes contemplate our terrier and consider with satisfaction that her forebears and mine have been together for nearly 12,000 years; in that time it is not just the dog that has made adjustments. We know that people who keep pets live longer on average than those who do not, and that the human heart slows when the hands stroke a friendly animal (10). Of course, in order

A young Spot-billed Duck cradled in caring hands. Ducklings have the endearing qualities of many small animals, and children find them especially appealing. Photograph by J. F. Leach.

to show that these facts have selective value we would need to show that families with pets have more children than those without, or that those offspring survive better. If results of this type were one day obtained, I should be quite unsurprised. I hope that this book, although a celebration of one group of birds, is also an expression of our dependence on the rest of the animal kingdom for a biologically sound 'quality of life'.

We are only partially 'tamed' ourselves, despite having been settled into agricultural communities, farming animals and cultivating grains, for ten thousand years. Most of us can digest milk as adults and, in this, are nearly unique among mammals (except for some of our pets). The selection of those individuals who retain the necessary stomach enzymes beyond weaning has been going on for so long as we have herded and milked the cow. But human allergies to milk and wheat are still commoner than to any other foods (14) – clearly, we have not yet completed the process of adaptation to a domesticated diet. Likewise, our evolution has not reached the point where we find contentment far from the natural world. We are closer to our wild origins than we often realise, and share with our recent ancestors our love of birds, our appreciation of their beauty, our desire to keep and hunt them, to sing and write about them, and to watch and protect them.

REFERENCES

1. Campbell, B. & Lack, E. (eds) 1985. *A Dictionary of Birds*. Calton: Poyser.
2. Diamond, A. W. 1987. A global view of cultural and economic uses of birds, in *The Value of Birds*, ICBP Technical Publication No.6.
3. Elder, W. H. 1955. Fluoroscopic measures of shooting pressure on Pink-footed and Greylag Geese. *Wildfowl* 7:123–6
4. Evans, M. E., Wood, N. A. & Kear, J. 1973. Lead shot in Bewick's Swans. *Wildfowl* 24: 56–60.
5. Harradine, J. 1987. More sauce for the goose! *Shooting and Conservation*. Autumn 35–36.
6. Kear, J. 1976. How wildfowl could improve our domestic breeds. *J.Brit. Waterfowl Assoc.* 1975–76: 37–40.
7. Lorenz, K. 1979. *The Year of the Greylag Goose*. London: Methuen.
8. Purseglove, J. 1988. *Taming the Flood*. OUP.
9. Scott, C. H. 1987. The socio-economic significance of waterfowl among Canada's aboriginal Cree: native use and local management, in *The Value of Birds*, ICBP Technical Publication No.6.
10. Serpell, J. 1986. *In the Company of Animals*. Oxford: Blackwell.
11. Short, R. V. 1976. The introduction of new species of animals for the purpose of domestication. *Symp. zool. Soc. Lond.* 40: 321–333.
12. Simoons, F. J. 1961. *Eat Not This Flesh: a Guide to Food Avoidances in the Old World*. Madison.
13. Whone, H. 1977. *Church, Monastery, Cathedral: a Guide to the Symbolism of the Christian Tradition*. Tisbury: Compton Russell.
14. Yudkin, J. 1969. Archaeology and the nutritionist, in *The Domestication and Exploitation of Plants and Animals*. London: Duckworth.

Appendix 1: Wildfowl and Wetlands Trust Centres open to the public in England, Scotland, Wales and Northern Ireland

Arundel: Mill Road, Arundel, West Sussex BN1 89PB. Telephone: Arundel (0903) 883355.

Caerlaverock: Eastpark Farm, Caerlaverock, Dunfriesshire DG1 4RS. Telephone: Glencaple (038 777) 200.

Castle Espie: Mahee Island, Comber, County Down BT23 6EP. Telephone: Comber (0247) 872517.

Llanelli: Penclacwydd, Llwynhendy, Llanelli, Dyfed SA14 9SH. Telephone: Llanelli (0554) 741087. (Opening 1991).

Martin Mere: Burscough, Ormskirk, Lancashire L40 OTA. Telephone: Burscough (0704) 895181.

Peakirk: Peterborough, Cambridgeshire PE6 7NP. Telephone: Peterborough (0733) 252271.

Slimbridge: Gloucestershire GL2 7BT. Telephone: Gloucester (045 389) 0333.

Washington: District 15, Washington, Tyne and Wear NE38 8LE. Telephone: Washington (091) 4165454.

Welney: Pintail House, Hundred Foot Bank, Welney, Wisbech, Cambridgeshire PE14 9TN. Telephone: Ely (0353) 860711.

Appendix 2: Decoys in England open to the public

Abbotsbury Duck Decoy, which is in the Swannery, is open from mid-May to early September every day from 9.30 am to 4.30 pm. The Swannery can be reached from the B3157 Weymouth to Bridport road and is signposted in the village of Abbotsbury. The approach from Bridport is recommended for the wonderful views of the coastline.

Berkeley New Decoy, which was restored by Peter Scott, is situated within The Wildfowl and Wetlands Trust Centre at Slimbridge, and may be overlooked from a gazebo and hides. Slimbridge is open from 9.30 am until 5.30 pm, or dusk if that is earlier, every day except 24 and 25 December, and is reached from the A38 at Cambridge via exits 13 and 14 on the M5 Motorway.

Boarstall Decoy is owned by the National Trust and operated for duck-ringing demonstrations by the Berkshire, Buckinghamshire and Oxfordshire Naturalists' Trust. The site lies adjacent to Manor Farm along the B4011 Bicester to Thame road, is north of Boarstall and two miles west of Brill near Aylesbury in Buckinghamshire. It is open from 10.00 am to 5.00 pm at weekends and Bank Holidays from Good Friday to the Summer Bank Holiday, and from 2.00 pm to 5.00 pm on Wednesdays during the same period.

Borough Fen Decoy is the only one of the four that is situated in East Anglia and is the sole survivor of the great commercial decoys; it opens on two Sundays every summer, and details may be obtained from The Wildfowl and Wetlands Trust Centre at Peakirk (see Appendix 1).

Appendix 3. Scientific names of plants, invertebrates, fishes, reptiles and mammals mentioned in the text

PLANTS

Périgord truffle *Tuber melanosporum*
Avocado *Persea americana*
Alder *Alnus* sp.
Grey Alder *Alnus incana*
Beech *Fagus sylvatica*
Sweet chestnut *Castanea sativa*
Oak *Quercus* sp.
Buttercup *Ranunculus* sp.
Lotus *Nelumbo nucifera*
Chickweed *Stellaria media*
Bistort *Polygonum* sp.
Golden dock *Rumex maritimus*
Cocoa *Theobroma cacao*
Cotton *Gossypium herbaceum*
Hop *Humulus lupulus*
Fig *Ficus carica*
Squash *Cucurbit pepo*
Willow *Salix* sp.
Iceland yellow-cress *Rorippa islandica*
Swedish turnip *Brassica napus*
Rhododendron *Rhododendron ponticum*
Strawberry *Fragaria ananassa*
Clover *Trifolium repens*
Field bean *Vicia faba*
Peanut *Arachis hypogaea*

Manioc *Manihot esculenta*
Flax *Linum usitatissimum*
Carrot *Daucus sativus*
Ash *Fraxinus excelsior*
Sweet peppers *Capsicum* sp.
Potato *Solanum andigenum*
Tomato *Lycopersicon lycopersicum*
Tobacco *Nicotiana tabacum*
Pennyroyal *Mentha pulegium*
Mint *Mentha* sp.
Small fleabane *Pulicaria vulgaris*
Groundsel *Senecio vulgaris*
Gosmore *Hypochaeris radicata*
Canadian pondweed *Elodea canadensis*
Esthwaite waterweed *Elodea nuttalli*
Eelgrass *Zostera* sp.
Rye grass *Lolium perenne*
Wheat *Triticum sativum*
Yorkshire fog *Holcus lanatus*
Maize *Zea mays*
Cotton grass *Eriophorum angustifolium*
Spike rush *Elecharis palustris*
Pineapple *Ananas sativus*
Asparagus *Asparagus officinalis*
Onion *Allium* sp.

INVERTEBRATES

Liver fluke *Fasciola hepatica*
Zebra-mussel *Dreissenia polymorpha*
Mussel *Mytilis edulis*
Oyster *Ostrea edulis*
Jenkin's spire-shell *Potamopyrgus
  jenkinsi*
Goose barnacle *Lepas anatifera*
Wheat-bulb fly *Delia coarctata*
Cockroach *Blatta* sp.
Bee *Apis* sp.
Chironomid larvae *Chironomus* sp.

FISHES

Salmon *Salmo salar*
Bream *Abramis brama*
Trout *Trutta* sp.
Carp *Caprinus carpio*
Pike *Esox lucius*
Mullet *Chelon* sp.

REPTILES

Tortoise *Testudo* sp.
Terrapin *Testudo* sp.
Black cobra *Naja* sp.

MAMMALS

Rabbit *Oryctolagus cuniculus*
Mouse *Mus* sp.
Brown rat *Rattus norvegicus*
Black rat *Rattus rattus*
Grey squirrel *Sciurus carolinensis*
Guinea pig *Cavia porcellus*
Capybara *Hydrochoerus hydrochaeris*
Red Fox *Vulpes vulpes*
Arctic fox *Alopex lagopus*
Wolf *Lupus lupus*
Domestic dog *Canis familiaris*
Mink *Mustela vison*
Otter *Lutra lutra*
Mongoose *Herpestes* sp.
Hyena *Huaena hyaena*
Domestic cat *Felis catus*
Domestic pig *Sus scrofa*
Camel *Camelus* sp.
Llama *Lama glama*
Alpaca *Lama pacos*
Red deer *Cervus elaphus*
Roe deer *Capreolus capreolus*
Reindeer *Rangifer tarandus*
Eland *Taurotragus oryx*
Quagga *Equus quagga*
Oryx *Oryx* sp.
Domestic ox *Bos taurus*
Domestic sheep *Ovis aries*
Goat *Capra hircus*

Index